Beyond the Hundredth Meridian

JOHN WESLEY POWELL

AND THE SECOND OPENING OF THE WEST

BOOKS BY

WALLACE STEGNER

Remembering Laughter

The Potter's House

On a Darkling Plain

Fire and Ice

Mormon Country

The Big Rock Candy Mountain

One Nation (in collaboration with the editors of Look *Magazine)*

Second Growth

The Women on the Wall

The Preacher and the Slave

Beyond the Hundredth Meridian

The City of the Living

Beyond the Hundredth Meridian

JOHN WESLEY POWELL

AND THE SECOND OPENING OF THE WEST

by Wallace Stegner

WITH AN INTRODUCTION BY
BERNARD DEVOTO

SENTRY EDITION
1962

illustrated with maps

HOUGHTON MIFFLIN COMPANY BOSTON
The Riverside Press Cambridge

The Riverside Press
CAMBRIDGE • MASSACHUSETTS
Printed in the U.S.A.

For Bernard DeVoto

Dear Benny:

This is a book in the area of your vast competence, one that you might have written more appropriately and certainly more authoritatively than I. It is dedicated to you in gratitude for a hundred kindnesses, the latest of which is the present introduction, but the earliest of which goes back nearly twenty years. I could not omit a word of thanks for all this without feeling that I had neglected the most important as well as the most pleasurable step in the making of this biography.

AUTHOR'S NOTE

THIS BOOK is an attempt to write a biography that is the history not of a personality but of a career.

I am not interested in Major Powell's personality, though that is generally considered the excuse for a biography, and though he was a man, by the testimony of those who worked with him and loved him and hated him, electric with energy and ideas. I am interested in him in other ways: As the personification of an ideal of public service that seems peculiarly a product of the American experience. As the source and mouthpiece of ideas three quarters of a century ahead of their possible fulfillment, yet rooted in that same American experience. As the father of government bureaus far-reaching in their own effects and influential in the models they provided for other and later government agencies. Above all, as a champion and an instrument of social understanding and social change. Like Lester Ward, his one-time employee and firm friend, Major Powell repudiated that reading of Darwinism which made man the pawn of evolutionary forces. In his view, man escaped the prison in which all other life was held, because he could apply intelligence and will to his environment and bend it.

In these pages I have dwelt somewhat long on an early and relatively unimportant, though adventurous, episode: the running of the Colorado River. I have done so because though Powell's later activities were of much greater national importance, the river journey was symptom and symbol. Though some river rats will disagree with me, I have been able to conclude only that Powell's party in 1869 survived by the exercise of observation, caution, intelligence, skill, planning — in a word, Science. A man or a civilization could do the same. Major Powell's attempts to impose order on whatever he touched, and especially on the development of the western states whose problems he knew as no one in his time knew them, are the real subject of this book.

His understanding of the West was not built on a dream or on the characteristic visions of his time, for on one side he was as practical as a plane table. The mythologies of the seventies and eighties had as little hold on him as the mythological tales of Hopi or Paiute: he knew all about the human habit of referring sense impressions to wrong causes and without verification. His faith in science was a faith in the ultimate ability of men to isolate true — that is, verifiable — causes for phenomena. Also, he knew a good deal about the human habit of distorting facts for personal gain, and he fought western land interests and their political hatchetmen for years, out of no motive but to see truth and science triumph and the greatest good come to the greatest number over the greatest period of time, according to the American gospels.

More clearly than most of his contemporaries he demonstrated that fundamental affinity between Democracy and Science that made America after the Civil War, in spite of scandal and graft and unprecedented venality, one of the exciting and climactic chapters of history both intellectual and social. He was one of those who in his education and in his confirmed beliefs seemed the culmination of an American type, though his own family arrived in America barely in time for him to be born here.

Also, he was one of the illustrious obscure who within the framework of government science achieved unusual power. He did much solid good because he combined with personal probity an ability to deal with politicians. And if he was more optimistic about the future of America and the world than is now fashionable, a review of his career reveals that a large amount of his work both for science and for democracy has not only lasted but has generated more of the same. We have gone a good long way toward his principal recommendations with regard to the West; three generations after some of those plans were first proposed, they seem of an extraordinary prescience.

All of which is to say that though someone like Clarence King may warrant a biography because of his personality, his wit, the brilliance of his conversation and the glitter of his circle, Powell's effect upon his country was that of an agent, or even of an agency. I have tried to treat him accordingly.

In the preparation of this biography I have benefited from the help and advice of scores of individuals and organizations. Some of the work has been done under grants from the Milton Fund of Harvard University, the Henry E. Huntington Library and Art Gallery, and the John Simon Guggenheim Memorial Foundation. The American Philosophical Society has kindly helped with microfilm problems. Among librarians I have yet to find a surly or unhelpful individual: I think librarians will inherit the earth. And the list of those to whom I owe a debt of gratitude is appended here, not to form a cordon through which a reader has to break to get at Powell, but as an inducement: If such as these have been interested in him and his work, he must be worthy of attention.

For kindness and assistance of every sort, I am especially grateful to Bernard DeVoto of Cambridge, Massachusetts; Henry Nash Smith of the University of California; Dale L. Morgan of Salt Lake City; Francis Farquhar, George R. Stewart, Otis Marston, and Paul Taylor of Berkeley, California; William Culp Darrah of Gettysburg, Pennsylvania; Lindley Morris of Bloomington, Illinois; Charles Kelly of Fruita, Utah; J. C. Bryant, Superintendent of the Grand Canyon National Park; the late Norman Nevills of Mexican Hat, Utah; Professor Robert Taft of the University of Kansas; Beaumont Newhall of Eastman House, Rochester, New York; Ansel Adams of San Francisco; Paul and Frances Judge of Grand Teton National Park, Wyoming; Struthers and Katherine Burt of Three Rivers Ranch, Moran, Wyoming; Louise Peffer of the Stanford Food Research Institute; J. O. Kilmartin, Chief of the Map Information Service of the United States Geological Survey; Matthew Stirling, Paul Oehser, and Miss Mae Tucker of the Bureau of American Ethnology; Professors Ben Page, J. E. Williams, and the late Bailey Willis of Stanford University, and V. L. Vander Hoof, formerly of Stanford; Leroy Hafen of the Colorado Historical Society and Marguerite Sinclair of the Utah State Historical Society; Thomas Manning of Yale University; and by no means least, the staffs of the libraries where I have had the pleasure of working: Widener

Library of Harvard University; Bancroft Library, University of California; the Stanford University Library and the Branner Geological Library, Stanford University; the Henry E. Huntington Library; the National Archives, the United States Geological Survey, and the Bureau of American Ethnology in Washington; the New York Public Library; and the McClean County Historical Society of Bloomington, Illinois.

Thanks are due to the *Pacific Spectator* for the right to reprint the chapter "Adding the Stone Age to History" in Part IV, and to the *Western Humanities Review* for the chapter on "Names" in Part II.

CONTENTS

MAPS

The cover design by Samuel Hanks Bryant is transcribed from an illustration by William Henry Holmes which originally appeared in Clarence E. Dutton's *Tertiary History of the Grand Canyon District* (1882). It is a panorama of the Grand Canyon, looking east, south, and west from Point Sublime.

INTRODUCTION

A BOOK called *The Growth of American Thought* was awarded the Pulitzer Prize for history in 1944. At the end of a chapter on "The Nature of the New Nationalism" the central figure of Mr. Stegner's book makes a momentary appearance. A passage which all told is nearly two pages long is discussing "the discovery of the West by a group of scientists who revealed it to the rest of the country." (They revealed it, we are to understand, primarily as interesting scenery.) A paragraph pauses to remark that at the time these scientists made their discovery, the frontier was vanishing but it had "left distinctive traces on the American mind through its cult of action, rough individualism, physical freedom, and adventurous romance." Here are four fixed and indestructible stereotypes about the West, all of them meaningless. No wonder that on the way to them Mr. Stegner's subject is dismissed with a sentence which records that "the ethnologist and geologist, John Powell, who explored the Colorado River, the Grand Canyon, and the homeland of Indian tribes of the Southwest, promoted extremely important geological surveys for the federal government." In his bibliographical notes the historian of American thought adds, "Major John Powell's *Exploration of the Colorado River of the West and Its Tributaries* is a classic."

Thus "John Powell" was an explorer who embraced the cult of action, whatever that may be, and went down the Colorado and wrote an adventure story. He also had something to do with geological surveys which were "extremely important" but not important enough to be specified. Our historian perceives in them nothing that bears on the growth of American thought. Nor does he mention the classic which Powell wrote, *Report on the Lands of the Arid Region of the United States.* Indeed nothing suggests that he has heard of it. It states, and states systematically for the first time, the conditions that control human life and society in forty per cent of the area of the United States. But because the historian of thought approaches the West with a handful of clichés, the conditions of life and society are not important. What counts is the book he names, an "adventurous romance."

Which is fair enough and no doubt inevitable. True, one historian who understood John Wesley Powell and his importance, Mr. Walter Prescott Webb, had discussed him at length before the one I have quoted wrote his book. But most of his colleagues had not even heard of Powell in 1944, and still haven't. This unawareness represents a serious gap in historical thinking — which is the only reason for quoting a prizewinning book here. Otherwise it would be enough to say that Powell was one of those powerfully original and prophetic minds which, like certain streams in a limestone country, sink out of sight for a time to reappear farther on. It will not do to sum up so briefly. For the reason historians have ignored Powell is that the *preconceptions* with which they have approached the area Powell figures in correspond exactly to the *misconceptions* with which the American people and their government approached the West.

Powell's importance is that seventy-five years ago he pierced through those misconceptions to the realities. His career was an indomitable effort to substitute knowledge for the misconceptions and to get it acted on. He tried to repair the damage they had done to the people and the land and to prevent them from doing further damage. He tried to shape legal and political and social institutions so that they would accord with the necessities of the West. He tried to conserve the West's natural wealth so that it could play to the full its potential part in the future of the United States. He tried to dissipate illusions about the West, to sweep mirage away. He was a great man and a prophet. Long ago he accomplished great things and now we are beginning to understand him . . . even out west.

That is the burden of Mr. Stegner's memorable book. My part here is to explain why writers of history have for so long failed to understand the massive figure of John Wesley Powell and therefore have failed, rather disastrously, to understand the fundamental meaning of the West in American history.

One of the reasons for that failure is beyond explanation: the tacit classification, the automatic dismissal, of Western history as merely sectional, not national, history. No such limitation has been placed on the experience of the American people in New England, the South, or the Middle West. These sections are taken to be organic in the United States and cannot safely be separated from their functional and reciprocal relationships. When you write Southern history in the round you must deal with such matters as, for instance, the cotton economy, the plantation system, slavery, States' rights, the tariff, secession, the Civil War, and Reconstruction. They are so clearly national as well as Southern in implication that it would be impossible to write about them without treating them in relation to the experience of the nation as a whole. The same statement holds for the historical study of, say, Southern institutions, Southern politics, and Southern thinking — to ignore their national context would clearly be absurd. Southerners too are acquainted with "action" if not a cult of action, and are known to value "individualism" if not a rough kind of it. We may observe, even, that the South has had some awareness of "physical freedom" and "adventurous romance." But an intellectual historian would not write a summary which implied that history need inquire no further — would not dismiss Jefferson with a sentence about his governorship of Virginia or Calhoun with one about his term in the legislature of South Carolina.

The experience of the West is just as inseparable from the central energies of American history. Any major Western topic, or any commonplace Western phenomenon, involves those energies the moment it is glanced at. Thus a favorite garment in the West (as in rural places throughout the United States) is a shirt whose trade name is Big Yank. It is a cotton shirt — made of a fiber once grown only in the South but now grown competitively in the West. It is a manufactured article — a product of industry located outside the West. So it cannot safely be dissected out from the national system. And the more you look at it, the more clearly you see that this involvement is complex. You encounter the mercantile-colonial status of the Western economy, the drainage of Western wealth eastward, the compensatory process of federal benefactions, preferential freight rates, and myriad concrete facts related to these — all national in implication. Make the shirt a woolen one and you bring in the tariff, absentee ownership of the West, Eastern control of Western finance, and the stockgrowing portion of Western agriculture. And if you will look at the woolen shirt just a little longer it will lead you straight to the basic conditions of the West.

Unless you are deflected or dazzled by its "adventurous romance." Or by your historical preconceptions.

The West was the latest and most adventurously romantic of our frontiers, and its history has been written, mostly, as frontier history. When the word "frontier" is used in history it has, to begin with, been raised to a tolerably high degree of abstraction. And its inherent abstractness has been almost immeasurably increased by a hypothesis which has dominated much writing about the West and has colored almost all of it, Frederick Jackson Turner's theory about the function of "the frontier" in American life. That theory has, I suppose, begotten more pages of American history than any other generalization. Till recently no one dreamed of writing about the West without its help. Indeed its postulate of a specific kind of "frontier" independence, which it derives from the public domain and which it calls the principal energy of American democracy, has heavily buttressed our illusions about the West. So our problem here exists in a medium of pure irony. For, to whatever degree the Turner hypothesis may be applicable to American experience east of the 100th meridian, it fails almost altogether when applied to the West. The study of a single water war, in fact of a single irrigation district, should reveal its irrelevance. Indeed as one who has written extensively of our sacred Western symbol, the covered wagon, I have frequently found myself wondering if the study of a single wagon train ought not to suffice.

But two other facts affect our problem more. In general, historians have been content to postulate that American institutions, orientations, and habits of thought which developed east of the 100th meridian maintained their form and retained their content after reaching the West, whereas in fact a good many important ones did not. In the second place, historians have generally been ignorant of or incurious about natural conditions that determine life in the West, differentiate it from other sections, and have given it different orientations. Since the importance of John Wesley Powell is entirely related to those differences, historians have naturally had no reason to perceive it. Presumably anyone nowadays is well enough informed to understand that the engaging nonsense of William Gilpin, which Mr. Stegner uses so effectively to illuminate Powell's achievements, is and always was nonsense. But the point is that anyone who is not well grounded in Western geography, topography, and climate could easily be led to dismiss Powell as precisely the kind of eccentric Gilpin was.

Well, there isn't much rain out west. There is not enough rain to grow crops and so additional water has to be brought to them for irrigation. The additional water falls as snow on the mountains, it melts, and it flows down the brooks to the creeks and down them to the rivers. If you build dams, you can hold the runoff for use when and where it is needed. Then if you construct systems of canals — increasingly complex systems as you take the melted snow farther — you can bring the water to town mains and to the fields that won't grow crops without it. The historical process which we call the westward movement shattered against these facts. Neither hope nor illusion nor desire nor Act of Congress could change them in the least. But they were even harder for the American people to accept than they have been for historians to understand.

There is no need to describe how the "quarter-section" acquired mystical significance in American thinking — the idea that 160 acres were the ideal family-sized farm, the basis of a yeoman democracy, the buttress of our liberties, and the cornerstone of our economy. It was certainly true, however, that if you owned 160 acres of flat Iowa farmland or rolling Wisconsin prairie, you had, on the average, a farm which would support your family and would require all its exertions to work. So the quarter-section, thought of as the proper homestead unit, became the mystical one. But in the arid regions 160 acres were not a homestead. They were just a mathematical expression whose meanings in relation to agricultural settlement were disastrous.

To begin with, what kind of land? A hundred and sixty acres of redwood or Douglas fir or Western white pine never could be a homestead — but they were a small fortune. Hence the personal and corporate timber frauds which stand high in the record of our national corruption. A hundred and sixty acres of arid range land could not provide forage for enough stock to support a family. Hence two kinds of land fraud, on a large scale by wealthy or corporate stock-growers to acquire big ranges, on a small scale by poor individuals trying to acquire the self-supporting homesteads that they could not get legally. What about 160 acres of valley farmland with the rich mineral soil of the West and capable of being irrigated? Two considerations: to irrigate so large a tract would usually cost more than an individual owner could afford, and the farming made possible by irrigation would mostly be so intensive that so big a farm could not be worked by a single family.

So the land in the arid country had better be classified, and the unit of ownership, the size of the homestead, had better be adjusted to the realities. Our system had always resisted land-classification for the public domain — the official ruling that standing timber was not farmland — in the interest of speculation and graft. But in the arid country not to classify land would on the one hand facilitate monopolization of land, and on the other hand would perpetuate and institutionalize the bankruptcy of Western homesteaders. And unless the unit of ownership was changed there would be no way of squaring either public or private interests with the immutable facts. But both changes would mean fundamental alteration of our legal and land system, and would produce further changes in many institutions related to them. The sum of change required was so great that the American mind did not take it in — and went on believing that there must be some way of licking climate or that climate would adapt itself to men's desires. Against this inherited set of mind, the tumultuous and tragic experience of the West could not prevail.

Again, not only what kind of land but whereabouts? A small holding that included a water source could prevent access to the basis of life and so would give its owner the usufructs of a much larger area which he could keep others from owning. Adjoining holdings along a stream could similarly dominate a much larger area. So at small expense (and by fraud) a corporation could keep individual stockgrowers from a really vast area it did not own but could thus make use of. Or a corporation could not only charge its own price for water, that is for life, but could control the terms of settlement with all that settlement implies. Here was another powerful force making for monopoly and speculation. Clearly, that is clearly to us now, the West could exist as a democratic society only if the law relating to the ownership and use of water were changed. The changes required were repugnant to our legal system and our set of mind, and again the experience of the West produced turbulence but not understanding.

Moreover, to bring water to land at any distance from the source was an undertaking expensive beyond the ability of an individual landowner to afford. As the distance increased it would become expensive beyond the ability first of co-operative groups, then of profit-making corporations, and finally of the individual states to afford. At the heyday of "individual enterprise" elsewhere in the United States, therefore, the natural conditions of the West demanded federal action in the procurement of water. And this was repugnant not only to our set of mind but, especially, to our mystical vision of the West, the very citadel, so we insisted on believing, of "rough individualism."

Furthermore, if in large parts of the West the individual landowner required a homestead of at least four square miles, then the traditional pattern of settlement would result in his living in fearful isolation from his kind. Loneliness, hardship, and social deterioration would inevitably follow. (Which is the history of the high plains down to the automobile and the coming of good roads.) What the Western realities demanded was not the ranch pattern of the Dakotas but the village pattern of the Spanish-American Southwest and of Mormon Utah. And in the arid region the traditional political organization within the states, by counties, would be cumbersome, illogical, and intolerably expensive. Far better to avoid such irrational units and to organize politically in accord with the Western realities, by river valley or watershed.

This does not state all the immutable conditions of the West against which institutions and eventually ideas shattered but it will do here. The history of the West derives from them — a history of experience failing to overcome in time our thinking, our illusions, our sentiments, and our expectations. The results were hardship, suffering, bankruptcy, tragedy, human waste — the overthrow of hope and belief to a degree almost incredible now, and only now beginning to be understood in the historical context.

These principles are described and analyzed, and most of the institutional changes necessary to bring Western society into effective accord with them are stated, in Powell's *Report on the Lands of the Arid Region of the United States.* In fact, they are set forth in the first forty-five pages of that monumental and astonishing book, a book which of itself opened a new era in Western and in national thinking. It is one of the most remarkable books ever written by an American. In the whole range of American experience from Jamestown on there is no book more prophetic. It is a scientific prophecy and it has been fulfilled — experimentally proved. Unhappily the experimental proof has consisted of human and social failure and the destruction of land. It is a document as basic as *The Federalist* but it is a tragic document. For it was published in 1878 and if we could have acted on it in full, incalculable loss would have been prevented and the United States would be happier and wealthier than it is. We did not even make an effective effort to act on it till 1902. Half a century after that beginning, we are still far short of catching up with it. The twist of the knife is that meanwhile irreversible actions went on out west and what we did in error will forever prevent us from catching up with it altogether.

Yet those statements, though true, will not hold of themselves. For meanwhile, before the effective beginning was made, institutions which Powell founded were amassing the knowledge that made the beginning possible. And they were steadily changing American opinion as they added to knowledge — to the treasury of knowledge that is the heritage of all mankind. And they, with what has issued from them, have steadily changed not only American social and political institutions but the structure and functions of the government of the United States. Finally, as this change has progressed it has become a force which, joined with others working in the same direction, has greatly changed our ideas of what government ought to do and how it should do what it ought.

That story, however, is Mr. Stegner's book. I began by alluding to a gap in historical understanding which has caused distortions in the writing of American history. Mr. Stegner has now filled the central and biggest part of that gap. Henceforth a prizewinning book about American intellectual history will not dismiss Powell as a believer in the cult of action who wrote an adventure story.

Mr. Stegner's subject is nineteenth century America and the part the West played in creating twentieth century America — wherein, how, but most of all why. He has added a basic book to the small shelf of books that give history basic knowledge of Western experience. As recently as twenty years ago there were no such histories, at least there were none sound enough and understanding enough to be used for interpretation. There are just about enough of them now, they have amassed just about enough basic knowledge, to justify someone in bringing them together to construct a new general synthesis of American history. Any day now we may expect the appearance of a historian with a generalizing mind who is bent on achieving a hypothesis about the West in American history that will square with the facts. When someone achieves it, it will be a more realistic and therefore a more useful theory than Turner's.

BERNARD DEVOTO

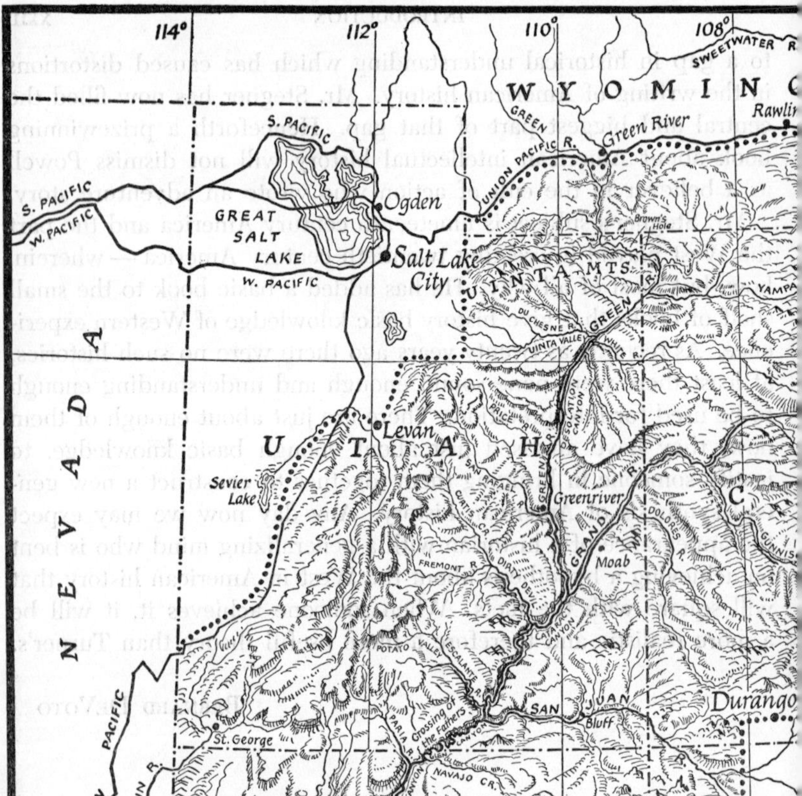
114°
112°
110°
108°
SWEETWATER R.
Green River
GREEN R.
UNION PACIFIC R.
S. PACIFIC
W. PACIFIC
GREAT SALT LAKE
Ogden
Salt Lake City
Brown's Hole
UINTA MTS.
DU CHESNE R.
UINTA VALLEY
WHITE R.
DESOLATION CANYON
PRICE
Levan
U T A H
N E V A D A
Sevier Lake
SAN RAFAEL
CURTIS CR.
Greenriver
GRAND R.
DOLORES R.
Moab
FREMONT R.
DIRTY DEVIL
CATARACT CANYON
POTATO VALLEY
ESCALANTE R.
SAN JUAN
Bluff
Durango
Crossing of the Fathers
PARIA R.
GLEN CANYON
St. George
NAVAJO CR.
MARBLE CANYON
ECHO CLIFFS
UNION PACIFIC
VIRGIN R.
COLORADO R.
GRAND CANYON
CATARACT CREEK
LITTLE COLORADO R.
PUERCO
RIO
AT. TOP & S.F.
COLORADO PLATEAU
Prescott
A R I Z O N A
SALT R.
GILA R.
COLORADO R.

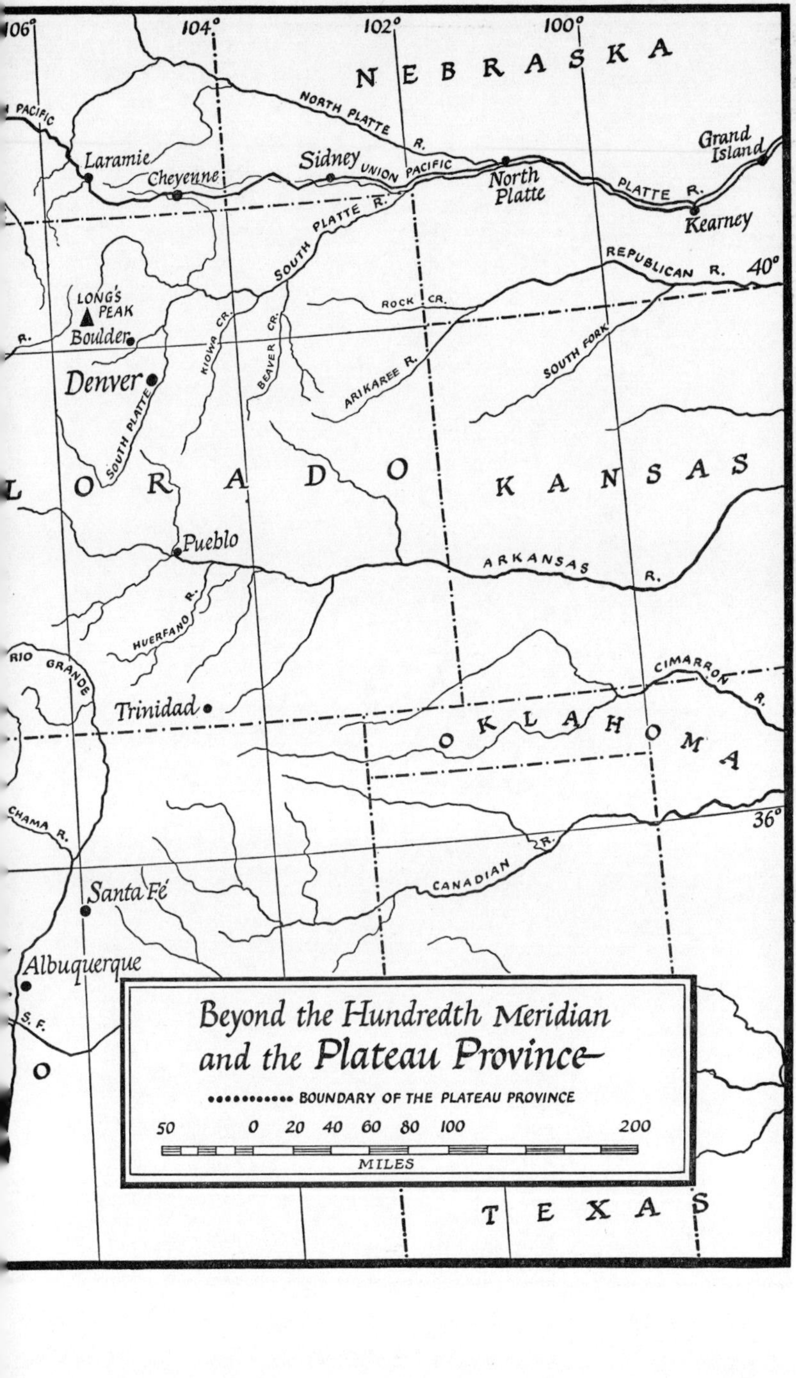
106°
104°
102°
100°
NEBRASKA
PACIFIC
NORTH PLATTE R.
Laramie
Cheyenne
Sidney
UNION PACIFIC
North Platte
PLATTE R.
Grand Island
Kearney
SOUTH PLATTE R.
REPUBLICAN R.
40°
LONG'S PEAK
Boulder
R.
ROCK CR.
KIOWA CR.
BEAVER CR.
ARIKAREE R.
SOUTH FORK
Denver
SOUTH PLATTE
LORADO
KANSAS
Pueblo
ARKANSAS R.
HUERFANO R.
RIO GRANDE
CIMARRON R.
Trinidad
OKLAHOMA
CHAMA R.
36°
R.
CANADIAN
Santa Fé
Albuquerque
S. F.
O
Beyond the Hundredth Meridian and the Plateau Province
BOUNDARY OF THE PLATEAU PROVINCE
50 0 20 40 60 80 100 200
MILES
TEXAS

I

THE THRESHOLD

1. Independence Day, 1868

ON JULY 4, 1868, about the time when Henry Adams was turning back toward New York to face a new and sharply altered America after ten years of study and diplomacy in the service of the old, two men who would have been worth his attention as a historian were going about their business on the western edge of the Great Plains.

One, the Honorable William Gilpin, was at fifty-five a veteran of large actions and an old Western hand.[1] He had been a friend of Andrew Jackson's, and Jackson's personal appointee to West Point; his brother had been Attorney General in Van Buren's cabinet. Gilpin himself, blown westward by an accidental encounter with Frémont's expedition in 1843, had gone with Frémont as far as Walla Walla and then continued to Fort Vancouver by himself. He had brought back to Washington the 1844 petition of settlers in the Willamette valley for American occupation, and had become an authority and adviser on Western affairs to Washington statesmen, including Thomas Benton of Missouri. As a major in Doniphan's First Missouri Volunteers he had fought Mexicans in 1846, and later than that he had joined expeditions against the Comanches and Pawnees. When Abraham Lincoln went to Washington to face the consequences of his election as President of the United States, William Gilpin went with him; for weeks he slept in the White House as one of the volunteer bodyguard of one hundred, a service which he relinquished to become the first territorial governor of Colorado. In that office he had been active and effective in holding Colorado for the Union, and he had been through all his life a consistent and impassioned advocate of the imperial dynamism of Old Bullion Benton.

Speaking to the Fenian Brotherhood in the capital of the seven-year-old territory of Colorado on this Fourth of July, 1868, he repeated and summarized the things he had been saying in speeches and books since before the Mexican War and would go on saying until his death. It is almost awe-inspiring to contemplate this veteran Westerner, with twenty-five years of hard firsthand experience behind him, as he stands up in the raw frontier town of Denver and looks clear over the continent of facts and into prophecy.

"What an immense geography has been revealed!" he shouted at the sweating Fenians and their guests. "What infinite hives of population and laboratories of industry have been electrified and set in motion! The great sea has rolled away its sombre veil. Asia is found and has become our neighbor. . . . North America is known to our own people. Its concave form and homogeneous structure are revealed. Our continental mission is set to its perennial frame. . . ."

Gilpin's version of America's continental mission he had already elaborated in 1860, in a book entitled *The Central Gold Region, The Grain, Pastoral, and Gold Regions of North America with Some New Views of Its Physical Geography and Observations on the Pacific Railroad.* He would reprint it with additions in 1873 as *The Mission of the North American People,* and extend its ideas in 1890 in *The Cosmopolitan Railway.* The Manifest Destiny which he had learned from Benton, and which was a creed and a policy of his generation, was a passionate vision to Gilpin. He saw the West through a blaze of mystical fervor, as part of a grand geopolitical design, the overture to global harmony; and his conception of its resources and its future as a home for millions was as grandiose as his rhetoric, as unlimited as his faith, as splendid as his capacity for inaccuracy.

All the wishful convictions of his time and place had his credence. The Great American Desert whose existence had been vouched for by travelers and vaguely indicated on maps at least since the report of Zebulon Pike in 1810 was waved away with a gesture. The semi-arid plains between the 100th meridian and the Rockies, plains which had barred settlement and repelled Spaniard and Anglo-American alike, were no desert, nor even a semi-desert, but a pastoral Canaan. Belief in such a desert, he said, had preceded settlement, the location being put ever farther west like the homeland of the White Indians, until now it pinched and disappeared before the eyes of gold seekers and pioneer farmers. Gilpin joined the politicians and the railroads, eager for settlers, in finding most of the plains region exuberantly arable. He had distinguished corroboration for his belief that artesian waters would unlock the fertility of the whole subhumid region east of the Rockies, and if he had chosen to he could have quoted everything from frontier folklore to government geologists in support of the theory that settlement improved the climate, that in very truth "rain follows the plow." [2]

No hindrances to settlement now existed, Gilpin said; the Mississippi Valley which now supported eighteen million people could easily support eighteen hundred million, ten times the total population of the Roman Empire under Trajan and the Antonines. On the more westerly plains, though there was little surface timber, a beneficent Nature had so disposed the rooting system of the low growth that settlers were able to *dig* for firewood and find plenty. And on these plains, once the wild herds were exterminated, three domestic animals could be pastured where one wild one had formerly roamed.

Throughout the vast concave bowl of the continental interior was illustrated the unifying effect of geography, for here where everything ran toward the center instead of being dispersed and divided by central mountains, the people could never be divided into a hundred tribes and nations as in Europe, but must be one. The native race was an illustration: all the tribes from Florida to Vancouver's Island exhibited a "perfect identity in hair, complexion, features, religion, stature, and language." To this same healthful homogeneity our fortunate geography would within a few generations bring white Americans also.

But marvelous and fecund as the valley was, the great plateau region, including the parks of the Rockies, was more wonderful.

Superlatives were futile for the description of the salubrity, richness, health, prosperity, and peace this West offered. The painful struggles of earlier times and harsher climates would not be found. Even houses were unnecessary, so temperate were the seasons. The aborigines used none, and Gilpin himself, in six years of living there, had rarely slept under a roof. (The Mormon handcart companies who starved and froze on the Sweetwater in 1856 might have been astonished to hear this; likewise the men of Frémont's 1848 expedition, reduced to the practice of cannibalism in the Colorado mountains.)

Agriculture was effortless: no forests needed clearing, manual tillage was not required, even the use of the plow was not essential, so eager were seeds to germinate in this Paradise. As the plains were amply irrigated by underground and artesian waters, the plateau was watered by mountain streams of purest melted snow, and to arrange fields for irrigation was no more trouble than fencing, which the ditches here superseded. No heat or cold, no drouth or saturation, no fickle climate or uncertain yield, afflicted this extensive region, and no portion of the globe, even the Mississippi Valley with its potential eighteen hundred millions, would support so dense a population. San Luis Park would in time become as renowned as the Vale of Kashmir; South Pass would be a gateway more thronging than Gibraltar. And all up and down the length of the cordillera that stretched through two continents, the unlimited deposits of precious metals assured the people of a perennial and plentiful supply of coin. In a moment of caution, keeping his feet on the ground, Gilpin admitted that there were a few — a very few — patches of gravelly and unproductive soil in the mountain parks, but he hastened to add that these could be depended upon to contain placers of gold.

Owning a territory that stretched from sea to sea and brought America face to face with Asia on the West as it was face to face with Europe on the East; possessed of unlimited gold and other resources; endowed with a population energetic and enduring, which the peculiar geography of the continent would soon blend into one people; blessed with a political system divinely appointed to emancipate the world's oppressed millions and set an example that would recreate the globe; tested and unified by the late bloody civil strife, and with a geographical position squarely upon that isothermal zodiac which had nourished all the world's great civilizations, America lacked nothing for the most extravagant future. On the brink of the mountain West (and already past the threshold of the Gilded Age) Gilpin looked into the sunburst dazzle of Manifest Destiny and panted for words to express his triumph and his vision.

And he had some justification. West of the hustling capital on Cherry Creek the gulches were pouring out gold. North of it the Union Pacific tracks had crossed the pass between Cheyenne and modern Laramie and were approaching the continental divide at Creston. The tracks that had already surmounted altitudes greater than any railroad had surmounted before would ceremoniously mate with the Central Pacific rails north of Great Salt Lake on May 10 of the next year. Instantly the hardships of a continental crossing would be replaced by the luxury of Mr. Pullman's palace cars, and the symbolic union at Promontory would convert virtually a whole nation to the optimism of seers like William Gilpin. The cattle which would replace the buffalo were already coming north from Texas, beginning the fleeting romantic history of the cowboy West. The buffalo which were to be replaced were already being hunted to death for their hides or the sport of tourists, and it would not be too many years before the pioneer farmers of Kansas would make two and a half million dollars simply by clearing their fields of bones and shipping them east to fertilizer mills. Within five years of the time Gilpin spoke, literally millions of hides would go east via the Union Pacific, Kansas Pacific, and Santa Fe.[3] The West was ready to welcome its happy settlers.

But on the same day when Gilpin summarized his geopolitical and prophetic extravaganza for the Fenians, an exploring party was camped a few miles out of Cheyenne, in what would in three weeks become Wyoming Territory. It included something over a dozen people, among them the wife and sister of the leader. Some of the rest were college students, some were teachers, some were amateur naturalists, one or two were merely tourists. All were so recently arrived that the camp was a disorderly collection of duffle and half-broken mules and half-organized intentions. Backing the expedition was an assortment of scientific and educational institutions, all in on a penny ante basis: the Illinois Natural History Society, the Illinois Normal University, the Illinois Industrial University, and by virtue of some donated instruments and some good advice, the Smithsonian Institution.

Leading the party was a man who before he was through would challenge almost every fact and discourage every attitude that William Gilpin asserted or held about the West — challenge and attack them coolly and on evidence — and in place of Gilpin's come-all-ye frenzy would propose a comprehensive and considered plan for the opening of the regions beyond the 100th meridian. That plan, beside Gilpin's, would be so sober as to seem calamitous; it would employ consistently what a recent historian rather unhappily calls "deficiency terminology"[4] when speaking of the West, and it would be decades before parts of it would get a calm public hearing.

If William Gilpin was enthusiastically part of his time, yapping in the van of the continentally confident, Major John Wesley Powell was just as surely working against the current of popular optimism in the policies he developed, and decades ahead of it in his vision. It was to be his distinction and in a way his misfortune that in an age of the wildest emotionalism and nationalist fervor he operated by common sense, had a faith in facts, and believed in system. It was also one of his distinctions that in an age of boodle he would persist in an ideal of public service which most public men of the time neither observed nor understood.

Major Powell was no pioneer Westerner as Gilpin was. The summer of 1868 was only his second summer in the West, and he was thirty-four years old to Gilpin's fifty-five. As yet he was not much of anything — not much of a scientist, not much of a schoolteacher, not much of an explorer. But to the problems which the West suggested, and which from this time on absorbed his interest and shaped his career, he brought eventually science where Gilpin brought mythology, measurement where Gilpin brought rhetoric; and he brought an imaginative vigor as great as Gilpin's but much better controlled and much closer to fact. In his one trip to the Rockies in the summer of 1867 he had learned more basic truths about them than Gilpin would ever know. By the end of his career he would know the West as few men did, and understand its problems better than any.

He would know enough to correct Gilpin in all his major assumptions and most of his minor ones. Even in 1868 he knew enough not to say that "North America is known to our people." On the maps he carried there were great blank spaces: in less than a year he would be embarked on an exploration that would replace hundreds of square miles of cartographical guesswork with information. As part of his mature work he would plan and begin the systematic mapping of the whole country, a project that even yet is incomplete and will never be finished as he planned it. Through years of public life he would resist with all his energy the tide of unreasoning, fantasy-drawn settlement and uncontrolled exploitation that the Gilpins explicitly or implicitly encouraged. He would continue to believe in a modified Great American Desert, to talk in "deficiency terms," to insist that instead of supporting eighteen hundred million people the Mississippi Valley could be made, in its trans-Missouri reaches, a barren and uninhabitable wasteland by the methods used to irritate it into fertility. He would protest the plow that broke the plains, he would deny that rain followed the plow, he would fight Western Congressmen and Senators and land speculators and dreamers who persisted in the Gilpin belief in ample artesian water under the Dakota buffalo grass. Instead of taking on faith the existence of unlimited seams of metals and coal, he would have a large hand in the careful survey of all these resources, and he would have the vision to add water and grass and land and timber to those limited and destroyable riches. He would have the courage to seek a revision of the public land laws and a modification of the sacrosanct freehold of 160 acres to match the conditions of the West, and would fight for his proposals cunningly and tenaciously. He would labor to conserve the public domain and to withdraw lands from entry in order to protect for posterity and the public good watersheds and dam sites and playgrounds. The irrigation which to Gilpin was simpler than building fence would be a lifelong study to Powell, and he would father a public interest in the subject that would eventually flower in the Newlands Act of 1902, establishing the Reclamation Bureau which has remade the face of the West. He would be a prime mover in the establishment of the federal government as the sponsor of science for the public welfare. Instead of preaching unlimited supply and unrestrained exploitation he would preach conservation of an already partly gutted continent and planning for the development of what remained.

And even the matter of racial homogeneity. It is hard to imagine what enthusiasm could have led Gilpin to say that all of the North American Indians were of one stature, language, complexion, religion, and culture. A glance at Gallatin's work would have told him differently; his own experience with Indians should have forced him to other conclusions. Powell would demonstrate, the first to bring a comprehensive order and system to the study, that the Indians were on the contrary of an incredible variety in every way. He would undertake the classification of all the Indian languages, would study Indian myth and folklore, and would found a government bureau whose whole purpose was the scientific investigation of that variety before the tribes were obliterated by the tide of Gilpin's settlers. In the course of those ethnological studies, he would contribute to the remaking and enlarging of the science of cultural anthropology.

But all of these activities, knowledges, and achievements were in the future. On July 4, 1868, they lay around in Powell's mind half realized and half intended, as much in need of thought and discipline and organization as the half-organized camp of the Rocky Mountain Scientific Exploring Expedition.

2. *The Dynamics of a Homemade Education*

THE BOY HENRY ADAMS, appraising the careers that were open to him, felt that of all the possibilities, the West offered him least. "Neither to a politician nor to a business-man nor to any of the learned professions did the West promise any certain advantages, while it offered uncertainties in plenty."[1] Adams could not have been expected to know in 1854 the shape of things to come, but the reminiscent Adams who was writing his *Education* in 1905 might have admitted that to certain politicians — Lincoln, Grant, and Garfield among them — as well as to certain businessmen — Miller and Lux, Isham, Henry Villard, Leland Stanford — as well as to numerous teachers, preachers, writers (Twain, Howells, Bret Harte, Hamlin Garland, Edward Eggleston) — the West had offered not merely opportunity but golden opportunity. One did not have to like everything the West brought into the nation's life to be aware that it had brought *something,* even that long before 1905 it had come to have a certain dominance in national affairs. Yet Adams, forgetful or not of how the nation's center of gravity had shifted from the Quincy and Beacon Hill of his boyhood, was certainly right in not going west to grow up with the country. Whatever his education had prepared him for, it had not prepared him for that. That took an education of a special kind. To grow up with the West, or to grow with and through it into national prominence, you had to have the West bred in your bones, you needed it facing you like a dare. You needed a Western education, with all the forming and shaping and the dynamics of special challenge and particular response that such an education implied.

The thing that many western boys called their education would have seemed to Adams a deprivation, so barren was it of opportunities and so pitiful were its methods and equipment. Considered in any way but in terms of its results in men and women, it *was* a deprivation. But the men it produced over a period of several generations showed such a family resemblance that until immigration drowned them under they constituted a strong regional type, and their virtues as exemplified in a Lincoln or a Mark Twain force the conclusion that this crude society with its vulgar and inadequate culture somehow made noble contributions to mankind. John Wesley Powell, without being a Lincoln or a Mark Twain, was of that persuasion, one of a great company. It is worth looking for a moment at how he was made.

It is easy enough to summarize: he was made by wandering, by hard labor, by the Bible, by an outdoor life in small towns and on farms, by the optimism and practicality and democracy of the frontier, by the occasional man of learning and the occasional books he met, by country schools and the ill-equipped cubs or worn-out misfits who taught them, by the academies and colleges with their lamentable lacks and their industry and their hope, by the Methodism of his father and the prevailing conviction that success came from work and only to the deserving. If there were not many opportunities, if the cultural darkness was considerable, it was also true that in that darkness any little star showed as plainly as a sun.

A homemade education did something to the people who acquired it, and a homemade education was not the exclusive invention of the western settlements. Any rural area, once frontier, retained some of the stamp: the boyhood of a Thurlow Weed or a John Burroughs or a Jay Gould in upstate New York was not greatly different from the boyhood of a Lincoln or a Garfield or a John Muir in the Midwest. But in the Midwest, over immense regions of a peculiar homogeneity in climate, geography, people, and economic status, the homemade education was typical, and it was made more typical by the way in which successive westering waves repeated the whole process in new country. Ohio and Kentucky repeated the backwoods experience of Massachusetts and New York and Pennsylvania; Indiana repeated Ohio; Illinois and Wisconsin and Michigan repeated Indiana; Iowa and Minnesota and Missouri repeated Illinois and Wisconsin; the Dakotas and Nebraska and Kansas repeated, or tried to repeat, Iowa and Minnesota.[2]

The bearded, one-armed young man who commanded the Rocky Mountain Exploring Expedition, and who had acquired the lifelong title of Major in the same volunteer service that cost him his arm, was almost classically a product of that special frontier education. His character, his ideas, his very weaknesses and his peculiar strengths derived from a social and intellectual climate nearly rudimentary, nearly unformed, but of a singularly formative kind. He is not comprehensible as man or as career except in the context given memorable expression by Lincoln, and containing, among Powell's own contemporaries, such distinguished names as Garfield, Mark Twain, Howells, Eggleston, Muir, Garland and Lester Ward. These, and many others like them, at once expressed and helped to shape the emerging West. The education of John Wesley Powell is less interesting as a personal than as a regional experience.[3]

Wandering was a part of it, and the wandering led always west.

Born in Mount Morris, New York, the eldest son of an immigrant Wesleyan preacher, young Powell spent his boyhood in Jackson, Ohio, near Chillicothe, and knew what it was to be stoned as an abolitionist for his father's sake, and learned something of the southern Ohio country from the reports his father brought home from the circuit, and watched a town grow up from raw beginnings around him, and had some chance to observe leading men of the town and region. By the time he was twelve he was adding the rural experience to that of the small town, taking over the major responsibility for a frontier farm in Walworth County, Wisconsin, southwest of Milwaukee. By the time he was eighteen he was helping his family to move across into Bonus Prairie, Illinois, and was ready himself to break loose on a series of summer trips and summer jobs that took him from St. Paul to New Orleans, from Pittsburgh to St. Louis, across Michigan, Wisconsin, Missouri, up and down the Mississippi and its tributary rivers. The principal purpose of those trips was amateur natural history, but they were adventure too — and education. The Civil War could hardly be said to have dragged him away from home; his home had been hardly more than a wharf to tie his boat to for years. And no sooner was the war over than his itchy foot led him west. His migratory family finally came to rest, long after Powell had broken away, in Emporia, Kansas.

An acquaintance with books and learning was not a thing that a frontier boy like Powell could take for granted; he had to seize it as he could. Abe Lincoln said it for every such boy with brains and dreams in his head: "The things I want to know are in books; my best friend is a man who'll git me a book I ain't read." A frontier boy with a lust for books was not choosy. It is hard, in an age with more books than it wants, to comprehend the enduring passion for reading that kept Lincoln up half the night with his bushy head almost in the fire, and led John Muir to rise at one o'clock in the morning to read and work on inventions, and induced Powell, hauling grain to market from the Walworth County farm, to put under the wagon seat any books he happened to have available, to be read on the slow tedious road. A frontier child who liked to read read what he could lay his hands on, and he laid hands on some peculiar things and in odd quarters. The boy who got a homemade education rarely could buy books until he was well grown, though Edward Eggleston's father took the precaution of providing in his will for a library for the use of his sons. Generally a boy borrowed his reading, and generally there was someone whom accident or ambition had tossed out on the frontier who brought his love of books and some of the books themselves to the wilderness. *Inferretque deos Latio.* Acquiring learning in the rural Midwest was like an elaborate egg-hunt — but the rules were fair; there were always eggs if you hunted long and hard enough. Somebody always turned out to have a book you hadn't read.

Quite as often, somebody in town or within reach turned out to have some sort of intellectual or professional or scientific interest or capacity, too, and that when it showed was a very bright star to tell direction by. In an extraordinary number of cases that first man of learning or enthusiasm that a frontier boy encountered gave his life a twist that it never outgrew. It happened that when Lincoln walked twenty miles to borrow books in Rockport, he borrowed them from Pitcher, and Pitcher was a lawyer. It happened too that from Dave Turnham, the constable at Pigeon Creek, he borrowed *The Revised Laws of Indiana, adopted and enacted by the general assembly at their eighth session. To which are prefixed the Declaration of Independence, the Constitution of the United States, the Constitution of the State of Indiana.* And it happened that Ann Rutledge's father sponsored a debating society, and that Abe Lincoln came. The accidents of his light-starved youth pushed him toward the law and politics just as surely as Edward Eggleston's contacts with Julia Dumont and with his stepfather in Vevay pushed him toward literature and the ministry, or Mark Twain's and William Dean Howells' experience in the print shops that Lincoln called the "poor man's university" pushed them toward a career in words.

There was more than one "poor man's university," and more than one profession into which a boy with a homemade education could be directed. Though free schools did not come to the Midwest until after 1848, and though illiteracy in 1840, when Powell was six years old, ranged from about 5½ per cent in Ohio to more than 14 per cent in Indiana and Illinois,[4] there were forces which had some of a school's effects. The Methodist circuit riders were one such force, both through their preaching and through the books and tracts they distributed. Peter Cartwright is said to have given away as much as a thousand dollars' worth of reading matter in a single year, and the very character of the circuit rider's mission took him to places where reading matter was most needed. Three fourths of the early students of Asbury (DePauw) University came from homes that were visited by itinerant Methodist preachers. What impulse toward learning and a wider world was generated by the crude culture of those men it would be impossible to measure, but it was undoubtedly great. Powell, like Eggleston, had it in his own home — though that fact probably made it less rather than more acceptable. The Powell family also had, as virtually every pioneer household had, a Bible, and they read it, and read it aloud.

Lawyers too rode a circuit, and they too were a civilizing force, though considerably more tainted with rum and broad stories than the preachers. The offices which they maintained at home, and the libraries of law books with which they stocked them, were universities just as surely as the print shops were, and more Americans than Andrew Jackson and Lincoln got much of their learning reading law with a patron. But the law never touched Wes Powell; and the Methodism of his father was so far overcome by his more secular reading that he refused to study for the ministry and by the refusal threw away his father's help toward a college education. He wanted to study for something quite different from the ministry, and the reason he did was that in Jackson, Ohio, he had met one of those frontier men of learning who so often gave a homemade education its motive and its direction.

This man, George Crookham, was a successful farmer, an abolitionist active in the Underground Railroad, and a self-taught man of science. Crookham had a private museum filled with Indian relics and natural history specimens. He had a library of scientific works of which he was very proud. His friends among the scientific and political leaders of Ohio included William Mather, the state geologist, Salmon P. Chase, the head of the Liberty Party, and President Charles Grandison Finney of Oberlin. And he had adjoining his museum a room in which without fee he gave instruction to all young men who wanted it. When the heat of the slavery issue made the common school unsafe for young Wes

Powell in that border town, Crookham undertook to instruct him.

They read Gibbon and Hume, among other things, but Gibbon and Hume were not the sources from which Powell learned most. For a boy of less than ten, even a light-starved frontier boy, those were pretty tough going. But natural history excursions into the fields and woods, sometimes with Crookham alone, sometimes with Crookham and Mather, were pure delight. Crookham, who partook of that taste for "natural philosophy" that kept the eighteenth century alive on the nineteenth-century American frontiers, was not particular in his intellectual tastes. He was botanist, geologist, zoologist, ethnologist, archaeologist, historian, philosopher, in the best tradition of the self-taught rural savant, and his life overflowed with scientific, political, agricultural, religious, and human interests. He was Wes Powell's guide for only a short time, and the wonders of his museum and library were available for an even shorter time, for a gang of pro-slavery hoodlums burned it down. But the few years of Crookham's company and instruction had a thousand times more immediate effect on the boy than all the years of his father's piety and orthodoxy.

When Wes Powell began to develop grown-up interests, they were by and large Crookham's interests. When he began to collect books, they were the sort of books that Crookham had collected, perhaps some of them those scientific treatises emanating from the Owenite colony of New Harmony, which Say and Lesueur and Troost and the rest of the "boatload of learning" made for a while the scientific capital of the Midwestern frontier. When he grew old enough to follow his own whims, his whims led him into excursions in search of natural history specimens, and at the first opportunity he began collections in pure imitation of Crookham's — flowers, shells, reptiles, relics from the mounds, animals, especially fresh-water shells and fossils. When he came, as he almost inevitably did, to Crookham's profession of schoolteaching — that common but often temporary recourse of the bright farm boy on the way up — he taught school Crookham's way, with field trips and an enthusiastic emphasis on natural history. And when he came to seek mature companionship in his intellectual life he found himself active in societies similar to the informal groups of which Crookham had been the center in Powell's Ohio boyhood. That is to say, the influence of Crookham was crucial and definitive: it was an influence calculated to make young Powell a leading citizen of some rural Athens, a member of the debating club, a lecturer on Lyceum circuits, a pillar of the crude structure that learning was building in the wilderness. He did not remain in that mold — the mold was too small for him — but he was shaped by it.

The years of the Powells' residence in Wisconsin were from one point of view years of hardship and deprivation for the boy, for his brothers Bram and Walter, and for his two sisters. The back-breaking, stunting labor of a frontier farm was his from the age of twelve on. Starting only three years later and sixty miles farther north, a Scotch boy named John Muir would go through a virtually identical experience of the hard manual labor necessary to break a frontier farm, and in his autobiography Muir would give classic expression to those fifteen-hour working days and the stolen hours when sleep was put off in favor of books. The parallel is exact even to the religious opposition of the father, for Joseph Powell objected to his son's museum, his natural history, his scientific interests, in the same way that Muir's father protested against reading and invention. Both boys were confirmed in their scientific interests by the surroundings of a backwoods Wisconsin farm, by nature in its intimate variety, by wandering Indians, by the persistent, constant stream of questions that the mind proposed and clamored to have answered. Both boys broke away for long rambling excursions justified by scientific collections; both sought college at their own expense and interrupted their schooling by intervals of teaching and farm labor; and both ultimately got what the schools could give them, but never graduated.

Powell's academic career was actually more restless and broken than Muir's. He tried the Illinois Institute which his father had helped to organize and which after collapse and reorganization became Wheaton College, and found when he went to register that not a single scientific course was offered. He tried Illinois College at Jacksonville for a year, and left it to go on a long collecting trip across Wisconsin. In 1857 he was back at Illinois Institute in Wheaton, and in the year following at Oberlin, from which he quietly departed with a smattering of Latin and Greek after one term.

No college in the Midwest was really equipped to teach a scientist, though there were a few courses in botany and natural philosophy. Powell had taught himself geometry in order to give it to his students in the country schools he had taught in off and on since the age of eighteen. He taught himself the sciences in the same way, and supplemented what he got from books with what collecting in the field could teach him. The 1855 trip across Wisconsin kept him rambling for four months. The next year, following a road Lincoln had traveled, he went down the Mississippi in a skiff from the Falls of St. Anthony to New Orleans, and on that long lonely wonderful passage he may have met or been passed by a steamboat on the texas of which a cub named Sam Clemens was learning the river from a pilot named Horace Bixby. In the spring of 1857 Powell took the train to Pittsburgh and floated down the Ohio to St. Louis, following the classic natural history route into the West that had been followed by Lewis and Clark, Say, Schoolcraft, Nuttall, Maximilian of Wied-Neuwied, and a dozen other of the West's first scientists. That same fall he was down in Missouri in the Iron Mountain country, collecting fossils. The following spring he rowed down the Illinois River to its mouth, and thence up the Des Moines as far as the mouth of Raccoon Creek. He won prizes for his mollusk collection at the 1860 fair of the Illinois State Agricultural Society, he found time to woo his cousin Emma in Detroit, against the family's wishes; he tried his hand in the spring of 1860 as a lecturer on geography and geology around a tanktown lyceum circuit in Kentucky, Tennessee, and Mississippi, and in that same year when he cast a vote for Abraham Lincoln for President he was made principal of the public schools of Hennepin, Illinois, near the junction of the Illinois River and the Illinois and Mississippi Canal, where he had been teaching since 1858.

What distinguishes this early career of Powell's is not its unusualness, but its intensity. He did the things that many of his contemporaries were doing, but did them with a kind of ferocity and a restless, driving will to completeness and perfection that distinguished him among local Illinois naturalists while he was still a very young man. When the State Natural History Society obtained a charter and elected its first officers in March, 1861, Principal John Wesley Powell, then aged twenty-seven, and the possessor of a homemade scientific education of more variety than depth, was made its secretary. Within little more than a month he was in the army as a volunteer; his education took a sudden turn toward military engineering, and the amateur scientist became for the next four years an amateur soldier.

He was not the kind to remain still, even in the army. He entered on April 14 as a private. By June he was a second lieutenant, by November a captain and something of an expert on fortifications, solidly enough established on Grant's staff at Cape Girardeau to ask as a personal favor a few days' leave to go to Detroit and marry his cousin Emma Dean. On April 5, 1862, he came out of the smoke and roar of Shiloh, mounted on General Wallace's horse and with his right arm smashed by a Minie ball. They removed his arm above the elbow in Savannah three days later.

Losing one's right arm is a misfortune; to some it would be a disaster, to others an excuse. It affected Wes Powell's life about as much as a stone fallen into a swift stream affects the course of the river. With a velocity like his, he simply foamed over it. He did not even resign from the army, but returned after a leave and a stretch of recruiting duty, and served as an artillery officer with Grant, Sherman, and Thomas. On January 2, 1865, after tasting more battle at Port Gibson, Grand Gulf, Raymond, Jackson, Charapini Hill, Big River, Vicksburg, the Meridian Raid, Nashville, and having risen to the command of the artillery of the 17th Army Corps, he resigned. His brother Walter, a lieutenant in Powell's battery, had been captured at Atlanta and had lain for a time completely mad in Camp Sorghum. A month after Powell's resignation Walter Powell was exchanged, a walking skeleton. His brother Wes was not much better off, for he came out of the war with a painful, twice-operated-upon stump, and weighing barely 110 pounds with a full beard.

By the fall of 1865, Major Powell had moved up to a professorship of geology at Illinois Wesleyan University in Bloomington. What he gave his students was essentially Crookham. He taught science classes with field excursions, he lectured on natural science, he formed a chapter of the State Natural History Society. In 1866 he arranged a move to the Illinois State Normal University, practically next door. The new post gave him a fresh impetus. Between November, 1866, and February, 1867, he personally steered through the legislature in Springfield a grant in support of a museum of the Illinois Natural History Society in Bloomington. The grant provided a thousand dollars a year for the maintenance and increase of the Society's collections, and it provided $1500 a year as salary for a curator. Curator was precisely what Major Powell wanted to be.

Considering his later success as an imaginative and tenacious bureau head in Washington, his success in this, his first minor local piece of promotion, seems a trivial thing. Yet his campaign in 1866–67 was brilliantly conducted, and it showed for the first time the politician and promoter superimposed upon the earnest amateur naturalist. Something new had been added to Crookham's disciple, a confidence and dash and capacity to manipulate men that nothing but the army could have taught him so fast. He was a finished performer as he appeared before the legislature in Springfield, argued for and got his grant on his own specifications, took the legislature's decision home and presented it to the Board of Education, meeting in Bloomington in March, and permitted the Board to press the curatorship upon him as an extension of his professorial duties. When he had modestly accepted this position, he told the Board about a dream he had of taking an expedition of students and naturalists to the Rocky Mountains or the Dakota badlands, where science had made only the barest beginnings and where a museum's collections could be quickly enriched. He came out of the meeting with the Board's promise that half the new maintenance fund of the museum could be devoted to support of the expedition, and with their almost breathless approval of everything he had asked.[5] The whole operation was small, but the only thing that was minor-league about it was the modesty of Powell's requests. He would learn to ask for more later, but he would never improve upon his performance as a promoter.

Actually, his first try for something bigger was prompt. In the latter part of April, 1867, he made up his mind to go to Washington and try for a Congressional appropriation to support his expedition. As one of that rush of office-seekers and petitioners and peddlers of schemes, that mob which the lobbyist Sam Ward likened to rutting stags, Powell did not do quite so well as he had before the

Illinois legislature.[6] But he did call on Grant, his old commander, who was then Secretary of War, and Grant did advise him to present a written request for army rations for twelve men, which Grant promised to provide. He also promised a military escort for Powell's party from Fort Laramie through the Badlands of Dakota. That was the best Powell could get out of the pork barrel, and it turned out that he could not use the second part of what he did get, for when he went out to see General Sherman in Council Bluffs a month later, Sherman advised him against stirring up the Sioux, and steered him instead toward the Colorado Rockies, where things were quieter.

By enlisting volunteers eager for excitement, by playing upon the railroads' universal desire to cultivate good will through favors to anyone with a potential grain of influence or prestige, and by gaining support from several institutions of learning, the Major managed to get his expedition to the mountains in 1867, and he and Emma climbed Pikes Peak and Lincoln Peak and took their crew up and down the Front Range and through Middle and South Parks and shipped their natural history specimens home. That limping reconnoissance was behind him now; it had demonstrated that imagination and perseverance could make a successful expedition out of very little. Now he was back at the edge of the Rockies, still with only ration-card support from Washington, still pinched for money, still depending on free railroad fares and free freight, on contributions from the Natural History Society and Normal University and the Illinois Industrial University and any other institution that wanted to buy in, but with something important on his mind. Slight, tough, well recovered from his wound and bristling with energy, Major Powell was not inclined to lament his failure both last year and this to extract an appropriation from Congress. His two trips to Washington had taught him something, made him acquainted. If he succeeded in the purposes of his expedition he could go back to Washington a third time and ask for what he wanted and get it. Weaknesses of equipment, personnel, finances, were troublesome but not fatal, and he was too busy looking ahead to worry about them. The farm boy trained in physical hardship, trained through the head and through the hands, trained in optimism and imagination as well as in a smattering of a half-dozen sciences, full of confidence and alive with ideas, was now coming face to face with the real West, and this was something he had been waiting for.

The inadequacies of a frontier education were all his: he had little formal background, he had never possessed adequate laboratory facilities and consequently did not have real laboratory skills, he had the brashness of the half educated that let him set up as an expert in a half-dozen specialized fields. By strict standards he was a "collector," a "natural historian," rather than a scientist. It was not pure accident that in this same summer of 1868 Othniel C. Marsh of Yale would pop off the Union Pacific train for a hurried few hours at a Nebraska station and in those few hours make discoveries of a thousand times greater importance than all the collections of Powell's party in two years. Specifically, Marsh would pick up the first of the fossils that gave him a complete developmental history of the horse from *eohippus* to *equus,* and let him publish the clinching documentation of the theory of evolution.[7] But Marsh was trained at the Sheffield Scientific School and in Germany; he was a thorough professional. He knew what he was looking for and he knew where to look and he knew what to do with what he found. Not that much could be said of Major Powell.

Nevertheless he had his strengths, and those too came largely from his border education. He had the independence, the confidence, the practical ability to accomplish things, that many better trained men lacked. He did not know enough to be discouraged. The war had given him a lesson in organization and the command of large numbers of men. It had shown him that an amateur soldier could accomplish things as well as many a professional. It had given him a taste for leadership that now responded to the challenge of a barely opened West.

Powell would have thought Henry Adams' doubts about the West the sheerest nonsense; he would not have understood the mind from which they came, for where Powell started low and West, Adams had started high and East. Where the one was crippled with doubts and ironies, his ambition constantly weakened by a divided mind, Powell was as single-minded as a buzz saw, and as resolute, and as little bothered by the agenbit of inwyt and the pale cast of thought. He was a doer, of a kind that Adams thought he admired but did not really understand and perhaps was a little afraid of. In later years Powell and Adams were friends of a sort, and at least once Powell dined at the Adams house on Lafayette Square, and Adams was one of a group that in 1878 met in Powell's parlor and organized the Cosmos Club, and they had a mutuality of friends and interests and a perfectly amicable relationship. But admiration and real liking apparently never flowered. Adams' admiration went out instead to Clarence King, the brilliant and volatile athlete and connoisseur and scientist and administrator, in Adams' opinion the best educated man in America for the job an American had to do, and engaged in a geological reconnoissance that both for science and for economics was of absolutely major importance.

But note that Clarence King, Yale educated, eastern-born, well to do, failed to live up to the extravagant predictions that Adams and John Hay made for him. He failed, Adams said, "for lack of money." That is hardly an accurate, though it is a humane and protective, judgment. Clarence King failed for lack of character, persistence, devotion, wholeness. For that important job he seemed to Adams cut out to do, John Wesley Powell was actually much better equipped. Despite his homemade education, and just possibly because of it, he would do more than Clarence King would do and do it better.

3. *The Rocky Mountain Scientific Exploring Expedition*

TOO LATE in time to be called explorers, too unskilled to deserve the name of frontiersmen, most of them strangers to the mountains, scientists only by an indulgent frontier standard, the members of the Rocky Mountain Scientific Exploring Expedition[1] were not, apart from their leader, a very likely looking crowd. Their zoologist was a Methodist preacher, their assistant zoologist an Illinois farm boy. Their ornithologists were distinguished more for ability to shoot birds than for capacity to make taxonomical heads or tails of them.

Their entomologist, as in 1867, was Powell's brother-in-law, Almon Thompson, the superintendent of schools in Bloomington. Though he would achieve a solid reputation later, it would be as a topographer, not as an entomologist. Their botanist was a bona fide and able naturalist, George Vasey, whose name still persists on the maps in the little curtain of maidenhair and redbud and ivy called Vasey's Paradise, deep in Marble Canyon on the Colorado. Emma Dean Powell and Nellie Powell Thompson were ornithologists, entomologists, or botanists as the occasion demanded, and Powell's brother Walter had a similarly vague function. Powell himself was listed as geologist, though his principal contribution to science thus far had been his extensive collection of shells. Dr. Henry Wing, of the Illinois State Board of Education, was along for the ride, as was the Reverend W. H. Daniels, an eminent Illinois divine and a historian of Methodism. Of the student volunteers, Sam Garman would become a Harvard professor and an assistant to Alexander Agassiz, and L. W. Keplinger would wind up a Kansas City judge. The others would not make history.

Motley and green, they camped outside Cheyenne filling their eye with the strangenesses: the prairie dog towns, the wild horse herds, the outline of romantic mountains breaking the horizons west and south, the restlessly moving Indians. They bought wild mounts, both horses and mules, and universally bit the dust when they tried to climb on. For two weeks, half their mornings and most of their nights would be spent chasing and cursing runaways.

Organized into messes of four, and supplied from the army warehouse at Cheyenne, they started south toward Denver on July 8, little by little hardening themselves for their contemplated expedition into the mountains by the easier travel on the plains. They put their mouths around the names of unknown streams and lonesome little stations on the Denver road; Lone Tree, Box Elder, Big Thompson, the "Cashalapoo." Rhodes Allen, one of the bird shooters, roused up from a violent attack of colic to note in his diary an encounter with "Old Fridey," chief of the "Ropahoos." Minor adventures befell them: a government agent chased them and confiscated one of their mules as a stolen animal; Powell chased the agent and got the mule back. Eventually, recovered from their first sun and wind burn, hardened to the saddle and feeling like buckaroos, and with a pack full of prairie dog and bird skins and pressed prairie flowers, they arrived in Denver, a somewhat more competent crew than had left Cheyenne.

Not explorers, in spite of the sounding title of their expedition. And yet the country they were headed for was not exactly a tourist playground yet, the mountains westward clear to the twenty-year-old Mormon settlements in Utah were only skimpily known. Not all the passes had been crossed, not all the peaks climbed, not all the rivers tracked from mouth to source, only the most obvious flora and fauna had been collected and classified.[2] There were miners on the metal lodes and placers, a few trappers and traders in the mountain valleys or parks, but beyond was a little-known wilderness, Ute country, full of game and not without danger, roadless except for game and Indian trails and the uncertain tracks by which Frémont in 1844, '48, and '53, Gunnison in 1853, Berthoud in 1861 and the Third California Veteran Infantry in 1865 had crossed those mountains. Lowland folk, excited and a little awed by what they approached, Rhodes Allen and Lyle Durley and W. C. Bishop and Keplinger and the rest of the greenhorns sat in camp on the bank of the South Platte, or stood night guard over the horses, and felt the loom of the Front Range over them like a portent of mystery and adventure, and were moved, authentically enough for beginners, with the thrill explorers feel.

Partly for the sake of the inexperienced, partly because even in relatively settled country collecting was possible, Powell moved slowly. There was much rain, the nights were cold, the greenhorns continued to have trouble with breachy horses and balky mules. They bitched to their diaries like old campaigners, grumbling about everything from the camp ants to the insistence Mrs. Powell made that they read the books she loaned them. They got piled from their horses and learned about prickly pears; they tried swimming in the icy water of Clear Creek and learned better; they had to make trail and discovered some of the facts of mountain travel; they encountered mosquitoes, "worse than I ever saw them." By the time they made the mining camp of Empire they felt themselves considerable voyageurs. But at Empire they met a man with whom Powell had arranged a rendezvous the autumn before, the trader and mountain man and guide, Jack Sumner. Sumner looked over their outfit in silence, and they shrivelled quietly back to size.

Many years later, when his friendship with Powell had soured to an enduring grudge,[3] Sumner wrote of the party that they were "about as fit for roughing it as Hades is for a Powder house." But he got along with them well enough. He was used to dudes. From his trading post at Hot Sulphur Springs in Middle Park he acted as factor for his brother-in-law, William N. Byers, editor of the *Rocky Mountain News* and later historian of Colorado. When politicos or bigwigs were to be entertained on a fishing or hunting or packing expedition, Sumner made an admirable guide. Bayard Taylor had used and liked him on a journey through the mountains in 1866;[4] Powell himself found him useful the next summer. Blond, cool, tough, a good hand with Indians and a good shot, he would have made a first-class partisan for one of the fur brigades if he had lived twenty-five years earlier. But he had been a Union soldier during the war; he had, through his sister, distinguished connections; he was himself originally a farm boy from Iowa. He could adapt himself to these dudes and college boys, especially since he and Powell had the previous autumn cooked up a project far more exciting than the collection of specimens for natural history museums.

By his own testimony,[5] Sumner was impatient to start immediately on the exploration of the Green and Colorado Rivers that he and Powell planned. It was that project which had induced Congress to pass a special resolution authorizing the 1868 expedition to draw rations from Western army posts. But Powell had obligations to his academic sponsors as well as to his own maturing and enlarging plans. The expedition must be justified, and its continuation assured, by successful collecting. Without regard either for the impatience of Sumner or the presence of Byers, who joined them at Empire bent on a pet expedition of his own, they camped for a week on the summit of the range in Berthoud Pass. At that season, Alpine plants were an unbelievably flowery carpet on slopes and ridges. Apparently neither of the women of the expedition kept a diary, but both Emma Powell and Nellie Thompson must have become assistant botanists for the time.[6] The early bloomers, moss campion and alpine lilies and alpine phlox and rock jasmine and forget-me-nots, were gone or fading, but others were coming on: alpine goldflower like a squat obese sunflower; alpine avens, bistorts, yellow-green alpine paintbrush, sandwort, saxifrages, sky pilots, chiming bells and harebells; and under the cold edges of melting snowbanks snow buttercups, king's crown, rose crown, marsh marigold; and away up on the bare windy slopes pigmy shrubs, cinquefoil and red gooseberry, and skyland willow hardly an inch high bearing its catkins snugly among the protecting grass and flowers.

Neither of the diarists, Allen and Durley, mentions the flowers. Durley was making trail with Sumner. Allen was out all day lying in ambush to shoot birds, and he was preoccupied with the snow and hail that fell two or three times during the week, the mudholes in which his mare bogged down, the mosquitoes that ate him alive as he lay in wait. Allen had a certain eye for scenery, and could appreciate the beauty of their camp on a meadowy saddle at 11,500 feet, with a north-running creek flowing toward Middle Park and the Grand River, and thence to the Colorado and the Gulf of California, and a south-running creek that dropped steeply into Clear Creek and on to the Platte, the Missouri, and the Gulf of Mexico. But discomfort could kill off scenery fairly fast for young Allen. His diary, full of the bad trails, fatigue, and "fussing and blundering around" that he saw in the trip, is probably a fair expression of the feelings of the majority of the party. They were all working as unpaid volunteers. They had a right to grumble.

They were an expedition organized and supported for the purpose of stocking a museum with natural history specimens. The members were selected more for their availability, willingness, or relationship to the leader than for their attainments in science. Yet they could hardly fail, in the virgin territory of the Rockies, to serve science every time they went out, and in view of Powell's appetite for learning, they could hardly fail to do much more than collect specimens.

So much was new, so much untouched and unknown and undone. Weather, topography, zoology, botany, geology, entomology, ornithology, herpetology, all the branches of science of which Powell had a smattering, could be enriched. In a week on Berthoud Pass a student with a shotgun, so ignorant of science that he later shot a jack rabbit under the impression that it was a young antelope, might bring in varieties of birds rare or even undescribed. The two ladies of the party could go wild among the alpine gardens and supplement Linnaeus in the act of picking a casual bouquet. A pair of schoolboys with a barometer, stuck up on top of some peak to take hourly readings through eight or nine days, could help establish so basic a scientific datum as the barometric fluctuation for the region, and lay the base not only for future weather reports but for the accurate measurement of altitudes.

Powell was running an all-purpose scientific reconnoissance, a large, loose, sketchy survey of the natural history resources of the Rockies. But he was not one to be content with minima. He wanted the most he could get in every line, and he drove his packers and collectors until they groused and grumbled to their diaries. As they moved down off Berthoud Pass into Middle Park to the base camp at Hot Sulphur Springs he had the country scoured for fifteen or twenty miles on both sides of the line of march. Once at the Springs, he scattered his party up and down the park after birds and mammals and minerals and barometer readings, and with a small picked group started out to fulfill one of the two agreements he had made the summer before. This one involved exploration of a kind, and exploration was a lust that burned in him. The canyon of Clear Creek up to Empire, and Middle Park around Hot Sulphur Springs, were populous parts of the mountains. But on top of Long's Peak, where he and Byers were headed now, no man had yet stood.

Four years earlier, Byers had attempted the ascent of Long's Peak, for no particular reason except a sportsman's zest in activity. Energetic, literate, sanguine, Byers was an ardent sportsman, a keen fisherman. While Durley and Allen and others of Powell's party threshed the waters of Grand River and a dozen creeks in vain, Byers caught all the fish he could carry. And he had an additional interest in this part of the mountains: the hundred and sixty acres on both sides of the Grand that contained the hot springs (now the heart of Hot Sulphur Springs, Colorado) he would buy in his wife's name the next year, and he already used Middle Park with a proprietary air, as if it were a playground to which he was privileged to invite guests. Some of Gilpin's faith in the future of the mountains was in him; his 1866 excursion with Bayard Taylor had made him aware of how much the mountain parks could offer an adventurous tourist. In his letters to his paper from the Springs [7] he glowed about the fishing, the grass, the color and pageantry of the Utes of Antero and Douglas, eighty lodges of them, camped along the river. Byers was a pioneer, an opener, a pass-crosser of a pure American breed, one for whom an untrodden peak was a rebuke and a shame to an energetic people. For his purposes he could not have found a better coadjutor than Powell.

From their camp on the west side of the Grand Lake, at the head of the park, the climbing party beat its way toward the peak through rough country and a tangle of down timber. The first night they slept at timberline, corralling their horses on a bare ridge by piling rocks across the only down path. In the morning, loaded with bacon and a batch of Major Powell's personal biscuits — gray, leaden, with a grain like fine limestone — they set off on foot. In climbing as in biscuit making Powell asked no odds and made no apology for his maiming. He stuck with the party across an intervening peak and found on gaining it that Long's, beyond, was separated by two miles of gorge from the main range. With great difficulty they worked down the precipitous northern face "which upon looking back appeared utterly impassable," and eastward along a ridge. This culminated in another peak only a little lower than Long's, from which they looked at their objective across another uncrossable chasm. In the end they had to descend clear to the valley and start over.

Of the group, which included Powell, his brother Walter, Byers, Sumner, and the students Keplinger, Garman, and Ned Farrell, the mountain man was the least enthusiastic. He had other things on his mind; he had not anticipated fooling around Middle Park all summer. At one point, inching along in the lead on a knife-edge of stone, he sat down and spit over the edge and balked. Keplinger, behind him, asked what was the matter. "By God, *I* haven't lost any mountain," Sumner said. Finally Keplinger passed him, and though Sumner followed, the tenderfoot had a chance to triumph over the frontiersman. Where the youth walked, Sumner "got down and cooned it."

That ridge led nowhere. They crawled back and finally made camp in what is now called the Wild Basin. From there they could see a route that seemed possible, and Keplinger, flushed with his afternoon's triumph, volunteered to reconnoiter. Climbing with all his hands and feet, he made his way up the Estes Park side to within a short distance of the summit. There he made the mistake of stopping to look at the view. It almost knocked him off the mountain. On his left, within ten feet, the edge dropped away in what seemed "the eaves of the world's roof." The disinclination that had visited

Sumner earlier visited Keplinger now. Clinging like a cat in the high branches of a tree, he slid and clawed down until he could drop to the ice in the northwest corner of the Notch. It was ten o'clock, and Sumner was working up the ridge lighting little fires of grass and twigs for beacons, when Keplinger made contact with the party again.

But he had found the way up. In the morning, without great difficulty, they worked up the last seven hundred feet and stood on the summit.

Sam Garman, a Quaker, and serious-minded, reported the experience to his friend Gertrude Lewis back in Bloomington:

> After a pretty hard climb we did it, built a monument on the top, raised a flag, threw some wine on the monument & the little that remained in the bottle was drank by 5 of the party. 2 of us withstanding all entreaties did not drink on Longs peak, whatever the papers may say to the contrary.

Garman does not name his fellow abstainer, nor say who took the trouble (it could only have been Byers) to carry a bottle of wine through two strenuous days of scrambling over cliffs and ridges. He does, however, remark on the discoveries Science made on top.

> Three hours we stayed on the top during which time my journal was written up and my collection enriched by several rare specimens. Nothing but Granite on the top afforded a poor foothold for Botanists yet some pretty mosses grew in the shadows of some large rocks, or close to the edges of the patches of snow, where they might keep damp for mosses love damp shady places; a few Lichens, i.e. only a few kinds, but many of a species grew and flourished on the otherwise bare sides of the Granite rocks. High and dry were they, for Lichens love the dry places, thousands of years had they flourished there and no human eye had beheld them. We exulted just a little in the thought that here if anywhere on the footstool were things just as God made them. — No flowers here too high for them. A Bird of the Shore larks: A few species of flies gnats &c. Several species of Beetles: and many thousands of a peculiar Grasshopper were all the living things I found. No not all a very pretty white Butterfly, what its name was can't be told unless another comes in my way, passed over the top which contains 5 or 6

> acres of a snarly level, & caused me quite a chase besides nearly tumbling me down over the side as an eager grab was made just as the insect got out of reach. . . .

Sam Garman was a serious young man, devoted to the study of natural history and the instruction of Friend Gertrude. But young Keplinger, recovered from his scare of the night before, was of a horsier kind. When the monument was built and it came time to put into it the can containing the names of the party and the thermometer and barometer readings, Keplinger produced another can containing one of Major Powell's limestone biscuits, which he wanted to put in the cairn as an "everlasting memento" of the Major.

Powell thought this not quite up to the dignity of the occasion, and the biscuit eventually was removed. The Major even, before they started down, made a speech, saying that they had achieved something in the physical way which had been thought impossible, but that there were more formidable mountains in other fields of effort. He expressed the hope that their success of this day, August 23, 1868, might be an augury of yet greater achievements in other ways.

There is no record which would indicate that he was being facetious or indulging in mock heroics. He took the climbing of Long's Peak seriously, far more seriously than Byers, Sumner, the students, even than Sam Garman. He took seriously too the thought of other challenges to overcome, other unknowns to mark with writings in a cairn. A serious and intense young man, hardier in spite of his maiming than most of his companions, and as visionary as William Gilpin though in different ways — a young man serious and a touch pompous and perhaps even somewhat ridiculous, making speeches on top of a mountain and refusing to permit a joke that might have taken away dignity from the occasion — he may well have been the second climber who refused the celebratory wine.

He meant his speech. He insisted on the meaningfulness of the moment, and his vision of what might be accomplished must have expanded on that windy knob of rock as the view expanded below him, forty mountain lakes, a welter of mountains, the bowl of Estes Park, and the Great Plains lying sealike, the horizon so high from that perspective that he seemed to look upward to it, and the plains floating high like an expanse of cirrhus cloud. One thing he had wanted to do was done, a minor thing, unimportant either to science or himself. It would be recorded by historians of American mountain climbing and remembered by no one else. But an omen. Turning his back on Estes Park far below him, turning away from the cloudlike reach of the plains, he could look down across the great forest of Middle Park through which the Grand River cut its way, and beyond that to the Gore Range, the Rabbit Ears, the westward and little known mountains, the unexplored canyons of the Colorado.

So much was new. So much was unknown and untouched and undone.

4. Hot Sulphur Springs

HOT SULPHUR SPRINGS was rich in celebrities during the last week of August, 1868. Schuyler Colfax, the meteoric young Speaker of the House, orator and public darling, the Great Smiler, destined as Grant's first Vice-President to be one of the sad casualties of the Gilded Age, was camped on the bank of the Grand with a party that included Governor Hunt of Colorado Territory, ex-Lieutenant Governor Bross of Indiana, a collection of generals and politicos and mere gentlemen, several ladies, and one of the most eminent journalists of his time, Samuel Bowles of the *Springfield Republican.*[1] As Colfax would become a symbol of the corrupting influence of boodle, and have his ethical edges blunted by the indefinitely expansionist and exploitative temper of Grant's regime, Sam Bowles would develop into his resistant opposite: a public man of probity, a voice in the wilderness, a member of that group of Liberal Republicans, including Carl Schurz, Abram Hewitt, Whitelaw Reid, and by fits and starts Henry Adams, which through the seventies fought against bribery and collusion and the piracy of the national domain.

There is no evidence that Colfax learned anything in particular from his excursion into the Rockies, or that the West meant any more to him than it did to most politicians. Since the war had wiped out all the paired rivalry between slave and free, of which Missouri Compromise, Wilmot Proviso, Clay's Great Compromise of 1850, and Stephen A. Douglas' Kansas-Nebraska Bill were all political and historical milestones, politicians could relax about the western territories, let them form and come on as nature and population directed. Colfax was more interested in the ladies of the party anyway. One of them, Nellie Wade, he married shortly after their return.[2] But Sam Bowles was a man who had been to see the elephant, and could name some of his parts. As the author of *Across the Continent,* published in 1865, the record of an excursion which Colfax had shared but not so much taken to heart, he spoke with authority on western travel and resources and problems. On this trip, as on the previous one, he was writing regular letters back to his paper,[3] and after an evening around the campfire talking with the returned mountain climbers he devoted one to the Powell expedition.

Powell could have asked for no better break than the respectful attention of Bowles. Because of the presence of Byers, the party was already getting local publicity in the *Rocky Mountain News.* Hometown Illinois papers, especially the Bloomington *Pantagraph,* were keeping their ears open for word of the expedition's doings. Now word would go wider, to a national audience. And though Bowles was not an infallible judge of men — he had called Lincoln a "Simple Susan" — Powell could have been under no misapprehension about the value of his good opinion.

Bowles wrote that he had made "familiar and friendly acquaintance with Professor Powell's scientific exploring party," and said pleasant things of their zeal and the value of their collection of more than two hundred species of birds. He commented too on the finances of the expedition, and on the fact that "Professor Powell . . . draws upon his private purse for all deficiencies, and these must be many thousands of dollars before he gets through." (Powell would not have sown that seed without hoping that governmental help might grow from it.)

But Bowles was more interested, as Powell was, in the future plans of the party than in its past accomplishments. "From here the explorers will follow down the Grand River, out of the Park into western Colorado. and then strike across to the other and larger branch of the great Colorado River, the Green, and upon that or some of its branches, near the line of Utah, spend the winter in camp . . . preparing for the next summer's campaign. The great and final object of the expedition is to explore the upper Colorado River and solve the mysteries of its three hundred mile canyon. They will probably undertake this next season by boats and rafts from their winter camp on the Green."

Thus the plan that Powell and Jack Sumner had talked over around the campfire the year before, the project that above all other aims of the expedition fired Powell's imagination, but the part about which he had apparently said least when lining up his backing among the universities and museums. Collecting was never a major aim, but an excuse. "The continent," Gilpin had bawled at the Fenians on July 4, "is known to our people." Powell knew better, and so did Sam Bowles.

"The mocking ignorance and fascinating reports of the course and country of the Colorado ought to hasten them to this interesting field. The maps from Washington,[4] that put down only what is absolutely, scientifically known, leave a great blank space here of three hundred to five hundred miles long and one hundred to two hundred miles broad. Is any other nation so ignorant of itself?"

He spoke of the river, of the legendary canyons, cataracts, falls, and of the widespread belief among Indians and mountain men that no one who ventured on that river would ever emerge from it alive.[5] But in talking with Powell, he was struck not only by his enthusiasm but by his coolness and resolution: "The whole field of observation and inquiry which Professor Powell has undertaken is more interesting and important than any which lies before our men of science. The wonder is they have neglected it so long. Here are seen the central forces that formed the continent; here more striking studies in physical geography, geology, and natural history, than are proffered anywhere else. New knowledge and wide honors await those who catalogue and define them. I can but think the inquiry, vast and important as it is, is fortunate in its inquirer. Professor Powell is well-educated, an enthusiast, resolute, a gallant leader. . . . He is in every way the soul, as he is the purse of the expedition. . . ."

High praise, and early in his career, and in a place where it might serve him later.

To put against the legendary terrors of the Colorado River Bowles could find only one hopeful thing: the reputed passage of some part of the Colorado canyons down to the Mormon port of Callville by James White, a trapper, in 1867. Though White's full story did not make the columns of the *Rocky Mountain News* until January, 1869, it had been written a full year earlier and published both in General Palmer's *Report of Surveys across the Continent* and in the *Transactions of the St. Louis Academy of Science,* and so fascinating a tale was bound to circulate among miners and mountain men. There is plenty of evidence that Powell as well as Bowles knew the story; there is also evidence that Powell did not believe it, even after he had hunted up White and talked to him.[6] James White's tale of a wild river journey of eleven days on a crude raft tied together with lasso ropes had some elements of truth in it. At least White had floated out into the edge of civilization at Callville on September 8, 1867, half naked, blackened with sun, starving and demented, on a cobbled raft. But he was either so far out of his head that he had lost all capacity to observe clearly and measure distance accurately, and had come a far shorter distance on the river than he thought he had, or he was one of the West's taller liars.

In any case, much of his story belongs in the tradition of Gilpin, whose own vision of the future took account of these same canyons with equal, but different, fantasy: "The dorsal mass of the Andes [the American cordillera or Rocky Mountains], thus perforated through from base to base, and athwart its course, by a river of the first magnitude, is formed, to its snowy summit, of the upheaved auriferous and igneous rocks!"

In this, as in other judgments, Gilpin could hardly have been less accurate, but his gaudy speculations were certainly matched around many a prospector's fire, and the canyons which lured Powell with their possible doors to knowledge and fame lured Jack Sumner and some of Sumner's friends with the dream of bars where no man had ever dipped a pan, ledges where gold could be crumbled off with the fingers. Yet there were the tales Bowles spoke of, that the river went underground, leaped falls higher than Niagara, ran between walls vertical to the water's edge for scores of miles. And even if one believed that James White had really run all the rapids of the Colorado on his raft, and so proved the river navigable, one could not take serious comfort from the spectacle of his shriveled, blackened, gibbering body being hauled ashore at Callville. However one looked at it, the prospect was adventurous.

The passing of August and the departure of the Colfax party marked a change in the composition and temper of Powell's Rocky Mountain Scientific Exploring Expedition as specific as the chilling of the mountain weather into fall. During the first week of September the greenhorns, no longer so green, had the experience of digging rifle pits and standing all-night watch against an expected Indian attack. Word came through that the town of Montgomery had been burned to the ground and dozens of whites massacred. A few days later the report was amended, by grapevine from Empire, to say that the town of Montgomery was safe, but that nineteen men of the Powell expedition had been killed.

Finding this report somewhat exaggerated, they had their jumpiness allayed. But the atmosphere had changed, nevertheless, as Middle Park cleared of dudes and the party prepared to move westward into the real wilderness toward a winter camp first projected somewhere on the Green but later changed to the valley of White River. White or Green, it would be a sterner experience than they had yet had, and the journey westward along the unused stage route that Berthoud had blazed in 1861 with Jim Bridger as a guide would be a wilder wayfaring than any of them had made.

Their membership had altered too. Professor Thompson and his wife had gone east, as had the Reverend Daniels. Mrs. Powell was now the only woman. The college boys, Keplinger and Farrell and Durley and Allen and Bishop, were still along; so were Doctors Vasey and Wing and Powell's brother Walter, big-voiced, rather surly, and unpredictable. But along with this nucleus of Illinois intellectuals and college boys was a group of mountain men that Sumner and Powell had recruited in Middle Park.

One was O. G. Howland, once a printer on Byers' *Rocky Mountain News*, a literate atavist from Vermont, who wore a patriarchal beard. Others were his younger brother Seneca, Bill Dunn, Gus Lankin, and Billy Rhodes, all trappers. Rhodes, for reasons he kept to himself, went sometimes by the name of Rhodes and sometimes simply as Missouri. He was a camp cook, something of a joker, an uneasy sleeper, and on the trip westward along Berthoud's uncertain and difficult track he once shot a flying hawk with his rifle at two hundred yards.[7]

They were all men who had sniffed the wind westward. By Sumner's account, which is by no means reliable, they had planned on their own hook a prospecting trip down the river, and threw in with Powell for the mutual assistance they could give each other. The trappers' mountain experience and knowledge of Indians would be of advantage to Powell, as would their pack outfits. Powell's scientific intelligence and his potential ability to enlist governmental or institutional support would help the mountain men where they were weakest. The trappers' rifles were insurance against hunger during the winter months, while the semi-official status of the Powell party, and their privileges at army posts through the resolution of Congress, might be a deterrent to too great insolence on the part of the Utes.

5. *The Country of the White River Utes*

FOR A TIME they were in three sections, one cleaning up the summer's business, one packing supplies over the pass from Empire, and one, under Walter Powell, breaking the trail west.[1]

The road they were traveling, if it could be called a road, had been laid out by E. L. Berthoud and Jim Bridger for the Overland Stage Company in 1861. It reached from Golden, Colorado, almost due west to Provo, Utah, spanning 413 miles of utter wilderness. And it had never been used since its laying out, except by 150 men of the Third California Veteran Infantry on their way to Denver in the summer of 1865.

Along the fading track of the volunteers' wagons the advance party starting from Hot Sulphur Springs made fifteen miles the first day, and camped on the Troublesome. The second day they lost the trail and made only eight miles. The third, they crossed the Rabbit Ears range and lost the trail again, camping on what they assumed to be the headwaters of the Bear (Yampa) River. The fourth, following an obscure trace down the creek, they had a mild mutiny when Gus Lankin and young Bishop, mistrusting Walter Powell's groping, stopped in a grove and unsaddled, saying they were camping there no matter what the others did. The main party went on down the creek, and before night the mutineers rejoined them. There were no words, but there were sneers, and in the evening the mountain men had the contemptuous edification of watching Keplinger sight a sextant on a star in Scorpio trying to determine where they were.

Next morning they had the irritation of meeting the Berthoud trail exactly where Keplinger had said they would. The day after that, they woke to find Gus Lankin gone with a horse, a mule, three sacks of flour, a sack of meat, and other plunder. And after that, going off the trail to pick up some traps that he and Lankin had cached in August, Billy Rhodes, accompanied by Bill Woodward, was fired on from ambush. The party spent an angry afternoon and evening hunting Lankin with the intention of putting him beyond further thievery and bushwhacking.

They did not find him, but Durley, Keplinger, and Allen, who with Walter Powell made up the posse, had their summer's experience capped with an earnest manhunt. The four were twenty-four hours without food, slept out alone, and had a rough eight miles of guesswork before they found their way back to camp. Billy Rhodes did not come off without suspicion, either. Bishop even slept with him for a few nights to keep an eye on him, for fear he and Lankin planned a quiet wilderness massacre with the pack train for a prize. But Missouri kept the peace, Lankin never showed again, and the excitement died down.

Young Bishop, who did not go with the manhunters, had his summer capped in a different way. Berthoud's trail was so obscure that the advance party lost it constantly, and finally Walter Powell sent four men back to the springs with the pack train while he remained to locate the route. Meeting Major and Mrs. Powell with the main train, bringing up a double load by hauling half of it one day's journey and then going back for the other half, Bishop was sent clear back to Empire for mail with instructions to return along the party's trail and join them on the White.

Only one thing was wrong with Bishop's instructions. No one told him that there were two large streams besides the Grand flowing westward. After picking up the mail and spending a week with the squatter Sampson at the springs, he followed the well-marked Indian trail down the Grand and across the Gore Mountains. But when he found himself at an abandoned campsite on a beautiful clear stream he assumed that he was on the White. Actually he was on the Yampa. On a tree he found a note for him: "We have moved camp to a point on White River, 50 miles distant. General directions South of West. You will find provisions cached in the rocks 20 steps north. Come along as fast as you can. Keplinger."

The ravens had beaten him to the provisions. Salvaging a little sugar and flour, Bishop went on, but he went down the river, thinking himself already on the White, instead of cutting southwest as instructed. When he realized that he was good and lost he sat down to think, and then backtracked to where he had found the note. Snow stalled him in the timber; his food was all but gone when he managed to kill an antelope and jerk a supply of venison. Hoarding his ammunition and coddling his mule, he felt his way along the snow-obliterated track of the party by such tenuous spoor as broken twigs and the marks of passage on sagebrush and trees. He even shot a grizzly bear and tried to take its pelt along, but the mule vetoed that. More than a month after he had left Hot Sulphur Springs, he caught up with the rest on the White River.

They were glad to see him, but not half so glad as he expected. Everything had grown harsher: the most Powell had been able to do about his lost member was to send Keplinger back to the Springs to inquire. After that they took their choice of explanations. He had been murdered by bad Indians or bad whites, he had deserted, or he was lost. But he had demonstrated a considerable capacity to take care of himself, and Powell cordially invited him to make one of next year's river party. Bishop calculated that he had had his fun, and elected to go back to the States with the dudes.

The dudes were not quite through with their seasonal labors, however. In the wide valley on the White River which now shows on the maps as Powell Park or Powell Bottoms, just below the modern town of Meeker, they spent the last two weeks of October, 1868, cutting winter hay for the stock and building cabins for their winter camp, and had snow for a warning as they worked. Green River Crossing, now Green River, to which the Union Pacific tracks had reached, was a hundred and seventy-five miles northwest of them in Wyoming. Those who were going out would have to be moving.

Ten of them left on November 2 for the last stretch of mountains the tenderfeet would see. Moving down the White through a valley full of game, they eventually broke off northeastward across the divide between the White and the Yampa, and then north of west until they hit the Yampa in a country sandy, eroded, grown to sage and cactus, and empty of both game and timber. The weather was bitter. On the night of November 5 they made a dry and grassless camp; to make matters worse the cook set the sagebrush afire and they parched themselves putting the blaze out.

Very thirsty, they set off in the morning with the intention of heading for the first green that showed, but the high points revealed nothing except dry hills, gulches, and endless wasteland. The best they could do for their thirst was a handful of snow drifted against the comb of a ridge. Moving north and west, sometimes swinging east to head arroyos, they entered a dry creekbed and followed it down to a frozen puddle, but when they chopped through the ice they found the water so alkaline that they did not dare drink it themselves or give the animals more than a taste. An all-day struggle put them nine or ten miles farther northwest, but for the second night they camped without grass or water. To hold the thirst-crazed stock they barricaded an arroyo at both ends and camped in the bottom.

Before daylight young Allen, tormented by a two-day thirst, woke to see clouds coming from the west. Hopefully he spread rubber blankets in the ditch, and before the flurry blew past he caught a cupful of dirty water mixed with snow.

It was noon the next day when they found water. That night it began to snow, so that they pushed hard all the next day, making eighteen miles. But the mules were used up and hard to move. In the afternoon Durley's gave out and had to be abandoned; he loaded his saddle and pack onto Allen's, and that same afternoon they lost the pack mule they were driving and never found him again. Into a bitter wind, their faces peppered with snow like harsh sand, they went on until that night they discovered willows, good grass, a herd of thirty-five strayed steers from some railroad point to the north or some herd being trailed up from Texas. Stronger for the provi-

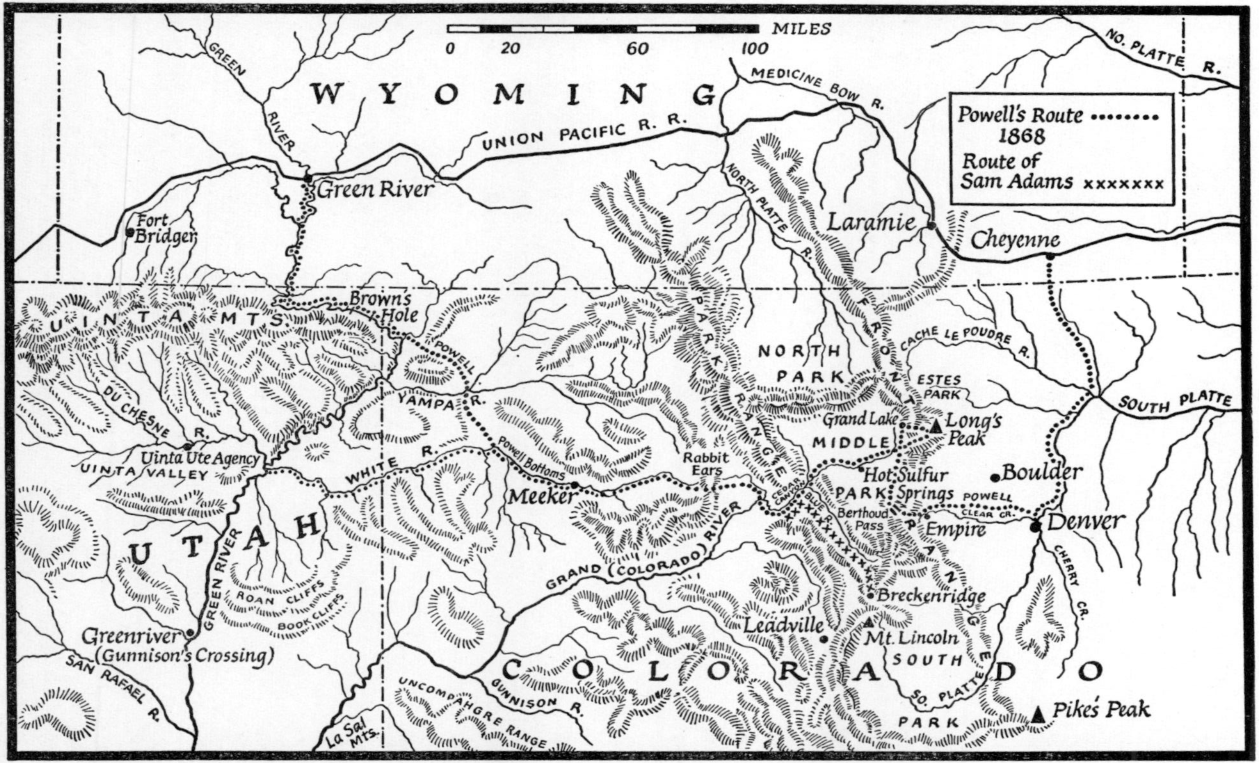

MILES
0
20
60
100
WYOMING
GREEN RIVER
UNION PACIFIC R. R.
MEDICINE BOW R.
NO. PLATTE R.
Powell's Route
1868
Route of
Sam Adams
Green River
Fort Bridger
Laramie
Cheyenne
NORTH PLATTE R.
Brown's Hole
UINTA MTS.
POWELL
FRONT
PARK RANGE
NORTH PARK
CACHE LE POUDRE R.
ESTES PARK
YAMPA R.
DU CHESNE R.
Grand Lake
Long's Peak
MIDDLE PARK
SOUTH PLATTE
Uinta Ute Agency
UINTA VALLEY
WHITE R.
Powell Bottoms
Rabbit Ears
Hot Sulfur Springs
Boulder
Meeker
CEDAR CANYON
BLUE R.
Berthoud Pass
POWELL
CLEAR CR.
Empire
Denver
UTAH
GREEN RIVER
ROAN CLIFFS
BOOK CLIFFS
GRAND (COLORADO) RIVER
CHERRY CR.
Breckenridge
RANGE
Leadville
Mt. Lincoln
SOUTH
Greenriver
(Gunnison's Crossing)
SAN RAFAEL R.
COLORADO
GUNNISON R.
UNCOMPAHGRE RANGE
SO. PLATTE
PARK
Pike's Peak
La Sal Mts.

dential fresh beef, they encountered next day a wagon track running down the valley of Little Bitter Creek, and that night they slept in cabins with woodcutters who told them that Green River, the end of the line for Union Pacific passenger trains, was only fifteen miles north. On November 15, after disposing of their mules for what they could get, all but Powell and Howland were on the train for the States.

Thus far the tourists, the temporary volunteers, those who in Bowles' words were "eager for border experiences." They had had them. Some had climbed a major peak with the first party to make it. Some had hunted a man with the intention of killing him. Some had stood guard all night in rifle pits awaiting an Indian attack. All had been reported killed by these same Indians. One had spent a month wandering through the wildest kind of country, living on what he could shoot and finding his way by signs that a few months before he would never even have seen. And all in the last ten days had experienced some of the dubious pleasures of the real explorer.

Doctors Wing and Vasey, along with Bishop, Durley, Farrell, Akin, Poston, Allen, and Taylor, called it a summer at Green River. Woodward and Keplinger had already gone out by the White River route. Powell and O. G. Howland went back in late November, 1868, across the snow-drifted sagebrush country, around the eastern end of the Uintas, and back to the camp in Powell Bottoms where now there were only Mrs. Powell, Walter, and Sam Garman of the prairie tribe, plus Sumner, the younger Howland, Bill Dunn, and Missouri Rhodes, who sometime now, safely west of possible embarrassment, began to go by his real name of Billy Hawkins.

During the winter, in spite of heavy snow, Powell pressed his investigation of the country out from Powell Bottoms: the mesas dark with juniper and runty pine, gray with sagebrush, whose terraced flanks dropped into the floodplains of creeks feeding the White, the Yampa, and the Grand. He went down the meandering cottonwood-belted valley of the White to where in a great basin blocked by the roll of the Uintas to the north and by broken fantastic buttes to the south the little river flowed into the wide dirty ice of the Green. He climbed to high places and saw the barren badlands country and the difficult canyons and gulches that had made trouble for his party on the trip to Green River in November.

What he was doing was making a map in his mind; upon that map, later, he would trace the imperfectly known course of the river.

Powell Bottoms was populous with Indians, mainly the White River Utes of Antero and Douglas, the same who had camped earlier in the season at Hot Sulphur Springs and irritated Sam Garman into temper tantrums with their incorrigible begging. They still begged, but they were an opportunity for study that Powell did not neglect. Though they had most of the attributes and culture patterns of the plains, they were a mountain people, protected by their remoteness and far less altered by contact with white men than the plains tribes. He spent days and weeks with them learning the Ute language, collecting an extensive vocabulary, trading for buckskin leggings, ceremonial bonnets, pottery, beadwork, all the artifacts in which their culture was given form. He had known Indians before, but never on such intimate terms as this. For more than thirty years after this winter he would retain and extend the interest he felt now, and what he learned from Antero and Douglas and the warriors and squaws and children who tracked the deep snow of the bottomland and smoked the winter sky with their fires would grow into an encyclopedic knowledge of Indian cultures and languages.

Not that he knew everything to begin with. In fact, he knew so little that in pursuing some topographical studies and running a line he drove stakes into the ground. If Jack Sumner had not been an old friend of Antero's that row of stakes might have cost the whole party their scalps, for the Utes, who knew little enough about white men, knew enough to know that stakes meant surveys, land parceling, white settlers. On that same ground, in some of those same cabins, those same Utes ten years later would murder Nathan Meeker and every man of his agency, and in the ensuing war all but wipe out a detachment of United States Cavalry, for a breach of cultural relations not much more serious. Meeker, friend of Emerson and Hawthorne, agricultural editor for Greeley's New York *Tribune*, founder of towns and scholarly enthusiast of pioneering, would make the mistake of plowing up a favorite race course of the Utes and trying to coerce them into becoming agriculturists and observers of the Sabbath.[2]

Powell, though he might be so gauche as to put out stakes, was not so bullheaded that he would not pull them up again. He was an ex-officer, and the habit of command stuck with him, but he was also a learner, and one of the growing few ready to grant the right of the Indian to his own habits and attitudes. In all his work in the West from that winter on, he never went armed, and he never had trouble, and this in years and in regions where other scientific expeditions would hardly venture outdoors without a military escort.

Actually they did not have to go outside their own group for trouble. Five months is a long time to be shut in. The trappers made one compact unit, the three Powells another; Sam Garman, the sole remaining student, was a little extraneous. Sumner thought he was homesick, but Sam himself, in a letter to Friend Gertrude, put another complexion on his dissatisfaction: "I can't afford to stay with the expedition as it requires too much of my time & too complete an abnegation of one's own affairs to present very great attractions to a student and traveler who is receiving no pay and not learning enough to pay for the time." So when the White River rose in mid-March, 1869, and flooded their cabins and drove them to a sopping and miserable camp on higher ground, and the camp took that occasion to break up and start moving toward Green River, Sam Garman kept right on going and began an expedition of his own. "The Major and myself had no difference except that he found I could do almost any work he had to do and that appeared to be excuse enough for setting me at it, no matter what became of the work I had come to do; besides Mrs. Powell thought me too independent and tried to make me understand that *herself* and the major *commanded* the expedition and *members* until I announced my intention of leaving when matters changed suddenly and took a much pleasanter aspect, but too late."

A little cabin fever, a little rubbing on the irritated nerves. Perhaps Sam Garman had a legitimate grievance. The trappers in their independence and solidarity would be hard to command, and Powell's maiming kept him from many tasks. There remained only Garman to fall back on, since Walter Powell, moody and difficult, was hardly a dependable helper. And Mrs. Powell, though by every testimony a woman of hardihood and courage, had a fair idea who was boss.

But the five months had hardened them further, they were better acquainted with the habits and language of the Indians, they had some notion of the country through which the Green and its tributaries ran. They had looked into the canyons along the Yampa and the Green, and from the country of the Uinta Utes where White and Green flowed together they had looked far southward toward the deeper unknown at the foot of Wonsits Valley. They had talked about the boats they would use; the drawings and specifications were in their kit.

Through deep snow, but without the hardship and danger of the November trip, they packed out to the Yampa, where Sumner, O. G. Howland, and Dunn settled down in good grass while Seneca Howland and Billy Hawkins accompanied the Powells out to Green River. From there the Major and Emma went east alone, headed for Chicago where he would order the boats built, and then Washington, where he would try his promotional talents for a third time on all the available sources of money and support.

Sumner, Howland, and Dunn loafed around on the Yampa for a while, looked over the country along the Little Snake and the Vermillion, moved on to Brown's Hole just as the spring ducks were coming over, hung around there for two weeks fattening up on duck and roast ribs, and then in a leisurely spring hegira cleared out and fooled their way up to Fort Bridger and thence to the town of Green River. There, reunited with Walter Powell, Hawkins, and Seneca Howland, they camped below the Green River bridge, spending their days and nights trying to drink up all the whiskey in town, but finding that Jake Fields could make it faster than they could drink it, and waited for Powell to return.

6. *Green River: the Gateway*

THEY WAITED below the Green River bridge on the bank of the Green, the old Seedskeedee-agie of the mountain men, until Powell should come with the boats. While they waited they might have thought of the blankness of the map south of them, the half-known course of the river, the remote junction of Grand and Green to form the Colorado,[1] the unlocated mouth of the San Juan and other tributaries, the unknown and unnamed creeks, the untouched country that stretched back away from the canyons on both sides. That country had been barely penetrated here and there. Coronado's men had reached the south rim of the Grand Canyon in 1540 and peered over into that awesome ditch. Father Garcés had visited the Supais in Havasu Canyon before the American Revolution. Escalante had crossed the Green in the Uinta Valley in 1776, and come back across the southwestern marches to ford the Colorado at the foot of a canyon that Powell would name Glen Canyon, where James Ohio Pattie may have trapped beaver in the eighteen-twenties. Frémont had crossed the northern edge of the region in 1844, the southern edge in 1853; he had all but died in its mountains in 1848. Ives in 1857 had come up the lower Colorado as far as Diamond Creek, within the lower Grand Canyon, and had traversed the plateaus south of the Grand Canyon to the Hopi towns and across the Painted Desert to Fort Defiance and the New Mexico settlements. Captain Gunnison had surveyed a railroad route, some of it impracticable, along the 35th parallel in 1853. Captain J. N. Macomb in 1859 had run an exploration out from Santa Fe in an unsuccessful attempt to reach the junction of Grand and Green. Berthoud and Bridger in 1861 had gone from Golden, Colorado, across the western slope and the Uinta Valley and down through the canyons of the Wasatch to Provo, Utah. From the eighteen-twenties until the near-extermination of the beaver the mountain men had trapped eastern and northern Utah, southern Wyoming, western Colorado. But these were traverses only, touches; this country had never been spread out and walked over and brought within the control of definite lines on paper. Large parts of it had only been circumnavigated, never really visited at all. The real unknown lay between the Uinta Valley and Gunnison's Crossing, now Greenriver, Utah; and between that crossing and the mouth of the Paria, now Lee's Ferry, Arizona; and below that to the foot of the Grand Wash Cliffs, south of present St. George, Utah. The crossings had been located; the hinterlands were a tantalizing blank marked, in a cartographer's neat lettering, "Unexplored."

They were a meager force with which to conduct a major exploration: five trappers, a war-psychotic ex-captain and a one-armed ex-major of artillery. It was important, and would have serious consequences, that both Powells represented military discipline and the officer class, and that the men who were to accompany them represented frontier independence and a violent distaste for discipline of any kind. Sumner, Dunn, Seneca Howland, and Hawkins had all been Union soldiers, but all had served in the ranks, Hawkins so obstreperously that he was wanted by the law in Missouri. Oramel Howland, the oldest man of the party, was a printer, an outdoorman by preference rather than by calling.

In purpose, as in background, the party split. Powell himself was intense, ambitious, intellectually curious, wanting to know, committed to the abstract cause of Science. But of the mountain men, only Oramel Howland and perhaps Sumner had any notion what science was about, or any understanding of Powell's motives. Their view of all his activities was likely to be tinged by that contemptuous amusement with which they had watched Keplinger try to find a lost wilderness trail by squinting at a star through a sextant. But action they understood, hardihood they all had. And there were the possible gravel bars. Green and Grand together drained a vast semicircle of mountains from the Wind Rivers in Wyoming through all the ranges of western Colorado and on down to the San Francisco peaks in northern Arizona. Where water ran and rock disintegrated, gold would wash down; where a river cut through thousands of feet of rock, veins would be exposed. Gilpin had said it for them. These were things the trappers understood well enough, and they appreciated Powell's gift of being able to tell one rock from another, however cold his other scientific achievements might leave them.[2]

Four trappers in buckskin pants, a printer, two ex-officers. And for backing, financial support? That was the principal reason, aside from the boats, for Powell's trip east.

Leaving the specifications for the four boats with a Chicago boatbuilder, he went on to Washington, one more among the throng of office-seekers, carpet baggers, pork-barrelers, men with schemes, thronging those muddy streets. He was not quite the unbacked unknown Illinois schoolteacher who had wangled a meager bone from Congress the year before, but he had little better luck. His hope was for a Congressional appropriation like that enjoyed by other government explorers and scientific investigators, Clarence

King and Ferdinand V. Hayden among them. That hope failed him; an acquaintance with Grant, with Professor Henry of the Smithsonian, with Senator Trumbull and a few others, was not enough, and he had little time. When he came away he had exactly the same kind of governmental help that he had had the previous season. A joint resolution of Congress implemented with an order from the office of the Adjutant General allowed him to draw rations for 12 men from any western army post; to draw other supplies in lieu of the regular army rations if they were available; and (what actually gave him the bare minimum of cash he needed to proceed) to commute certain unneeded parts of the ration into money.

As Powell took pains to explain later in a letter to the Chicago *Tribune* from Green River,[3] just before he shoved off, the party was not a government exploration at all. It was under the auspices of the Illinois Natural History Society, of which he was secretary. The funds available from the Society totaled less than a thousand dollars annually, and additional funds donated by the Illinois Industrial University[4] amounted to only $1100 in all. Certain favors had been extended, principally in the form of instruments, by the Chicago Academy of Sciences and the Smithsonian Institution.

And that was all. Powell apparently arranged some sort of wages for the hunters[5] by taking cash in lieu of part of the bacon ration, on the theory that fresh meat was a legitimate part of the ration if it could be provided. The hunters would help manage the boats, as they had for the past year managed the pack train. Sumner later asserted, without proof, that he was in on a partnership basis, providing part of the outfit and some of the supplies for the winter of 1868. Powell provided the rations and the boats, and obtained free transportation for men and supplies from several railroads as well as from Wells, Fargo and Adams and the American Express.

So except for the wages provided the hunters, it was entirely a volunteer party. Before it started down the swollen current of the Green three more volunteers would join it, and one comic-valentine volunteer would try.

Two of the three actual volunteers simply happened by at Green River. One, Frank Goodman, a red-faced Englishman rattling around the West in search of adventure, wanted so badly to go that he even offered Powell money to take him. There is no record of whether Powell took his money or not, but he took Goodman. Another, Andy Hall, was a cheerful, husky, eighteen-year-old bull-whacker and vagabond whom Powell saw resting on the oars of a homemade boat and enlisted on the spot. The third, George Bradley, Powell went to some trouble to get. He had met Bradley the autumn before, sadly sitting out an army enlistment at Fort Bridger and whiling away his time in melancholia and amateur fossil hunting. Bradley was a New Englander, and he knew boats, and he would do anything to get out of the army. Powell's one real success in Washington in May, 1869, was a War Department order authorizing Bradley's discharge to allow him to go on the river expedition. On May 14 the hypochondriac sergeant was mustered out and came down from Fort Bridger in time to teach the mountain men how to calk and paint the boats.

Of those boats a good deal has been written, and Colorado boatmen ever since have argued their virtues and their faults. It is not even clear who was responsible for their design, since Jack Sumner, in his later years of bitter grudge holding, claimed to have drawn them on the White River. The fact remains that Powell, who had taken solitary collecting trips by rowboat on the Ohio, Mississippi, Illinois, and Des Moines, undoubtedly knew more about river travel than Sumner or any other member of his crew. Whatever the boats' qualities, they were probably Powell's design.

Rivermen since have designed boats much better adapted for the running of rapids. In particular the variety of "cataract boat" perfected by Nate Galloway has been used by most of the expeditions since 1909 except the Clyde Eddy Expedition of 1927, which returned to Powell's heavy and clumsy craft. But Galloway, Norman Nevills, and the later boatmen have not had the double problem of constructing a boat that would both ride bad water and carry tons of supplies. And they were not facing an unknown river. Powell intended to stay in the canyons a full ten months. Because there was no sure way of getting out once he plunged in, he thought he had to take everything he needed, and prepare against every imaginable emergency, including the possibility of ice in the canyons. His boats, in consequence, even the light sixteen-foot pine pilot boat, were unwieldy, hard to handle, backbreaking on a portage, sluggish in rapids. But they were stoutly built, with airtight compartments at both ends. The three large boats, designed to carry forty-five hundred pounds apiece, were of oak, twenty-one feet long, with a long stern sweep for steering — as it turned out, an awkward and ineffective arrangement in the rock-choked rapids they would meet.[6]

The boats came off the cars at Green River with Major Powell on May 11, 1869, one day after Governor Stanford, General Dodge, and an extraordinary collection of celebrities, frontiersmen, saloonkeepers, Indians, Irish workmen, Chinese coolies, and plain spectators had ceremoniously put the transcontinental rails together between the cowcatchers of two facing locomotives at Promontory, a few hundred miles west. While the Powell party was still camped amid its stacked duffle below the Green River bridge, the first transcontinental train crossed the bridge above them and by its mere passing drew a line between periods of history.

Green River, which a little while before had had a population of 2000, and was now a diminished shacktown of a hundred or so, came to the riverbank to watch the party calk and paint and load. It speculated and spit and laid bets, and according to its constitution joked or looked solemn. In the river the four boats rode like a little navy, with the flag snapping at the jackstaff of the pilot boat, the *Emma Dean,* named for Mrs. Powell, now back in Detroit with her family awaiting the outcome. Under the bridge and past the camp the river went, swollen by the runoff from Horse Creek, the Pineys, Fontanelle Creek, and on the east the creeks from the Wind Rivers and the high bare divide along South Pass. In autumn almost pistachio green, the water now was thick with grayish mud. It moved fast, straining the flooded willows, hurrying with nervous whirlpools.

There is something ominous about a swift river, and something thrilling about a river of any kind. The nearest upstream bend is a gate out of mystery, the nearest downstream bend a door to further mystery. Even at Green River the waters of the Green in flood move swiftly. Powell's men watched the river pour by, and felt with their hands the powerful push of the current, and reflected that this was quiet water, perhaps as quiet as any they would have all the way except in Brown's Hole and at the mouth of the White. They looked southward at the badlands that hid the river's course, and sometimes climbed to the bluffs and looked across the broken, yellow and ocher and brown barrens, across an expanse of sage that in August would be purple with bloom, but was now faintly green with spring. Beyond the broken land and the tortuous, disguised cut of the river came up the blue roll of the Uintas, whose east end they had skirted on their trip from the White River, and into whose flaming canyons, threaded by the thin green line of the stream, they had peered from high cliffs. They would soon be looking up at those cliffs; they would be shooting on the river's back through the split mountains. Briefly, they would recognize the country where they had touched it in their explorations of the previous fall: in one or two of the Uinta canyons, at Brown's Hole, at the junction of White and Green in the broad Wonsits Valley. Then there would be the unknown again, a mystery clothed in rumor, secret water trails where perhaps not even Indians had passed.

It was a thing to hurry the pulse. Even in 1869, with the railroad demonstrably transcontinental at their backs, the northern and southern plains split in two, the Indians doomed along with the buffalo by whom they had lived, Omaha only four days by palace car from San Francisco and elegant passengers leaning from the windows to stare down on the little fleet, there was still this opportunity to look upon something, as Sam Garman had said on Long's Peak, just as God made it.

What they record in their journals and letters as they wait for the preparations to be finished and listen for the signal to start is not doubt, not fear, not any legitimate foreboding about a journey from which none of them might return. What they record is impatience and eagerness. The grumbling of the fall and winter, the cabin fever and distrust between dudes and mountain men, are gone and forgotten. They are tugged at as strongly as their four boats, pulling in the swollen current of the Green.

But before they leave, there is one final volunteer to be disposed of.

7. *Green River: A Volunteer of the Tribe of Gilpin*

WELL BEFORE Powell's preparations brought him to the water's edge at Green River, what one may call the Gilpin mentality had taken notice of the Colorado River. It was inevitable that it should have. Distances in the Southwest were so great, grass and water so uncertain, difficulties of travel so numerous, that the imagination of pioneers was sure to be seized by the possibility of a great river highway from the Rockies to the Pacific. The explorations up from the Gulf of California by Lieutenant Derby and Lieutenant Ives in 1857–58 both had the intelligent object of discovering the possibilities of steamboat navigation on the lower Colorado, and Brigham Young, contemplating in that same decade an empire that would reach from the crest of the Rockies to the crest of the Sierra and from Oregon to the Rio Grande, hoped for an outlet to the sea and a water route to Utah for settlers and supplies. To that end he sent Anson Call to establish the river port of Callville, just above the present Hoover Dam, in 1864, and he kept his apostle to the Lamanites, Jacob Hamblin, busy for years searching out crossings and exploring the possibilities of the Colorado as a thoroughfare. These investigations established the course and nature of the lower river and the resources of the country through which it ran, and they arrived at a logical navigational head just above Black Canyon, near Callville.[1]

What distinguishes the Gilpin approach from this methodical and factual investigation is the inability to be content with facts, or even to see them: the quality of incorrigible faith, the insistence upon introducing fantasy into geography. It would be a valuable and exciting matter if a practicable water route split the plateau country in two and gave easy access to the Pacific. Therefore it existed, in spite of logic and topography and triply demonstrated fact. There were people who from physiographic inference knew what the Colorado *probably* did between its known headwaters and its known lower course. Its canyons had been peeked into at enough points to prove their continuity over hundreds of miles, the amount of its fall was on record, its rapids were attested both by logic and by spotty observation. But the Gilpin mentality was capable not only of convincing itself, but at times of imposing its fantasy upon a public and government understandably ignorant of the facts. It was the wishfulness of the Gilpin mind that had gotten James White's raft story a respectful hearing the year before, in official as well as unofficial quarters. The same wishfulness at times imposed upon the Colorado some of the legendary properties of the Multnomah and the Buenaventura, those fabled rivers that drained the Great Basin into the Pacific until Jed Smith walked across the Nevada and Utah deserts and proved otherwise.

Of all the makers of fantasy who touched the history of the Colorado, few approached Samuel Adams.[2] His career is a demonstration of how far a man could get in a new country on nothing but gall and the gift of gab, so long as what he said was what people wanted to believe. He was one of a tribe of Western adventurers and imposters and mountebanks, cousin-german to James Dickson and Walter Murray Gibson;[3] and if his schemes were not so grandiose as theirs and his imagination not so lurid and his personal ambitions less godlike, he was still recognizably of that sib. As Dickson was to Sam Houston, as Gibson was to Brigham Young, so Adams was to Powell — a lunatic counterpoint, a parody in advance, a caricature just close enough to the real thing, just close enough to a big idea, to have been temporarily plausible and limitedly successful.

His spiritual relative William Gilpin, after half a lifetime in the West, could see through a glass eye so darkly that he denied geography, topography, meteorology, and the plain evidence of his senses, and his advice to America and his dream of the future floated upward on the draft of his own bombast. One who had frozen and starved and chewed his swollen tongue in thirst, he could still deny the facts of western deserts and western climate. Samuel Adams — Captain Samuel Adams he chose to call himself — with more actual experience on the Colorado than most men, could still talk of it as a thoroughfare.

He was posing as an authority on the Colorado before either Powell or James White ever saw it. In a letter to Secretary of War Stanton dated March 29, 1867, while Powell was still planning his first mountain expedition and had probably not even conceived the notion of exploring the river, Adams named himself and outlined his expert qualifications. He said that in 1865 he and Captain Thomas Trueworthy made a voyage up the Colorado from its mouth in a little sternwheeler for the purpose of "demonstrating that it was capable of being ascended with steamers for over 620 miles from the mouth." (Captain George Johnson in the steamer *Colorado* and Lieutenant Ives in *The Explorer*, shoving up the Colorado from Yuma, had demonstrated that in 1858.)[4] As a matter of fact, regular steamer service was already established when Adams arrived, as he admitted in the next breath without apparent sense that he was contradicting himself. But this California Navigation Company which by 1865 ran six or eight river steamers between Yuma and Callville was, Adams said, a ruthless monopoly determined to stamp out competition, by the "bullet and the knife" if necessary, or by cutting the timber on both sides of the river to destroy rivals' fuel supply. In spite of a letter of character he had carried there from Governor Low of California,[5] it appears that Adams' pretensions as an explorer had not made much impression on the lower Colorado.

But at least he was now convinced that steamboat navigation was possible as far as Callville, and he went eleven miles above Callville and built a raft and floated down with ease through Boulder Canyon, which he represented to Stanton as the biggest on the river. Before taking to his raft, he climbed the canyon wall and saw "an open valley, sixty miles in length, extending to the northeast." That would have been the Valley of the Virgin, now the Virgin Basin of Lake Mead. Beyond it, Adams said, the land had been considered a *terra incognita*. But from his talks with Indians, his observation of the terrain, and his study of "maps and correspondence" in the "Historical Society" in Salt Lake, he had satisfied himself "that there are none of those dangerous obstructions which have been represented by those who have viewed them at a distance, and whose imaginary canyons and rapids below had almost disappeared at the approach of the steamer."

Lieutenant Ives and his men would have been interested to hear this, for there, in one look and one sentence, went the whole canyon and plateau country that they had labored across on foot after being forced to abandon the river in 1858. It was imaginary. There went the Grand Canyon and Marble Canyon and Glen and Cataract and Labyrinth Canyons, there went the abysmal chasms into which Coronado's men had peered fearfully and which so impressed Baron von Egloffstein, Ives' topographer and artist, that his illustrations for the Ives report look like the landscapes of nightmare. There went the barrier canyons that had held in the southern edge of Brigham Young's empire, to join the Great American Desert that other Gilpins were busily dissolving. Down this misrepresented and maligned highway of the Colorado, Adams said, must come the ties and rails and supplies for the building of the southern railroad. The Colorado must become for the Pacific Coast what the Mississippi was for the Midwest. The whole rumor of impassable canyons and rapids was a flagrant lie of the corporations now entrenched on the river and jealous of possible competition.

The yeasty schemes stirring in Adams' head must have generated gases to cloud his eyesight. Eastward from that same canyon rim from which he looked up the Valley of the Virgin he could not have failed to see even at that distance the towering, level, four-thousand-foot rampart of the Grand Wash Cliffs, where the river emerges from the Grand Canyon into relatively open country. Those cliffs are the dominating element in the landscape Adams viewed. In mass and import they are enormously impressive — and the river, as Adams ought to have been able to see, either had to run along the cliffs or come straight out of them. Yet they did not impress him as a "dangerous obstruction."

All Adams got for his letter to Stanton in 1867 was a resolution of thanks from the House of Representatives. But that was something. It was symptomatic. More might be had.

What Captain Adams did for the next two years, aside from writing letters, does not seem to be known. But early in May, 1869, as Sumner and the trappers were waiting in camp on the Green for Powell to return with the boats, a young man of impressive presence and a fast tongue climbed off the Union Pacific's passenger train and made himself at home in camp. He said that he was to accompany the expedition in a scientific capacity; his mouth was full of big names. He had letters and orders which he would present to Major Powell as soon as he arrived.

The trappers, still concentrating on their quarrel with Jake Fields' forty-rod whiskey, shrugged and let him stay — "a young scientific duck," Billy Hawkins called him, part of Powell's incomprehensible busy-ness. He was not so different from the other young scientific ducks they had had half a year's experience with. And he spoke with confidence and particularity of his explorations on the lower river. He seemed to have qualifications, though they found him a finicky camper, and took a gentle pleasure in ribbing him.

When Powell arrived with the boats on May 11 Adams presented himself as one who had authorization from ex-Secretary of War Stanton to accompany the expedition. He might even have got away with his bluff if, as he thought, the expedition had been sponsored by the government. But Powell, who had himself planned and organized every detail of the trip, saw no reason why a retired Secretary of War should forcibly impose a recruit upon him, especially a lordly recruit who acted like the commander. He asked to see Adams' papers, and Adams brought them out: letters from Stanton and others thanking him kindly for his communication and wishing him success in the exploration he contemplated. Powell said later[6] that he read the letters and sent Adams about his business, but Billy Hawkins, whose reminiscences show more liveliness and more will to aggrandize Hawkins than to report the sober truth, had another version of Adams' departure. He said that Adams was hard to please at meals, and complained a good deal about Hawkins' cooking. One night Jack Sumner remarked something confounded queer about the coffee, and Hawkins, across the fire, reached down with his bowie and forked up one of Walter Powell's black and dripping socks from where it had been soaking in a kettle. It looked to Adams as if the sock had come out of the coffeepot, and that finished his desire for frontier adventure.

Actually Adams' desire for adventure and exploration was not in the least quenched, either by Powell's harsh judgment of his character and claims or by Hawkins' coffee. He was a hard man to quench. In Arizona Territory, his legal domicile, he had run for delegate to Congress in three consecutive elections, getting 31 votes the first time, 168 the second, and 32 the third. Now, swearing that he was misunderstood and abused, he climbed on the train and headed for Colorado Territory. If Powell would not accept his honestly proffered services, there were those who would.

There were, too. The Colorado was the natural highway, the beckoning door, of an empire rich in precious metals, timber, agricultural land, that empire of the Gilpin fantasy where fell not rain nor hail nor any snow, nor ever wind blew loudly. It would take more than a rebuff from Powell to discourage Adams from leading the nation into Canaan.

Let him go. We shall hear of him again.

8. The Green: Green River to the Uinta Valley

AT NOON on May 24, 1869, the population of Green River gathered on the bank, and an hour later they watched the four boats of the Powell Expedition spin out into the current [1] — the *Emma Dean,* the *Maid of the Canyon,* the *Kitty Clyde's Sister,* and the *No-Name,* all but the pilot boat heavy and low in the water with their loads. The men jumped to oars and sweeps, the Major swung his hat from the *Emma Dean.* In two or three minutes the current carried them left, then right, and one after another they disappeared around the bend. The crowd stood around a little, squinted at the rising river, passed predictions, and dispersed.

That was the last anybody heard of Major Powell and his nine men for thirty-seven days, until June 30. On that day the Corinne *Reporter,* mouthpiece for the sinful railroad camp at the north end of Great Salt Lake, reported that all of the party except the gunsmith had drowned in the terrible rapids of the Green.

Newspaper intelligence along the line of the Union Pacific was, in spite of the telegraph, closely related to rumor. Those expecting word of Powell's party waited uncertainly, unwilling to believe. Then on July 2 and 3 the Omaha *Republican* ran a lengthy but confused story of the disaster which it had got from a trapper named Riley, who said he had met Jack Sumner in Fort Bridger and from him, the only survivor, obtained the facts. Riley said that Sumner, detailed to a job on shore, had watched helplessly as all the laden boats plunged one after another over a twelve-foot fall in the first canyon south of Brown's Hole and were swept to destruction in the raging rapids below. There were those who wagged their heads and believed, remembering Jim Beckwourth, that loud and lying mountaineer, and his terrible "suck," [2] which was fabled to swallow any boat that entered it.

By July 4 the story had moved eastward. Chicago papers reported the arrival in Springfield of John A. Risdon, the only survivor of the Powell Expedition, and gained from him a circumstantial account of the disaster, the names of all the victims, and the story of Risdon's difficult struggle to make his way out to civilization.[3] The next day the Detroit *Post* published a letter from

Emma Powell denouncing Risdon as an impostor. No such man had ever been with her husband's party, and moreover she had received letters from her husband dated May 22, though Risdon said the wreck had taken place on May 8.

So here, hard on the heels of Sam Adams, came another impostor quite as cavalier with the truth and a good deal more ghoulish. His purpose was apparently no more than to get a free ride east, using his sad story for a passenger ticket. Like other liars, he may even have got to believing his own story as he repeated and embellished it, for he carried it brazenly back to Springfield and told it to Governor Palmer of Illinois, and he footnoted it with great particularity. For the adorning of his tale he invented a whole geography of rivers and canyons and army posts, all from the land of fable, and he put it over on Governor Palmer so thoroughly that the Governor publicly called him an "honest, plain, candid man," who told his story straightforwardly and seemed reliable. (In the same way Governor Low of California had borne testimony for Adams, and Brigham Young had given to Walter Murray Gibson a piece of paper that Gibson parlayed into a barbaric crown in the Sandwich Islands.)

A character out of fiction, an incontrovertible Duke of Bilgewater or poor lost Dauphin, Risdon wept as he carried his story eastward along the Union Pacific, and in general made such an unregenerate and conscienceless show of his lie that Byers in the *Rocky Mountain News,* summarizing the extent of Risdon's wickedness, first clamored for him to be hung and then came around to treating him almost with admiration for his illustration of man's capacity to "lie without object or provocation."

Risdon had a talent. From a few garbled rumors he had made a coherent fiction, invented a geography, created various people named Andrew Knoxson, T. W. Smith, William S. Dolton, Charles Sherman, and so on, plus a half-breed guide called Chic-a-wa-nee. The only name he got right was that of Durley, of the 1868 group, but he didn't know Durley's first name and so he doubled it, transforming the original Lyle into brothers named William and Charles. He took this motley crew of twenty-five, with teamsters and wagons, to a "small Indian settlement" on the Colorado called Williamsburg. There he kept them for seven or eight days making observations before he started them down the river to explore two tributaries known as the Big Black and the Deleban.

There is a certain advantage to living before maps have petrified geography. Risdon could give himself plenty of elbow room. He brought the Big Black and the Deleban into the Colorado within a mile and a quarter of each other, and in that distance gave the Colorado a drop of 160 feet. Powell, said Risdon, ordered him ashore to explore a way of getting up the Deleban, while the remaining twenty-five men packed themselves aboard a bark canoe, called a "yawl" by the Indians, and laughingly pushed off to paddle across the roaring Colorado. They had with them all the surveying instruments and all the Major's papers and notebooks. The Major stood in the stern steering, while seven paddlers dug water. Risdon shouted to them to be sure and come back in time for dinner, and they shouted back, "Goodbye, Jack, you will never see us again!" A moment later a whirlpool seized the yawl, spun it around, and swallowed it. The last man the astonished Risdon saw was Powell, still standing erect and brave at his post in the stern.

Risdon cried like a baby. Later he went up and down the river (why *up* not even the sardonic Byers could figure out) looking for bodies or remains. All he found was a carpetbag containing Powell's papers and records. After four days' searching Risdon gave up, took the two teams and what remained of the party's supplies, and drove off through the timber toward civilization. About June 1 he reached Leroy, a small military post deep in that Gilpin-Adams-Risdon land on a stream called the Red River. Here he reported to Colonel Smith, commanding, and was assisted to St. Louis. All of Major Powell's baggage, including the carpetbag, he said he had sent to Mrs. Powell.

In the long run, perhaps Powell should have been grateful to Risdon. His report of disaster could have been believed only by those who knew nothing about the country, the expedition, or its members, and the flurry of indignation when Risdon was exposed most certainly titillated interest in what was actually happening as the explorers went deeper into the canyons. For a brief while Risdon's yarn may have brought anxiety to Powell's wife and others, not because they ever credited its truth but because it named an eventuality that was perfectly possible. Knowing nothing

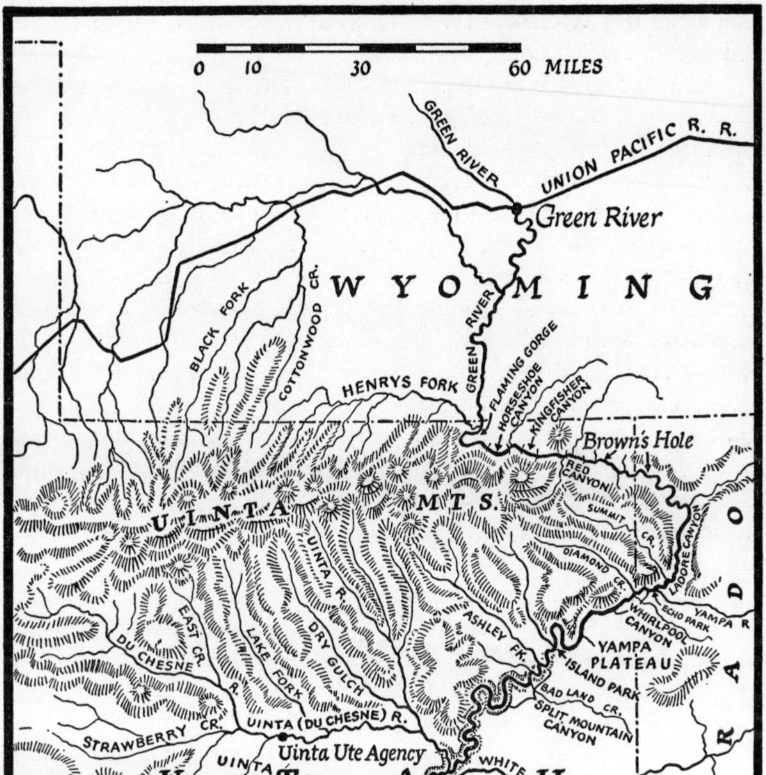

0 10 30 60 MILES
GREEN RIVER
UNION PACIFIC R. R.
Green River
WYOMING
BLACK FORK
COTTONWOOD CR.
GREEN RIVER
FLAMING GORGE
HORSESHOE CANYON
KINGFISHER CANYON
HENRYS FORK
Brown's Hole
RED CANYON
UINTA MTS.
SUMMIT CR.
LADORE CANYON
DIAMOND CR.
UINTA R.
EAST CR.
DU CHESNE R.
LAKE FORK
DRY GULCH
ASHLEY FK.
ECHO PARK
YAMPA R.
WHIRLPOOL CANYON
YAMPA PLATEAU
ISLAND PARK
BAD LAND CR.
SPLIT MOUNTAIN CANYON
STRAWBERRY CR.
UINTA (DU CHESNE) R.
Uinta Ute Agency
UINTA VALLEY
UTAH
WHITE R.
GREEN R.
BAD LAND CLIFFS
MINNIE MAUD CR.
INDIAN CR.
DESOLATION CANYON
CASTLE VALLEY
ROAN OR BROWN CLIFFS
BOOK CLIFFS
PRICE R.
PATMOS HEAD
RED PLATEAU
GRAY CANYON
EAST TAVAPUTS PLATEAU
ROAN OR BROWN CLIFFS
GRAND RIVER
COLORADO

except that Risdon lied, Emma had to wait, and the public had to wait, until some more authentic report should come out.

The next word, though more authentic than Risdon's tale, was not reassuring. On July 15 the Cheyenne *Argus* reported the experiences of Colonel Jackson, chief of a silver prospecting company, in the upper canyons of the Green. Jackson had headed down river by land six days before Powell's group. He reported that he had gone 160 miles, and had found the river passage utterly impracticable. Deep in the canyons, forty miles below where the Powell party was supposed to have been lost, Jackson's men were overtaken by the shattered remnants of a boat expedition which had started three weeks *after* Powell, determined to prove that if Powell could run the river they could. The leader of that reckless excursion, Frederick Hook, was now buried among the boulders in Red Canyon.[4] Returning together toward Green River, the Hook-Jackson parties had seen no trace of Powell or his men — not a footprint on the beach, not a dead campfire, not a rag in a rapid. The canyons had swallowed the ten of them; Jackson felt that they could not be alive.

But two days later the *Rocky Mountain News* was able to run two letters from its old employee Oramel Howland. One was dated from the mouth of the Yampa on June 19, the other from the mouth of the Uinta (modern Ouray, Utah, in the Uinta Ute Reservation) on June 30. And the same wilderness mail that brought Howland's letters out from the Uinta Ute Agency brought a letter from Andy Hall to his brother and letters from Major Powell himself to the Chicago *Tribune*, dated from Flaming Gorge, Brown's Hole, and the mouth of the Yampa.[5] The party had come down the Green for 160 miles, survived all the canyons that Jackson had called impassable, and run clean through the Uintas into the broad Wonsits or Uinta Valley of Utah. It was camped, when the last letters were written, less than two miles upriver from the mouth of the White, which it had visited the winter before. It was, in fact, temporarily in safe and known country. How it had got that far was news the papers would copy.

Luckily for the Powell Expedition's unpractised boatmen, the Green for sixty miles south of Green River is a relatively mild stream, flowing through broken badlands. Though there are low bluffs, there are no real canyons, and though the current is insistent and swift, there is nothing that can be called a rapid. In those sixty miles they had a chance to discover how their boats handled. Hall and Hawkins, heavily laden, found that when they wanted to land they had better start making preparations at least two hundred yards above the proposed landing place. They complained to Powell that their *Maid of the Canyon* was nine inches closer to the bottom of the river than the others, and got a redistribution of the load. They learned too what every man who has ever handled a boat on Green or Colorado or San Juan learns: how trivial a mistake can lead to trouble. The rivers are not "treacherous." They are only forever dangerous. One who has not tried it finds it hard to believe the instant and terrible force that such a current exerts on a broadside boat out of control on a sandbar or rock. On the San Juan it is possible in places to sit on the bottom, close to shore where the current is not nearly so strong as in the main channel, and with the hands grasping the ankles be sledded along the bottom at a coasting clip. On any of the rivers a spilled boatman, an upset boat, is swept off downstream as if by an avalanche. Powell's men, running aground, breaking an oar, spinning in eddies, learned respect for the river before it got dangerous. They took three days running down to the mouth of Henry's Fork, at the foot of the Uintas, where they had cached barometers and rations earlier in the spring on their way out from White River. The cache was untouched; they raised it and camped the third night in sight of the flaring red gateway they named Flaming Gorge, where for the first time the river broke directly into the barrier range.

Because they were an exploring party and not merely a group of thrill-hunters, they did not plunge directly in. For three days they sat outside the gate, mending barometers, measuring the height of the cliffs (1200 feet), climbing the walls to look around. The peaks of the Wasatch notched the west, the barren Wyoming plateau northward swelled up toward South Pass and the snowy Wind River Mountains. Below their lookout rim was the valley of Henry's Fork, old trapper country, and the lodge of Jim Baker, a squawman who had established a ranch against the mountain. And they could see the gorge of the Green with the river at its bottom splitting the red cliffs.

For a while the river flirts with the great mountain table rising east and west across its course. It cuts in through Flaming Gorge, emerges into a little park where today there are three or four remote ranches, and then wheels left into the mountain. But it does not cut through. The red walls turn it in a half circle, forcing it through a complete U out into the valley again, barely a half mile from where it entered. Powell named this stretch Horseshoe Canyon. In the part of it now called Hideout Canyon there is a footbridge across the Green to accommodate pack trains and deer hunters and sheep bands headed for the back country. This canyon gave the expedition its first real thrill — a curving rapid where the water plunged down among rocks. They ran it, at first scared and then exhilarated.

The walls widened out to make another little valley, pinched in to make another canyon. The river was broad and quiet here, and kingfishers playing along a tributary stream gave valley and canyon and stream a name. Just beyond their May 30 camp came a great domed point eroded into thousands of holes where swallows nested. They called it Beehive Point and followed the river around it, changing course from south to east as the river, having cut in close to the heart of the range, turned and ran along it lengthwise.

By now the walls were close to a half mile high, stepping backward in terraces, clean cliff and wooded slope and clean cliff again, to remote rims. Red Canyon they called it; it is one of the spectacular chasms of the Green. Today a tourist can look down into it from several spots on the rim, notably from Green Lake. But the tourist from that height sees only a thread of river, green in low water, reddish in high. He will not see the rapids that for the first time gave Powell and his men a touch of danger and exhausting work, and he will not hear what is perhaps the most nerve-wearing accompaniment of any voyage in these canyons: the incessant, thundering, express-engine roar of the water. In many parts of the canyons it never ceases, day or night. It speeds the heartbeat and deafens the ears and shakes the ground underfoot. It comes from every side, echoed and multiplied by the walls. A man's voice is lost, shouting in it.

The expedition would have plenty of experience with that roar of rapids. What they had of it here was a mere preliminary, for this was still a small river, unaugmented by the large tributaries.

The rapids in Red Canyon, though bad enough to force them to line their boats down several times, were not such rapids as they would meet later, and there were stretches of wonderfully fast exciting water. Powell records that they made in one hour, including stops, twelve miles. Some of the men guessed that at times they were doing a mile a minute.

Except in very bad places, the men all preferred running to the laborious technique of lining that Powell devised. He was exasperatingly cautious.[6] Going ahead in the *Emma Dean,* he scouted every stretch where the growing roar announced bad water, and as they went along he improvised methods of getting around the danger spots. The lining system that he used at what they named Ashley Falls was typical. Each boat was unloaded completely, and a line attached to bow and stern. The bow line was taken below the fall and secured. Then the boat was let down over the fall by five or six men straining back on the stern line. When they could no longer hold against the rush of water, they let go, the boat leaped the fall, and the rest of the crew snubbed it in below. Then they all got together and lugged the tons of supplies around the rapid and across the rocks. Bradley, whose journal is the only complete diary of the expedition besides Jack Sumner's, was undoubtedly speaking for all of them when he groused that they didn't run enough.

They had thought they were the first into these red rock gorges, but at Ashley Falls, as they would do several times, they crossed the path of history. They were portaging around the foot of the cliff when they came upon an inscription put there by a distinguished predecessor. The bullboat party of General Ashley, forty-four years before, had painted on the rock the words "Ashley, 1825." Powell did not know who Ashley was, for Ashley's narrative was not printed until 1918. He thought the inscription was made by a prospector whose story he had heard from the mountain man Jim Baker, and he misread the date as 1855.[7]

He was not yet opening new country, but he was collecting data as he went, climbing the cliffs at every opportunity to measure altitudes and take geological sections, and most of all to fill his eye with the view and let the sweep of the Uintas take their place in the map that was forming in his mind. Climbing out to the rim from Red Canyon he looked down the narrowing wedge of forested mountain between the Uinta crest and the gorge of the river, and came close to history again. On the same piney uplands beyond the rims of Red Canyon, Henry Adams would be camping in a little more than a year, formulating in campfire discussions with Arnold Hague and S. F. Emmons[8] some of the ideas that would mold a fascinating and cryptic career, and measuring his education against a primeval wilderness. And from the cliffs above Brown's Hole, where Powell climbed two days later, he could look eastward up the valley of the Vermillion through which Frémont had found his way to the parks of Colorado in 1844.

Ashley, Frémont, the Manly party of Forty-niners,[9] Henry Adams, Clarence King and his helpers Hague and Emmons, Powell himself — a curiously diverse history would casually brush that little-known range. From the mountain man's uncomplicated and ferocious dynamism to Adams' dynamo and second law of thermodynamics, ideas significant for the continent's knowledge and use of itself passed here. Not too many miles away one of the most incredible and successful hoaxes in our history, the great diamond swindle, would be staged in a little gulch on the south slope of the range. The mentality that permitted public credence of the words of Gilpin and Sam Adams would permit "investments" in these Uinta diamonds to the tune of $10,000,000 and personally cost a San Francisco banker, William Ralston, $660,000, and ultimately his life. The salted mine would be exposed by Clarence King, friend of Adams and Powell's later collaborator; the spot would retain its name Diamond Gulch as a reminder of how far the will to believe can go, even in the face of probability, in the land of Gilpin.[10]

Powell was not thinking of history as he camped in Brown's Hole, resting after the canyons, restoring the ears of his party with silence and birdsong, measuring the country he could reach or see. Some history had not happened yet, and some of it he did not know. He might glance up the Vermillion where Frémont had gone, but he glanced more frequently at the frowning gateway where the river, after miles of running down the east-west axis of the Uintas, turned south again and cut straight in. For him this was the real beginning. Up to here he had been anticipated by trappers and prospectors. Brown's Hole itself was a vast cattle ranch, there were cabins and herds, and the place had been known years back by trappers on the Seedskeedee. But from here on was something else. Two thousand feet above the Hole, hanging his feet over the cliff, Powell sat and wrote a letter, dated June 7, 1869, which he would send out to the Chicago *Tribune* if and when he had the chance.

> While I write [he concluded], I am sitting on the same rock where I sat last spring, with Mrs. Powell, looking down into this cañon. When I came down at noon, the sun shone in splendor on its vermilion walls shaded into green and gray when the rocks are lichened over. The river fills the channel from wall to wall. The cañon opened like a beautiful portal to a region of glory. Now, as I write, the sun is going down, and the shadows are settling in the cañon. The vermilion gleams and the rosy hues, the green and gray tints, are changing to sombre brown above, and black shadows below. Now 'tis a black portal to a region of gloom.
>
> And that is the gateway through which we enter [on] our voyage of exploration tomorrow — and what shall we find? [11]

He dramatized himself somewhat, this one-armed major, and he had perhaps been reading eloquent and rhetorical travelers of the school of Mungo Park. Circumstances would conspire to assist in the dramatization. Though he would not know it for months, the rumor of his death and the death of his whole party but one would shortly go out from the mountains, and the place of his reported death, before John Risdon began tampering with geography, was this same canyon beneath his feet.

The rapids Powell saw from the walls had not looked too bad, but they turned out to be sharp, fierce pitches in the riverbed, filled with boulders fallen from the cliffs. Powell went ahead, waving the boats ashore at every bad spot, reconnoitering on foot. Until noon they had short stretches of navigable water broken by rapids so furious that Andy Hall, remembering some schoolboy lesson, was led to exclaim, "Oh how the waters come down at Lodore!" They named it the Canyon of Lodore, to Sumner's disgust. Sumner's reason for carping, confided a little later to his journal, is not only a sharp reminder of the difference between leader and men, but has a quaintly modern sound: "The idea of diving into musty trash to find names for new discoveries on a new continent is un-American, to say the least." [12]

Just at noon on June 7 Powell's boat pulled ashore at the head of a bad place, and signaled the freight boats to land. Powell went along shore to scout a practicable portage. Over his shoulder he saw one of the boats pulling in, but when he looked again he saw the *No-Name,* with the two Howlands and Frank Goodman struggling at oars and sweep. Either they had not seen the signal, or had not started digging for shore in time. O. G. Howland later said [13] he could have made shore if he had not been half full of water from running the rapids above. But now the experience Hawkins and Hall had had in easy water the first day was repeated without the laughs.

Powell saw the boat hang for a breath at the head of the rapid and then sweep into it. He leaped onto a rock to signal frantically at the last boat, and after a long minute saw it pulling heavily toward shore well above the tongue. The moment he saw that one safe, he ran after the *No-Name.*

It had shot the first fall, only a few feet high, and was rearing down a steep rapid. He saw it strike a boulder and heave up like a bucking horse. All three men were thrown out, but when the boat jammed briefly against the rocks they managed to grab the gunwale, and as she slipped off and started down again Powell watched the dripping boatmen frantically haul themselves in. The boat was full of water; though her watertight compartments kept her afloat, she was unmanageable in the fierce current. She wallowed down through the rapid, pounded into the tail waves and on two hundred yards to a second rapid as wild as the first. There she struck solidly, broadside, and broke completely in two. For a moment the tiny dark heads of the swimming men were visible in the foam, and then the water swept them out of sight.

Powell ran, bursting his lungs, with the other men behind him. Around the bend he came in sight of a swimmer being washed and pounded on a rock to which he clung for his life. O. G. Howland, recognizable by his draggled beard, had made a stony island in mid-rapid and was scrambling out to stretch a pole to the man on the rock, who turned out to be Goodman. Goodman let go the rock, seized the pole, and was hauled out. Further down the island

Seneca Howland was dragging himself to the safety of the boulders.

They were safe for the time, but marooned in the middle of a bad rapid. Now the lightness and maneuverability of the *Emma Dean* proved out. The others lined her down to the foot of the first rapid, and Sumner, a brave man and by now a good boatman, was shoved off from there. Angling across the tail waves that swept almost to the tongue of the second rapid, he made the tip of the island. Then the four men pulled the boat upriver as high as they could go. Standing in water to his shoulders, one held it there while the others climbed in. Then a straining push, a scramble, the men in the stern hauling the pusher aboard, Sumner pulling furiously on the oars, and they made it in to where those on shore could reach them. There was a good deal of handshaking and thumping on the back — as much rejoicing, Powell wrote, "as if they had been on a voyage around the world and wrecked on a distant coast." [14]

The rapid was not Jim Beckwourth's suck, nor Risdon's whirlpool, but it was a reasonable facsimile. What made the wreck difficult to bear was that one whole boatload of rations, all the extra clothing of the *No-Name's* crew, and a good many instruments, were lost. What made it worse was that by an error all the barometers had been packed in that boat instead of being distributed as they should have been. What made it worst, perhaps, from the leader's point of view, was that the wreck need not have happened at all. A split-second error, a failure to bail fast enough or keep the eyes open, a momentary sluggishness in responding to signals, and they were in trouble.[15]

The loss of clothes was not serious; they needed little except the shirts and drawers they were wearing, and the other men still had spares to lend. But the loss of rations would make them move faster than Powell had planned, and the loss of all the barometers would seriously reduce the scientific usefulness of the expedition. Both the map that Howland was making as they went, and the prediction of where they were on the river's downward grade to tidewater, depended on those tubes of mercury. Powell lay awake that night, half inclined to try making his way out to Salt Lake to order new barometers from the east. But in the morning they saw that the wreck of the *No-Name* had washed fifty yards farther downstream. Her stern half had lodged where it might possibly be reached, and there was a chance that something remained in its compartment. Sumner and Hall volunteered to reach her, and did so. From their rummaging in the smashed after cabin they rose up to wave their arms and yell something across the roar of water, and in a few minutes they came back in triumph. No clothes and no rations were among their prizes, but they had found the whole package of barometers, unhurt, as well as a package of thermometers, plus what had inspired their cheers: a keg of whiskey smuggled aboard at Green River without Powell's knowledge. Powell's *Report* calls it a three-gallon keg; Sumner's journal says it was a ten. Perhaps there was some wishful thinking in both accounts. Howland's letter to the *Rocky Mountain News* modestly refers to it only as a "blue keg." He had reason to be modest. It was his whiskey.

Intent upon the success of the expedition, and perhaps (though neither he nor any other diarist ever suggests it) wondering if Howland's error of the day before might have been caused by that same keg, Powell might have risked the entire trip by throwing the keg back in the river. But the men were fagged, three of them had had a good scare and a good ducking and bruising, all of them had lost clothes, guns, outfit, and Howland had lost all his notes made up to that point. They were in need of a little morale building. Powell good-naturedly admitted that the river was cold, and accepted the keg as medicine.

Presumably it served its medicinal function. They were days getting past this portage, nearly a mile long, and letting the boats down successive rapids. At the bottom they lay over two more days to dry their spoiling rations, which had now become a worry. The wreck had sobered their exuberance, which in the fast water above had left them feeling, as Sumner said, "like sparking a black-eyed girl — just dangerous enough to be exciting." Now they encountered evidence of another wreck before their own — a broken boat, the lid of a bake oven, an old tin plate. Powell thought this might be Ashley's boat. Nobody has ever determined whose in fact it was. But it helped emphasize the prudence that Powell had emphasized from the beginning. It did not take sucks or Niagaras to wreck a boat or drown a man.

Lodore was not a succession of rapids such as they had passed before, but as Bradley wrote in his journal, one continuous rapid. The shores were cluttered boulders, without level ground on which to camp. Bitching like a good army man, Bradley remarked on June 11 that the Major had as usual chosen the worst campsite available. "If I had a dog," Bradley said, "that would lie where my bed is made tonight I would kill him and burn his collar and swear I never owned him." That same day, to give him better cause to grouse, he fell on the portage and cut his eye badly, so that thereafter, down the canyon where the river "roars and foams like a wild beast," he went sullenly with a notable black eye. Bedraggled, soaked, muddy, their shirttails dragging and their drawers clinging to their goosepimpled legs, they were all in Bradley's mood.

There are characteristic discomforts on a river voyage. Not the least is the incessant wetting and the sharp alternation of heat and cold. On a bright day a boatman swiftly sunburns the backs of his hands, the insteps of his feet if they are bare, every unexpected spot exposed by long sitting in one position. In the shade, in soaked clothes, the wind is often icy. And worse than either sun or wind is the irritation of sitting long hours on a hard wet board in sopping pants or drawers. The water is full of silt and sand, and so, consequently, are the clothes one wears. After a few hours there grows a sensation as if one has been gently coasting his seat back and forth across fine sandpaper. After a few more hours a boatman likes to stand whenever the river will let him.

Their clothes, even in the valises and carpetbags stowed under the cabin decks, were soaked. Their flour was wet and souring, their bacon gritty with silt, their coffee damp, their beans sprouting. Their muscles were sore and their bodies bruised and their tempers tried. When they took a rest on June 13 the saturnine Bradley commented that it was the first Sunday they had paid any attention to and he was inclined to believe that nobody but himself even knew it was the Sabbath. As they spread the spoiling rations out to dry on the rocks he prophesied dourly that they would soon be sorry they had taken no better care of them. "If we succeed," he said, "it will be *dumb luck,* not good judgment that will do it."

Thus the enlisted man about his commander, *ad infinitum.*

Lodore continued to rub its lessons in. They had barely started from their enforced rest camp on June 15 before the *Maid of the Canyon,* allowed to swing a little too far out into the current in the tongue of a rapid, smoked her line through the palms of the men holding her and broke clean away down the rapid and out of sight. Their spirits went down with her, for with only two boats they would be badly overloaded and underrationed. But they chased along shore, hoping against probability, and found her rotating with dignity in an eddy, unharmed except for a bruise or two.[16]

Still that was not enough. Accidents it seemed must happen by threes. A day after the breaking loose of the *Maid,* Powell climbed with Howland up the cliff above camp, which was pitched in willows and cedars on a bar. A few minutes later he looked down on pandemonium. With characteristic carelessness Hawkins had built his cooking fire too close to the dead willows. A whirlwind swept upriver, tore across the bar, and scattered burning sticks in every direction. Willow and cedar smoldered and burst into flame which in the stiff wind grew almost instantly into a conflagration. Trapped on the bar, the men had no escape except the river as the wind swooped tongues of flame across the camp. They jumped for the boats. Hawkins grabbed what he could carry of the mess kit, and ran with his arms full of kettles and bake ovens, but at the bank he stubbed his toe, and without a pause or a cry dove head first into the Green. He came up strangling and cussing, and without the mess kit.

By that time the whole point was ablaze. Their hair and beards were singed and the boats in danger. There was nothing to do but cut loose. From up on the cliff Powell watched the boats full of smoking, slapping men pour down the river and through a stiff rapid for almost a mile before they got under control and made shore. Their knives, forks, spoons, tin plates, and some of their kettles remained behind them in Lodore, along with the cryptic wreckage they themselves had found, to be a warning to careless travelers.

As if the lessons were now finished, the river relented, and on the morning of June 18 they floated down into a cliff-walled park where the Yampa flowed smoothly in, carrying more water at this stage than the Green. In a grassy, sunny bottom "the size of a good farm" they camped and rested and sent their voices against the cliffs that sent them back in diminishing echoes, six or eight echoes, or echoes of echoes. Behind them, as Powell now wrote in a fourth letter to the Chicago *Tribune*,[17] lay "a chapter of disasters and toils," but Lodore was "grand beyond the power of pen to tell. Its waters poured unceasingly from the hour we entered it until we landed here. No quiet in all that time; but its walls and cliffs, its peaks and crags, its amphitheaters and alcoves, told a story that I hear yet, and shall hear, and shall hear. . . ." With an ear cocked for the public sound of his voice, he could still sound perilously like Mungo Park.

In this Echo Park at the mouth of the Yampa Howland too wrote up their adventures, and Sumner, Powell, and Bradley brought their journals up to date, Bradley so secretly that nobody on the expedition, then or later, suspected he was keeping one. A moody man, he holed up alone away from the others and talked to his thoughts. Walter Powell, just as moody, rang his fine bass voice off the cliffs in song, especially in renderings of "Old Shady." He sang that song so much they called him Old Shady himself. The hunters, for whose skill Bradley had the most acid contempt, made no inroads on the game supply, but Bradley got personally irritated by fish that kept breaking his hooks, rigged up a quadruple-strength line, and brought in a ten-pounder. This was their first experience with the "Colorado River salmon," a sluggish and overgrown variety of minnow that often reaches four feet in length and thirty to forty pounds in weight. Jack Sumner remarked when they cooked Bradley's catch that it tasted like a paper of pins cooked in lard oil.

They had a pleasant camp, a good rest, a sense of having come to a place they knew, for they had camped on the Yampa many times, and crossed its canyon farther up. A comfortable sense of having passed perils with only moderate bad luck shows through the letters and journals they wrote here. Their morale was high. In his letter to the *News* Howland, the best reporter of the lot, put it for all of them:

> Our trip thus far has been pretty severe: still very exciting. When we have to run rapids, nothing is more exhilarating . . . and as a breaker dashes over us as we shoot out from one side or the other, after having run the fall, one feels like hurrahing. It must be some-

thing like the excitement of battle at the point of victory. . . . A calm, smooth stream, running only at the rate of five or six miles per hour, is a horror we all detest now. . . . As soon as the surface of the river looks smooth all is listlessness or grumbling at the sluggish current, unless some unlucky goose comes within range of our rifles. But just let white foam show itself ahead and everything is as jolly and full of life as an Irish "wake." . . .[18]

They were all feeling good as they camped in Echo Park and established altitude and latitude and longitude for the junction of the rivers — all but Bradley, the loner, and Goodman, the outsider whom nobody knew well and nobody much liked. Since his near-drowning, he had been looking thoughtful.

For a good many days it seemed that their prediction of better water ahead, and their belief that Lodore was as bad as anything they would hit on the river, were sound. Below Echo Park they portaged a couple of stiff little rapids, but in the main the river ran very swiftly and without serious obstacles — the kind of running they all most appreciated. Where a creek came in clear and cold, they had their first mess of trout. The hunters were given a chance to get up on the rims, and "wonderful to relate," as Bradley said, Hawkins shot a buck. It was the only fresh meat they had had, except for geese and ducks and fish, since Hawkins had trailed a band of mountain sheep on the second day out and thrown a lamb down the cliff. Bradley found ripe currants growing, and picked a gallon in the mountain pocket they named Island Park. Through the longitudinally cut spur that Powell christened Craggy Canyon[19] they boomed along well-fed and sassy, making, by their measurement, thirty miles in a day.

On the morning of June 26, slightly more than a month after their embarkation, they bounced down a lively little riffle toward a hollow-worn cliff of smooth salmon-colored sandstone, pulled stoutly to avoid being carried under the cliff, and rounded a bend to the right to see wide open sky, a quiet river fringed with cottonwoods meandering south and west through a great valley.

This again was known country, the Wonsits or Uinta Valley, the widest break in the series of canyons on all the Colorado. They had camped in it the winter before; Berthoud's wagon track crossed its center at the mouth of the Uinta River; Father Escalante, though apparently Powell did not know it, had forded the Green near the upper end of the valley and gone westward toward Utah Valley on his attempted passage from Taos to California in 1776. Manly had left the river here in 1849. Along its banks, as they rowed down the quiet, dirty stream, they saw evidence of many Indian camps.

Quiet water had its drawbacks. If they wanted to make time, they had to row. Even so, they dragged their log for sixty-three miles down the Green's meanders on June 27, fought mosquitoes all night, and in the morning made the mouth of the Uinta, the site of the present town of Ouray, Utah, less than two miles above the mouth of the White where they had camped the winter before.[20] The Third California Veteran Infantry had sunk a ferry barge in the Green here, in anticipation of its use on the stage road, and they probed for it halfheartedly, but they were not interested enough really to hunt. Other things were on their minds. This was the only opportunity along the whole course of the river for communication. From here letters could go out, and at the Uinta Agency, thirty miles up this creek, there might be mail waiting.

Powell sent his brother and Andy Hall on foot to the agency for mail, setting out after them two days later with Goodman and Hawkins. The ones left behind rather mournfully celebrated the Fourth by chasing ducks on the Uinta. When the Major, Hawkins, Hall, Walter and two Indian packers returned, Frank Goodman was not with them. His appetite for border experiences had been satisfied. Bradley and Howland, in their accounts, charitably grant him his reason that he had lost his whole outfit in the wreck of the *No-Name*. Sumner half contemptuously remarks that Goodman seemed fonder of bullwhacking than of rowing. Powell gives him credit for being a "faithful man," but he was not sorry to see him go, for with one boat wrecked he could do with a smaller party.

By the Ute packers who had carried 300 pounds of flour out from Uinta Agency, Powell sent back the small collection of fossils he had made coming downriver. Sumner, impatient to "cut loose from the last sign of civilization for many hundred miles,"[21] let himself be sharply critical of the pitiful little dab of provisions that the Major had brought. The fact was that Powell had very little money, and even if he had had the price, the agent's stores were so low that he could have given Powell little.[22] The boats, moreover, now carried three men each, besides the supplies, and the

Major obviously did not share the sanguine belief of his men that they had run through the worst of the river.

Bradley, though not as vehement as Sumner about the "weary, useless waiting" [23] while Powell fooled around at the agency, was quite as eager to be off. They were all impatient. Nevertheless, for a mixed group, they had so far managed to remain remarkably harmonious. The river equivalent of cabin fever, which comes on fast and in virulent forms, had hardly touched them. Goodman, the near-pariah, was gone. Bradley, the loner, might herd by himself but he was a good boatman and a cool head — "tough as a badger," Powell said — and he had their respect. Walter Powell, though moody and increasingly disliked, was insulated by his relationship to the leader, and accepted for the quality of his singing and his great physical strength.[24] As for the Major himself, in spite of his science they had to admire him. One-armed, he was as agile on the cliffs as any of them. He had nerve, and he had a variety of interests that excited him, and he participated fully in camp life. Actually he was a commander more likely than most to hold so centrifugal a crew in hand. All they really objected to in him was his caution and his "waiting around." Andy Hall, as wild as any of the party, wrote to his brother from the Uinta Agency that the Major was "a bully fellow you bett." [25]

Still, they grumbled at delay, and at caution, and at the demands of science. Quiet water and known valleys did not interest them, and there were no gravel bars to occupy their spare time here. Southward they saw the unknown country rising in buttes and mesas. The river went past them smooth and taffy-colored, spinning in quiet whirlpools, sucking at its mud banks. They had not come to sit by the side of so uninteresting a stream so long.

On July 6, to their universal relief, they pushed off on the second leg of the journey, this time into the incontrovertible Unknown. As if to document their wanderlust and their unfitness for civilization, a squatter's garden encountered at the mouth of the White poisoned them all so thoroughly that they floated through the lower end of Uinta Valley vomiting over the side and cursing Andy Hall, who had suggested that potato tops made good greens. By evening, almost imperceptibly, the valley closed in, the walls began to rise, the barren rock poked through, and they were in another canyon.

9. *The Green: Uinta Valley to the Junction with the Grand*

LOOKING UPON the unknown, they found reasons for its being so. On both sides of the river an increasingly barren and broken land closed in, topped with fantastic towers. On July 7 they were deep in an entrenched, meandering canyon, swinging in great bends and amphitheaters. By evening they had come again to bad water, the walls much broken by side canyons, sometimes so close together that holes had eroded out between them leaving natural bridges. On the high rims they could see pine forests, but down on the river there was little but baking broken rock.[1] It reminded them all of the arid plateau around Green River and Fort Bridger; they were agreeably surprised to be in tune with science when the Major found fossil fish teeth that told him these rocks were in fact the same lacustrine formations.

Wanting to know as much as he could about the unexplored land back from the river, Powell took Bradley and climbed up a steep, ledgy wall in blistering sun. Somewhere on the cliff he made the mistake of jumping from one foothold to another, grabbing a projection of rock with his one hand. Then he found himself "rimmed," unable to go forward or back. Standing on tiptoe and clinging to the knob, he shouted to Bradley, above him, but Bradley could not reach him with his hand, and there was no halfway foothold to which he could descend. The cliff had neither brush nor pole; they had carried no rope with them.

Below his feet was a hundred-foot drop, a terrace, and then a longer drop. If he let himself go he might fall clear to the river's edge. By now his legs were trembling, his strength beginning to waver. As a desperation measure Bradley sat down on his ledge and yanked off his long drawers, which he lowered to Powell. With nice timing, Powell let go the knob, and half falling away from the cliff, grabbed the dangling underwear.[2] That was the first, but by no means the only time he had cause to thank his stars for Bradley's presence on the party.

That day, and for several successive days, Powell scanned from the rims a country even more wild and desolate than the canyon through which the boats felt their careful way. A great plateau was

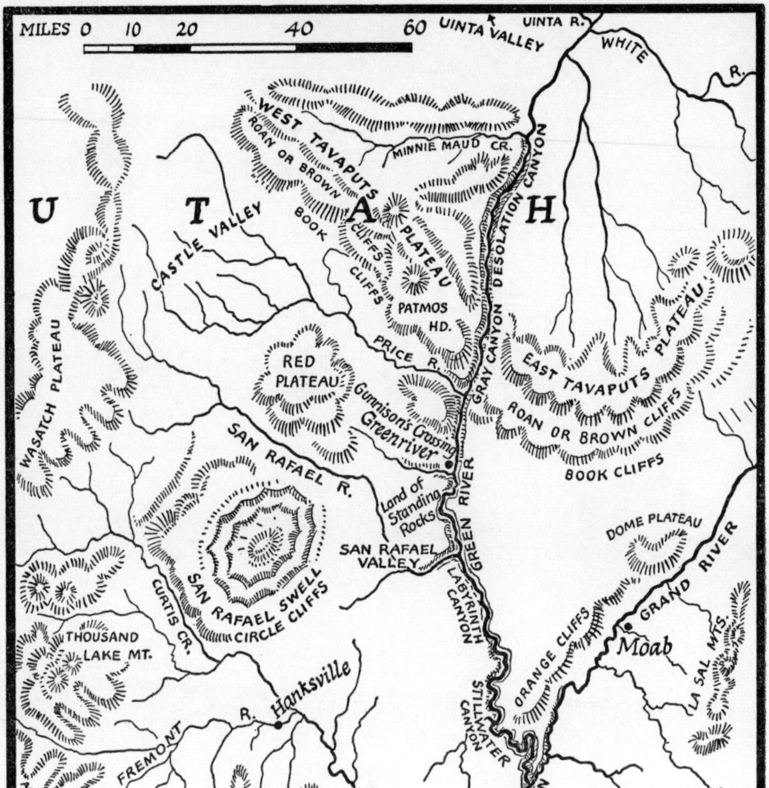
MILES 0 10 20 40 60
UINTA VALLEY
UINTA R.
WHITE R.
U T A H
WEST TAVAPUTS PLATEAU
ROAN OR BROWN CLIFFS
BOOK CLIFFS
MINNIE MAUD CR.
DESOLATION CANYON
GRAY CANYON
CASTLE VALLEY
PATMOS HD.
PRICE R.
RED PLATEAU
Gunnison's Crossing
Greenriver
EAST TAVAPUTS PLATEAU
ROAN OR BROWN CLIFFS
BOOK CLIFFS
WASATCH PLATEAU
SAN RAFAEL R.
Land of Standing Rocks
GREEN RIVER
SAN RAFAEL VALLEY
SAN RAFAEL SWELL
CIRCLE CLIFFS
CURTIS CR.
DOME PLATEAU
GRAND RIVER
LABYRINTH CANYON
ORANGE CLIFFS
Moab
LA SAL MTS.
THOUSAND LAKE MT.
Hanksville
FREMONT R.
STILLWATER CANYON
AQUARIUS PLATEAU
DIRTY DEVIL R.
CATARACT CANYON
TRACHYTE CR.
HENRY MTS.
Hite
Dandy Crossing
ABAJO MTS.
MT. LINNAEUS
Monticello
POTATO VALLEY
WATER POCKET FOLD
ALCOVE CR.
COLORADO RIVER
GLEN CANYON
Blanding
ESCALANTE R.
KAIPAROWITS PLAT
Bluff
SAN JUAN R.
GLEN CANYON
Navajo Mt.

cut completely in two by the river. From a tower which he climbed he looked across the high pine forest clothing the summits, and across dozens of canyons heading in mid-plateau and deepening toward their confluence with the Green or with the White and Uinta to the north. But he could see little that told him what lay to the south, only the widening gray and brown lips of canyons cutting down toward unknown junctions. He took barometric measurements of the depth of strata, height of walls, fall of river. He taught Jack Sumner to use a sextant. He came down from the cliffs, groping dangerously after dark, and stayed up nearly all night making observations, and with an hour or two of sleep pushed off to run a while and tie up for more climbing, more observations.

They met headwinds so hot and strong they could not run against them. Even in mid-river, soaking wet, they panted with the heat, and on shore the sand of their campsite blew over them so that they covered their heads with blankets and sweltered. And when the wind subsided enough so that they could run, they hit twenty miles of continuous cataracts that made them revise some of the superlatives they had applied to Lodore.[3] Sometimes running, sometimes (to the men's disgust) cautiously lining, they got through forty-five miles of what they named the Canyon of Desolation and thought the country ahead looked favorable for a break. Andy Hall, rising above sandstorms and headwinds and the grinding labor of the portages, lay on his back that night and sang to the glum Bradley in a voice like a crosscut saw:

> *When he put his arm around her*
> *She bustified like a forty-pounder,*
> *Look away, look away, look away, Dixie land.*

All the way down the river Bradley had been griping in his diary about the Major's habit of ignoring the Sabbath. Now he had a chance to crow. On Sunday, July 11, Powell started the *Emma Dean* down a brisk rapid and saw too late that it was a dogleg with a sharp kick to the left and a heavy pile-up of water against the wall at the turn. Earlier, two of their oars had been broken; the boat had only two now, not enough to pull them out of danger. All they could do was to point her nose downstream, wave frantically to the following boats to pull ashore, and hang on. They shot past a rock and were caught in a reflex wave that rolled the boat like a spinning log. Powell was thrown a boat's length away, Sumner and Dunn managed to cling to the gunwales. In a pneumatic life preserver,[4] and in water so swift, Powell could not sink. He struck out one-armed for the boat, wallowing swamped through the tail waves. The three of them, swimming and pulling at the waterlogged boat, managed to get her against a pile of driftwood before she could be swept over a second rapid below. But to Bradley's satisfaction they had lost two rifles, some blankets, a barometer, and both remaining oars, and the Major had had his comeuppance for laboring on Sunday. That day they made a half mile, most of it swimming, and spent the remaining hours of daylight whipsawing oars out of a driftwood log.

Next day Bradley got his own comeuppance for gloating. Coming to a long, curving fall between broken rocks and an overhanging cliff, the Major looked the rapid over and concluded to run it, keeping as close to the rocks on the left as possible to avoid the great waves and the overhang along the cliff. The *Emma Dean* made it, half full of water, but as Bradley's boat swept down out of the tongue a wave broke over his stern and knocked him overboard. His foot caught under the thwart, and head down, now contorting himself upward enough to get a hand on the gunwale, now dragging clear under, he rushed with the swamped boat through a series of battering waves before Walter Powell, pulling like a madman away from the threatening cliff, made it past the danger and could reach his strangling companion a hand.

The river played no favorites, and it showed no sign of conforming to their united wish for a letup. Beyond the Canyon of Desolation they ran directly into another, which they called Coal Canyon from the seams of lignite in the walls. It is now called Gray Canyon. And Gray Canyon was more of the same. In one bad rapid the river filled the channel from cliff to cliff, leaving not even the bare toehold of a portage. They had to let one boat down the full length of its line, then push off the second attached to it, and the third attached to the second, until all three were stretched out straining in the rapid, when the third was pulled in, then the second loosed and snubbed in, then the first. Then Bill Dunn, left on a rock in midstream, had to swim for it and be yanked in by those on shore.

It was bone-wrenching labor. Below that difficult lining job lay a portage, and below that a camp on a sandbeach in a hurricane of wind that blew all night and filled blankets, kettles, food, hair, eyes, ears, mouths, with sand. Desolation and Coal Canyons had been pretty continuous strain. Tempers were short, the rapids apparently endless. And then in a blink the unpredictable river gave them precisely what they craved: swift water, exhilarating little riffles and rapids that sped them along without labor and with a great lift of the spirit. They ran nineteen rapids in eighteen miles without the necessity of getting out of the boats, and at the end of Coal Canyon they burst out into open country again, a shimmering, blistered desert broken by circumeroded buttes of buff and gray and brown and slaty blue. Behind them, stretching in a long line east and west, were the Roan and Book Cliffs, cut to their base by the river's gorge, and meandering away in long wavy lines distorted by heat haze and the smoke of forest fires. To the northeast they saw snow mountains, the Uncompahgre Range in western Colorado. Across the valley the buttes lifted on the heat waves and hung dreamlike above the earth.

The river was deep, broad, quiet. Two hours below the mouth of Coal Canyon they found an Indian crossing where crude rafts were moored against the bank, and knew it for another of the very few practicable crossings in the canyon wilderness. At this point, now the site of Greenriver, Utah, where both Highway 50 and the Denver and Rio Grande cross, the old Spanish Trail, route of mule drivers between Taos and California, route of traveling mountain men and supply trains, found a way across the canyons. To this same point Captain Gunnison, surveying for the Pacific Railroad in 1853, had been compelled like water in a funnel.[5] The Powell party knew that Gunnison and seven of his men had been massacred by the Pahvant Indians a little farther west. When they landed and found evidence that Indians had recently crossed, they did not linger. Even such half-spoiled rations and depleted outfits as they had might be a temptation.

Beyond their brief meeting with the tracks of Indian and white they pushed on down the quiet river, one day, two days. At the mouth of the San Rafael, trickling from the west through a deep canyon, they found much Indian sign. Out from the river the buttes were evenly banded, brilliantly colored: pink, purple, brown, gray. As the river dug again into the rock and the walls rose higher around them they kept climbing out to look over the dunes of colored sand, maroon and orange and creamy white. The river began to pursue another entrenched meander, locked and baffled in the deep rock, swinging on itself in great bends under walls of homogeneous orange sandstone domed and hollowed into immense caves.

By now they had left behind them all familiarity; the country was such as none of them had ever seen. On the broken plains stretching away from rimrock there was no vegetation, only worn rock and sand and the bizarre forms of desert erosion; in the distance the Roan Cliffs were pale azure, the flat and tabular outlines of mesas and buttes were evenly bedded, colored like the rainbow. It *looked* like unknown country, and its heat fried their skins and beat on their heads and sucked the sweat from their pores as they rowed down the slow baffled current around bends that showed always more alcoves, more amphitheaters. The strangeness excited them to horseplay; they shot off their guns and loosed sharp yells to hear the confused echoes in the bowknot tangles of the river. They named it Labyrinth Canyon.

Like a teasing woman the river dawdled, meandered, surprised them with new forms, new colors, delayed and delayed and delayed the expected union with the Grand, now marked on the maps as the Colorado, at that point which on all the maps was frank guess work.[6] They watched, and rowed, and waited, and expected the rapids and cataracts that should accompany the junction in such a wild and moonlike landscape, but the river swept them on serenely through July 14, 15, 16. Again and again they climbed out, but they looked in vain for any canyon that could mean the incoming Grand. They walked over pavements of jasper and heard their foreign voices in painted amphitheaters and tracked the sand in the bottoms of lateral gorges and saw the Orange Cliffs flame under the harsh sun, but still their objective escaped them, and still the Green went smooth and quiet around more bends.

Late in the afternoon of the 16th the river broke into hurrying waves, became again a swift steep pouring on which the boats rode like coasting sleds. Stillwater Canyon was behind them. In another hour they broke without warning on the junction, the Grand coming in "in a calm strong tide" from the left. No falls, no cataracts, no tumult to mark the union. Lesser canyons, wet-weather streams, almost always meant rapids, for they bore down flood-washed boulders and left them at their mouths. But the Grand came secretly out of the concealing rock, clearer and colder than the Green and at this time of year with a greater flow. Below the junction for a thousand yards, as far as they could see, the doubled river went unrippled, undangerous.

From Green River, Wyoming, they had come, by Powell's computation, 538 miles. Caution had held their losses to one boat and its contents. Of the crew only one, the weakest, had given up. They were tightly knit, an expedition, camped on a spot probably no white man and perhaps no man of any kind had ever seen, unless the mysterious Denis Julien or other mountain men had found their way in. Macomb ten years before had predicted that the spot would remain forever unvisited, though a mendacious Colorado editor had once claimed that he had laid out a town at the junction. His town was in the land of Gilpin. Here was what Sumner described as "an apparently endless canyon in three directions — up the Grand, up the Green, and down the Colorado," with "not enough timber within ten miles to last one family six months."[7]

A quarter of a mile deep in the rock, the two rivers met to form a third with a formidable name. They camped at the fork of the waters and had some fun with the editor's "Junction City" and settled down for several days of observations and measurements. Now they were correcting the maps.

10. Interlude: "A Prosperous Passage ahead of Us"

IT IS TIME to return for a few minutes to Captain Samuel Adams, last seen carrying his dudgeon onto the Union Pacific cars at Green River. He had not been idle since. On July 12, four days before the

Powell party reached the junction of Grand and Green, Sam Adams was raising the curtain on a new scene of his low-comedy subplot. At Breckenridge, a mining camp on the Blue, on Colorado's western slope, he had made himself solid with a congenial group, of a mentality to suit his own. They were predisposed for the spiel he gave them, eager for the news he brought of riches and opportunities along the river, willing to play a long shot — or as they appeared to conceive it, a sure thing.

They fitted Sam Adams out with four boats, built on the spot out of green lumber, undecked and with no air compartments, and they enlisted in his expedition to the number of ten men.[1] They equipped themselves (for there is no reason to believe that Adams could have equipped them) with Spencer muzzle-loading rifles and two hundred rounds of ammunition apiece, and with a good many hundredweight of assorted supplies. For the flagship the ladies of Breckenridge made a flag upon which was inscribed, "Western Colorado to California, Greeting."

Adams' purpose, conceived after his rebuff by Powell, was to descend the Blue to its junction with the Grand a few miles southwest of Gore Pass, and from there float on down this unobstructed waterway to California. It was not quite clear how far away California was horizontally, but it was a cinch that from Breckenridge, at an altitude of ten thousand feet, it was almost two miles vertically.

Breckenridge gave him a large sendoff, with speeches and cheers, at the launching place two and a half miles below town where two of the boats pushed off. (The other two were hauled down twelve miles by wagon, and launched there). So full was Adams' heart that in his journal that day[2] he recorded a long paragraph in praise of Summit County, where "upon the extreme limits of civilization I had unexpectedly found a community which in intelligence, enterprise, and moral worth were superior to that of any other I had ever met."

Down a creek which Adams describes as falling 80 to 120 feet per mile, they ran nine miles. With scientific care Adams noted the width and depth of the river, leaving blanks for the figures to be filled in later, and that night in a jovial camp they dined upon the homemade bread of the wife of Judge Silverthorn, presented to them at parting. There had been no difficulty that day, Adams says, though his boat was twice upset.

Next day there was a new launching, after the wagoners who had brought the other boats had left. Judge Silverthorn made a speech and presented Adams with a dog. What ever happened to that miserable animal in the next month is one of the dark and tantalizing silences of history.

The experiences of the next day, July 14, might have given Adams a hint of what was coming. In what his journal calls Rocky Canyon they bounced around a corner full upon a bad rapid. Within seconds Adams, Waddle, Day, O'Connor, Twible, Lillis, Decker, and everybody else in the expedition except the occupants of the last boat were hanging onto rocks in midstream, trying to make themselves heard over the roar of water. Their "instruments," whatever those were, as well as Adams' box of papers, including his letters of "authorization" from the Secretary of War, went down the Blue. The fall in Rocky Canyon Adams estimated at over 250 feet in a mile and a half.

On Sunday, July 18, somewhat quenched by the ducking, and in need of repairs, they sent Mr. Lovell by land back to Breckenridge for more "instruments" and matches. Adams does not state what instruments would be available in the mining camp of Breckenridge; it is allowable to believe that it was the matches he really needed. As the rest of the group hung around Pacific Park waiting for Lovell's return they began to show the first signs of failing enthusiasm. On Tuesday, July 19, Adams' diary notes that they raised thirty dollars and gave it to Mr. Ricker and sent him back home as a "common nuisance."

Others had also begun to doubt, but Adams talked them into going on, saying that he would proceed though no one accompanied him. Heartened and with dry matches, they pushed off again, but had gone only a short distance when the boat of Lillis and Decker hit a rock and was demolished. Somewhat forlornly they stopped for the rest of the day to fish out of the rocks downstream whatever could be salvaged. Minus his instruments, Adams remained at a scientific disadvantage, and again had to leave a blank in his diary: "Distance by water from Breckenridge, —— miles."

By Thursday, July 22, dissension had begun to rend the little group of explorers to its foundations. O'Connor, Foment, Decker, and Frazier gave up and started back, as Adams' diary says contemptuously, "to tell of their heroic actions &c." That was the same camp where, looking around him with the eye of fantasy, Adams saw growing in great abundance crops of wild oats, wheat, rye, barley, clover, and timothy, in places and at altitudes where only the protecting hand of God could have let them grow.

The day after the great desertion, Mr. Waddle showed up temporarily missing, so that Adams had to run his boat alone. He swamped only once, when he drove under a fallen tree. For eight miles, according to his record, he had smooth and easy sailing to the junction with the Grand. There the party camped, fifty-five miles and twelve days out of Breckenridge, and one boat and five members fewer than they had started with.

Here for a week there is a gap in Adams' journal, perhaps because he was too busy to write, perhaps because his pencil floated off to join his instruments. Presumably they rested. Not impossibly, in this week the unhappy dog met his fate, whatever it was. At last on July 30 they started again and ran five miles, stopping at the mouth of what Adams calls the Grand Cannon. It appears to have been Cedar Canyon, where in 1867 Powell had first looked at white water and dreamed of hunting down the secrets of the unexplored plateaus.[3] Camped here for two and a half days, the party washed clothes, cleaned guns, brought journals up to date, and waited for Twible and Lillis to carry out dispatches to Hot Sulphur Springs and bring back newspapers and more matches. Adams totted up the river he had run and estimated the fall as 3500 feet. These figures gave him cause for self-gratulation when in a copy of the *Rocky Mountain News* that Lillis brought back he read Howland's letter written on the Yampa. "It was well written," Adams admitted to his journal, "but rather extravagant respecting the speed they made in going down a river of 15 fall per mile. Had their party come over a continued rapid of over 3000 feet in fifty five I do not think it would be attended with so much permanent excitement as that spoken of in the letter of my friend Howland."[4]

He wrote this on the bank of a calm river slipping through the level of Middle Park. Next day, when the boats entered the "Grand Cannon" through a slot "fifty feet in breadth," they had to line over several very bad stretches where Adams said he leveled and found the fall to be thirty-four feet in four hundred yards. Never on the Colorado had he seen such water, he said. Undoubtedly he hadn't.

Only a few hundred yards into the canyon one of the boats being lined swung out of control over a fall, filled with water, and was badly damaged. They lost a hundred pounds of bacon, a sack of flour, an axe, a saw, an oven, two canteens of salt, thirty-five pounds of coffee, and other articles. When they took stock after laboring past the bad spot they found that they had left two hundred twenty-five pounds of lumpy flour, fifty of bacon, and fifteen of coffee and salt.

Undaunted, they persevered. On August 3 they made paddles and repaired their boats and lined down an additional three hundred yards. Next day, lining with great difficulty through a roaring rapid, they found a slab of their lost bacon lying unhurt among the rocks, and were cheered as by an omen. It was the only good thing that had happened to them since they left Breckenridge.

By now they were deep in the gorge, with a huge domed mountain before them as if to stop the river, and the walls overhanging them so alarmingly that they began to wonder what they would do if Indians ambushed them from above. It was impossible to run, all but impossible to line or portage, difficult even to go back. The fall, Adams estimated, was fifty feet in five hundred yards, about the slope of a good coasting hill.

On August 5 one of the boats filled and swamped and was caught by its line among the rocks. They worked all morning to free it, only to see the line part in the afternoon and boat and load rush down into the falls and disappear forever. They had been four days of panting work making three quarters of a mile, and now, with one damaged boat remaining, they were faced with a seemingly impassable chute. But whatever Sam Adams lacked — ability to see, willingness to tell the truth, capacity to think straight — he lacked neither courage nor persistence. It gave him enormous satisfaction to assume that they were descending at the rate of one hundred twenty feet to the mile, for though the descent caused them great difficulty, they approached that much more swiftly the near-sea-level reaches that would give them smooth sailing. On August 6, stiffening their courage for trouble ahead, the members of the party threw away all extra clothing and equipment and stripped down for passage in the one boat. Adams says that he gave to the waves his box of papers (lost once already, on the second day out) and abandoned his instruments (which except perhaps for a hand level and a thermometer he had never had and wouldn't have known how to use) and on the seventh day they struggled from difficult portage to difficult portage until after the fourth round the boat swamped, broke its line, and rushed in disintegrating wreckage to join the other three.

Other men might by this time have begun to entertain doubts about the water route to California. By now the brave flag with its greeting from the ladies of Breckenridge was snagged in some rapid or driftwood pile, and all four inadequate boats were on their way to the Gulf of California in splinters. But Captain Samuel Adams was a dedicated man. With his five companions he built a raft and floated the skimpy remains of their provisions around a perpendicular corner, where on August 9 they sifted and dried their flour, of which they had one hundred twenty pounds left, along with twenty of bacon. Waddle, Lovell, and Day, musing over the stores and contemplating the river ahead, decided that day to start back by land. It was like the nursery rhyme of the ten little nine little eight little Indians. Adams now had left, besides himself, only two little Indian boys. The three indomitables went on, packing their stuff three miles down the canyon, passing en route the rocks strewn and plastered with discarded clothes that they had tossed overboard higher up. On August 10, square-jawed, they built a raft five by fourteen feet out of drift logs and took to the water again.

At the end of three miles the raft hit a rock and spilled overboard all their salt, all but ten days' ration of flour, and all their knives and forks, which were becoming fairly unnecessary anyway. They still had a camp kettle and a frying pan, but the raft was a wreck. When they had dried out they reconnoitered down the river. As far as they could see the water roared and pounded through one rapid after another. Reluctantly, on August 13, they decided to give it up and start back. The water-level route to the Pacific would have to wait a little while.

But to the eye of Sam Adams what he and his light-witted companions had come through had the look of a hard-won success. In the secondary and more polished version of his diary (figures are inked in, for instance), he wrote:

> I am fully satisfied that we had come over the worst part of our rout in 95 miles we had descended about 4500 feet. The vallies were open up river, the mountains bec smooth the pine and cedar

larger everything indic that a prosperous passage was ahead of us had we been in a position to have gone on. Three years before as I stated in my Report to the Sec of War, I looked up the Colorado River from a point 650 miles from its mouth and could then see a vally exten 75 miles to the NE. I could now look to the SW & almost see the narrow gap which divided us.[5]

That is to say, he was down, he had conquered all but the "narrow gap," he had demonstrated the passability of the Colorado waterway. But his statements continue to be haunted by illusion and contradiction. In one paragraph he is standing at the foot of Middle Park, Colorado, and all but seeing across to Boulder Canyon, Nevada. In the next paragraph he estimates the distance from where his expedition ended to the Gulf of California as 1300 miles, though Boulder Canyon is only 650 miles from the gulf. He was thus looking at least 650 miles — in fact nearer 800. In William Gilpin, though there was extravagance, there was also logic, coherence, a show of sense. Adams was over that shadow line which divides the merely extravagant from the lunatic, and yet the distance between Adams and Gilpin looks to the eye of history far narrower than that "narrow gap" that separated Adams from his goal.

In the canyon which halted his hairbreadth and hairbrained plunge down the western slope, Adams' straining eyes saw wild wheat more than six feet high. From first to last he demonstrated a mastery of things that were not there. The 4500 feet of fall which he thought he had navigated were actually between 2000 and 3000. The "prosperous voyage" from which he reluctantly turned away would have included stretches like the rapids along which Highway 50 now runs near Glenwood Springs. Anyone can drive it at any time during the spring runoff and test himself by imagining what it would be to put a boat or raft through that wildhorse current with its twenty-foot waves. That "prosperous voyage" would have involved, in the stretch past Grand Junction and Moab and down to the union with the Green in the Land of Standing Rocks, some fancy water in West Water Canyon and some stiff rapids below the mouth of the Dolores. And then would have come almost five hundred miles of river rough enough to daunt even the witless.

On August 13, the day when Sam Adams was turning back from the Grand below Cedar Canyon, assuring himself that he had passed the worst, Major Powell and his eight bearded, ragged, exhausted, snarling men were running through what Sumner called a "nest of rapids." That day they ran thirty and lined three in fifteen miles, and looking ahead they were moved to ribald mirth at the thought of James White running that water on a lasso-bound raft. That was the morning when they had left the Little Colorado's mouth, the River of Flax, and were just entering the 217 mile stretch, between walls that went up in places more than a mile, which would afterward be known as Powell knew it: The Grand Canyon, the real one. And that afternoon, as they camped at the head of a bad rapid, they saw rising from under the even sedimentary strata the black and ominous gneiss and schist that they miscalled granite. It seemed to come as if thrust out of the core of the earth, as in fact it almost did. It was Archaean rock, as ancient as any revealed in the world's crust, packed and metamorphosed by billions of tons of pressure, millions of years of anchoring the globe. Its very look was black and ugly, and it would take them less than a day to learn that its looks were not deceptive.

Many times they had had what they thought bad rapids. They would learn that whenever they met that black rock coming up into the canyon's bed the river would pinch in meanly, gather speed, burst and roll over buried boulders and uncorraded adamantine ledges, run sometimes a hundred feet deep and with waves ten or fifteen feet high.

Like Sam Adams, they had been interested in the amount of fall they had accounted for. In camp below the mouth of the Little Colorado they had figured their altitude with satisfaction and hope, for from Green River Crossing they had ridden down almost 3400 feet from their starting altitude of 6075, and this by measurement, with instruments that existed and worked. To the mouth of the Virgin, the known and easy reaches of the river, they had only around 2000 feet to fall. They were close to two-thirds of the way down.

But the further they went the higher the unclimbable walls soared up, winging back in wide ledges to remote, painted rims, or pinching in to the narrow congested granite. The deeper they went, the fiercer and wilder the river became, the more remote and lost they felt, like bugs swept helplessly along the bottom of a flooded ditch.

By Adams' kind of observation, a prosperous voyage lay ahead.

11. *The Colorado: The Junction to the River of Flax*

BUT LET US GO BACK and pick them up where we left them.

By the time they reached the junction of the Green and Grand the Powell party had been out almost two months, and in that time seen no man white or red except at the Uinta Agency. The ten-month supply of food with which they had started was diminished alarmingly by consumption, spoilage, and the loss of the *No-Name*. When they sifted their musty flour through mosquito netting and checked over the rations that remained, they found themselves with a frugal two-month supply — if they didn't lose any more to the river. Their barometers were battered and their clothes considerably used up; the Howlands had only hand-me-downs to clothe their shanks. Nevertheless their camp at the junction was a satisfying one, and they made the most of the opportunity for exploration back from the canyons. Powell's field notes report nothing for this period, since there is a two-week gap from July 7 through July 19, but his published report, elaborated and enlarged later,[1] has a full entry:

> July 19: — Bradley and I start this morning to climb the left wall below the junction. The way we have selected is up a gulch. Climbing for an hour over and among the rocks, we find ourselves in a vast amphitheater, and our way cut off. We clamber around to the left for half an hour, until we find that we cannot go up in that direction. Then we try the rocks around to the right, and discover a narrow shelf, nearly half a mile long. In some places, this is so wide that we pass along with ease; in others, it is so narrow and sloping that we are compelled to lie down and crawl. We can look over the edge of the shelf, down eight hundred feet, and see the river rolling and plunging among the rocks. Looking up five hundred feet, to the brink of the cliff, it seems to blend with the sky. We continue along, until we come to a point where the wall is again broken down. Up we climb. On the right, there is a narrow, mural point of rocks, extending toward the river, two or three hundred feet high, and six or eight hundred feet long. We come back to where this sets in, and find it cut off from the main wall by a great crevice. Into this we pass. And now, a long, narrow rock is between us and the river. The rock itself is split longitudinally and transversely; and the rains on the surface above have run down through the crevices, and gathered into channels below, and then run off into the river. The crevices are usually narrow

> above, and, by erosion of the streams, wider below, forming a net work of caves; but each cave having a narrow, winding skylight up through the rocks. We wander among these corridors for an hour or two, but find no place where the rocks are broken down, so that we can climb up. At last, we determine to attempt a passage by a crevice, and select one which we think is wide enough to admit of the passage of our bodies, and yet narrow enough to climb out by pressing our hands and feet against the walls. So we climb as men would out of a well. Bradley climbs first; I hand him the barometer, then climb over his head, and he hands me the barometer. So we pass each other alternately, until we emerge from the fissure, out on the summit of the rock.

That is an adequate description of the difficulties of travel in the heart of the Land of Standing Rocks. It was hard enough for an able-bodied man, difficult in the extreme for a man with one arm. And out on top?

> Below is the cañon, through which the Colorado runs. We can trace its course for miles, and at points catch glimpses of the river. From the northwest comes the Green, in a narrow, winding gorge. From the northeast comes the Grand, through a cañon that seems bottomless from where we stand. Away to the west are lines of cliff and ledges of rock — not such ledges as you may have seen where the quarryman splits his blocks, but ledges from which the gods might quarry mountains, that, rolled out on the plain below, would stand a lofty range; and not such cliffs as you may have seen where the swallow builds its nest, but cliffs where the soaring eagle is lost to view ere he reaches the summit. Between us and the distant cliffs are the strangely carved and pinnacled rocks of the *Toom̆-pin wu-near̆ Tu-weap̆*. On the summit of the opposite wall of the cañon are rock forms that we do not understand. Away to the east a group of eruptive mountains are seen — the Sierra La Sal. Their slopes are covered with pines, and deep gulches are flanked with great crags, and snow fields are seen near the summits. So the mountains are in uniform, green, gray, and silver. Wherever we look there is but a wilderness of rocks; deep gorges, where the rivers are lost below cliffs and towers and pinnacles; and ten thousand strangely carved forms in every direction; and beyond them, mountains blending with the clouds.[2]

Bierstadt never painted a more romantic landscape.

That July 19 was notable for one thing besides the view. On that day Billy Hawkins made his peace with Science. "While we are eating supper," Powell's *Report* says, "we very naturally speak of better fare, as musty bread and spoiled bacon are not pleasant. Soon I see Hawkins down by the boat, taking up the sextant, rather a strange proceeding for him, and I question him concerning it. He replies that he is trying to find the latitude and longitude of the nearest pie."[3]

It was July 21 before they pushed off into the real Colorado, the old man himself, an awesome river wide and deep and the color of cocoa. The thousand yards of serene current visible from the junction lengthened out to three miles. Then rapids, bad ones, in quick succession. They portaged and lined when they could, ran when there seemed no other choice. The *Emma Dean* swamped again, and Powell, Sumner, and Dunn clung to her through the waves and got her ashore below minus three oars. The other boats took a beating and came through leaking, so that they lay over half a day to calk them with pitch gathered on the rim and to saw new oars out of drift logs. Eight miles, one mile, five miles, three quarters of a mile a day, they fought their way down the furious river, more furious than anything yet. Powell estimated that the stretch ahead of them on July 23 dropped fifty feet in a mile, "and he always," said Bradley dourly and not quite accurately to his journal, "underestimates."[4]

Even lining was too dangerous at some of these cataracts. They had to unload, make a trail among the boulders and talus, and carry everything, including the two ponderous oaken boats, stumbling and staggering in hundred-degree heat down to the foot of rapids where as likely as not a careful look showed them another portage directly ahead. Grousing, underfed, with nothing to console them except the faith that every foot of fall meant calmer water below, they ran or lined or carried their leaking boats past cataract after cataract. Respect for Lodore and the Canyon of Desolation waned; those rapids now seemed mere riffles to these. Bradley, though still willing to run anything Powell would let him, began to speculate on the possibility of a fall too high to run, in a part of the canyon where there was no shore for lining or a portage. Once they ran through just such a slot blind, tense with anticipation of disaster.

A muddy stream not marked on any map swept in from a canyon opening on the right, and from that point on the river improved.

They named the bad stretch Cataract Canyon, and the unknown stream, from its color and smell, the Dirty Devil. Later Hawkins and Sumner intimated that Powell named the stream for Bill Dunn, as a deliberate insult,[5] which seems unlikely. But the toils of Cataract Canyon had left them edgy: Bradley wrote that the name Powell gave this creek was "in keeping with his whole character which needs only a short study to be read like a book."[6] What he meant by that is vague; probably it has to do with the Major's impiety and refusal to observe the Sabbath.

But not everything was sour. Full on top of their fatigue and hardship the much-ridiculed hunters brought down two desert bighorn and they feasted gigantically on wild mutton — the best meat, according to mountain men, in all the West.

And the fickle river relented. From the mouth of the Dirty Devil they had fast, easy water. Their daily run jumped from a hard-won mile or two to a comfortable twenty. The walls became lower, became smooth, monolithic, salmon-colored sandstone stained with vertical stripes of "desert varnish," with maidenhair fern dripping from wet seams in the rock.

Through most of its course the canyoned Green and Colorado, though impressive beyond description, awesome and colorful and bizarre, is scenically disturbing, a trouble to the mind. It works on the nerves, there is no repose in it, nothing that is soft. The water-roar emphasizes what the walls begin: a restlessness and excitement and irritability. But Glen Canyon, into which they now floated and which they first called Monument Canyon from the domes and "baldheads" crowning its low walls, is completely different. As beautiful as any of the canyons, it is almost absolutely serene, an interlude for a pastoral flute. Except for some riffles in the upper section its river is wide, smooth, deep, spinning in dignified whirlpools and moving no more than seven or eight miles an hour. Its walls are the monolithic Navajo sandstone, sometimes smooth and vertical, rounding off to domes at the rims, sometimes undercut by great arched caves, sometimes fantastically eroded by slit side canyons, alcoves, grottoes green with redbud and maidenhair and with springs of sweet water. The first white men to see it except possibly James Ohio Pattie, they felt what every river tourist has felt since: the stillness, the remoteness, the lovely withdrawn quiet of that 149-mile river groove. This country seemed kindlier to human intrusions. They saw their first Moqui ruins on the cliffs, and the Major, climbing out to survey the country, found and used a series of ancient steps hewn in the smooth face of the rock.

Yet idyllic as Glen Canyon was, they could not relax and enjoy it. Their bacon was down to fifteen rancid pounds; they were short of everything but flour, coffee, and dried apples. After two cyclopean feasts, the mutton had spoiled in the heat, and though they saw other bighorn they were unable to bring any down. Their eyes searched the east wall for the mouth of the San Juan. A Mormon map they had placed it fifty miles below the junction of Green and Grand, while the "official" map made in Washington indicated that it was "probably 100." [7] But the river's course lay farther west than the government map put it, and that meant that the mouth of the San Juan might be a long way from where it was supposed to be.

Past the mouth of the Escalante they went without even noticing the river; it is not very noticeable, and perhaps they were all watching the east wall for the San Juan's mouth. Then in the afternoon of the last day of July they floated down toward a massive awning-striped wall that turned the river in a sharp right-hand bend. Just before the bend the San Juan came in through a trenchlike gorge from the left, a swift, muddy stream as large as White River.

Now the whole enormous drainage basin of the river was floating them, melted snow from the high Wind River peaks, and from the Wasatch, and from the Uintas with their hundred cold streams, Black's Fork, Henry's Fork, Ham's Fork, Kingfisher Creek, Brush Creek, the Uinta; the western slopes of the Colorado Rockies whose creeks poured into the Yampa and the White; the waters all the way from Grand Lake under the shadow of Long's Peak, and the tributary springs and creeks and runoff gulches that fed the Grand all the way to modern Grand Junction and Moab; and finally the San Juan, muddy from recent rains, its headwaters tangled with those of the Rio Grande in the Five Rivers country of southwest Colorado, its gathering waters coming down from the San Juan Mountains through New Mexico and what would sometime be Arizona and across the southeastern corner of Utah through the country of the Navajo. It was a big river by now, a tremendous surge of muddy water. The whirlpools started by the muddy current of the San Juan hitting the Colorado at a right angle spun them on the bend. Along shore, where willows and alders had a foothold on the bars, the scouring eddies sometimes revolved back upstream with a current almost as strong as that which in the middle swept down.

But it was hot, and there was little shelter from the fierce sun at their campsite. Bradley found the junction desolate and uninviting — which is one sign of strain, for this stretch of Glen Canyon is as beautiful a place as exists in the whole canyon country, a Canyon de Chelly with a great river turned into it from wall to wall.

Bradley's grousing had a reason and a worry behind it. He was afraid Powell would wait here by the meeting rivers until the eclipse of the sun on August 7 in order to make astronomical observations, and he apparently reflected the attitude of the other men when he wrote, "Major has been taking observations ever since we came here and seems no nearer done now than when he began. He ought to get the latitude and longitude of every mouth of a river not before known, and we are willing to face starvation if necessary to do it but further than that he should not ask us to wait and he must go on soon or the consequences will be different from what he anticipates. If we could get game or fish we should be all right but we have not caught a single mess of fish since we left the junction."[8]

Rumblings of rebellion, hints of mutiny. Under pressure from the men, Powell moved on, and from the camp below the elfin grotto he named Music Temple they shoved off on August 3 and ran thirty-three miles through Glen Canyon. Powell's *Report*, a retouched description, is full of admiration for the scenery, but his own notes and the journals of Sumner and Bradley do not much dwell on it. They passed the mouth of Padre Creek and recognized this as the place where Father Escalante had made his way back across the river returning to New Mexico in 1776. None of them mentions the striking details of the country, neither the impressive dome of Navajo Mountain southeastward or the prominent Tower Butte directly south. The Navajo sandstone was running down, and coming in over it were red marly beds of a ledgier and more broken profile. They were at the bottom of Glen Canyon. On the afternoon of August 4 they ran into an open pocket, the canyon ending

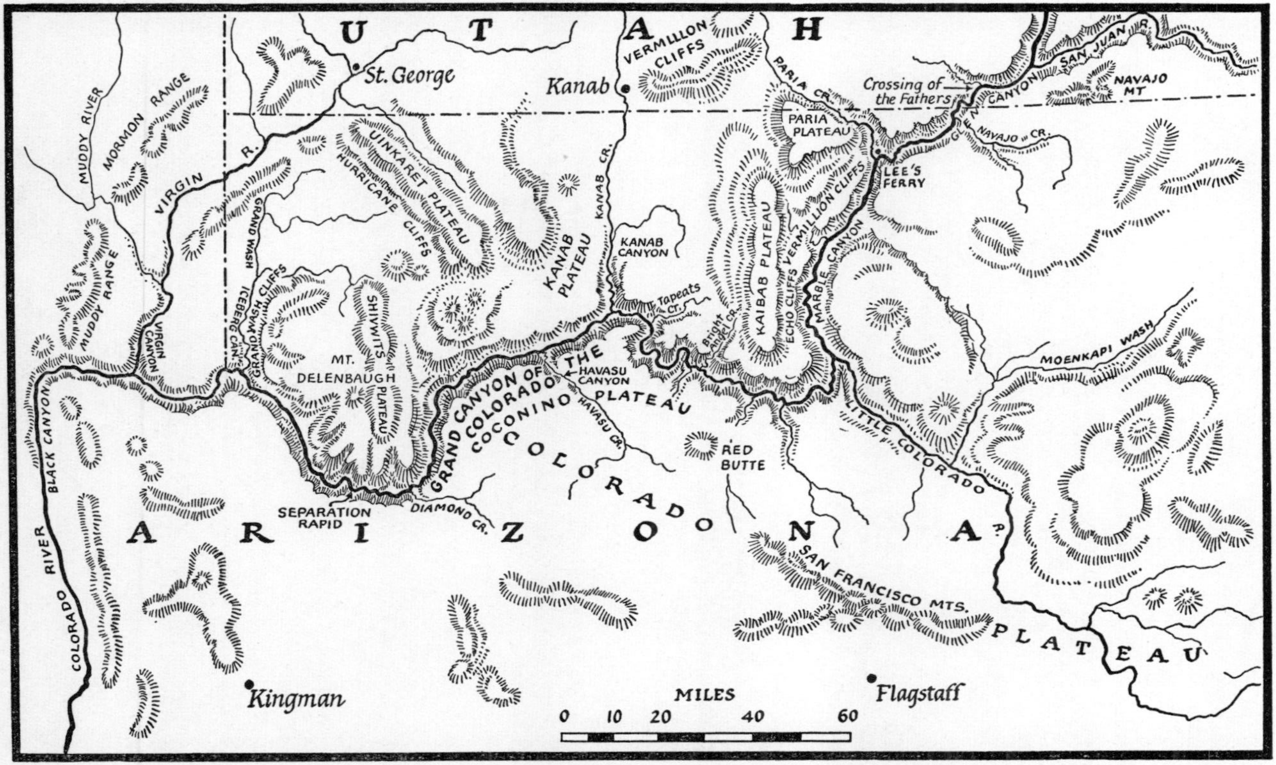

UTAH
ARIZONA
St. George
Kanab
Kingman
Flagstaff
VERMILLION CLIFFS
PARIA CR.
Crossing of the Fathers
GLEN CANYON
SAN JUAN R.
NAVAJO MT
NAVAJO CR.
PARIA PLATEAU
LEE'S FERRY
MUDDY RIVER
MORMON RANGE
VIRGIN R.
MUDDY RANGE
VIRGIN CANYON
GRAND WASH
ICEBERG CAN.
GRAND WASH CLIFFS
UINKARET PLATEAU
HURRICANE CLIFFS
SHIVWITS PLATEAU
MT. DELENBAUGH
KANAB CR.
KANAB PLATEAU
KANAB CANYON
Tapeats Cr.
Bright Angel Cr.
KAIBAB PLATEAU
ECHO CLIFFS
VERMILLION CLIFFS
MARBLE CANYON
THE GRAND CANYON OF COLORADO
HAVASU CANYON
HAVASU CR.
COCONINO PLATEAU
COLORADO PLATEAU
RED BUTTE
SEPARATION RAPID
DIAMOND CR.
LITTLE COLORADO R.
MOENKAPI WASH
SAN FRANCISCO MTS.
BLACK CANYON
COLORADO RIVER
MILES
0 10 20 40 60

sharply in a line of high cliffs that came in from the west on the north side of the river, turned at the line of a tributary creek, and crossed the river at right angles, heading in an irregular line into the broken country southward. Though Powell apparently did not recognize it at the time, and Sumner confused it with the Crossing of the Fathers,[9] this was the mouth of the Paria, one of the crossings which Brigham Young's scout Jacob Hamblin had searched out. The cliffs which, swinging southward across the river, mark an end to Glen Canyon were the Echo Cliffs, an extension of the Vermilion Cliffs, and the most striking and beautiful and persistent cliff-wall in the whole plateau country. Just below the Paria the Navajo Bridge now leads Highway 89 across the inner gorge and on across House Rock Valley and up the slope of the Kaibab to Jacob's Lake and the north rim of the Grand Canyon.[10]

Almost certainly, Powell would have stopped if he could have. His vision of a leisurely ten-month exploration could not have been abandoned without regrets. But by now he was facing dissatisfaction among the men, overworked and half starved. Jack Sumner had shot another sheep just above the Paria, and they still had a little half-dried mutton, but food was on their minds. It is clear from Bradley's journal that even he, who had always delighted in white water, had had about enough.

From the Paria camp, at what is now Lee's Ferry, they could look straight down river, and in that stretch see white foam for half a mile. They could see also that the river barely got out from the shadow of the Vermilion Cliffs before it began digging in again to make a new canyon. And the rocks below were not soft sandstone like those of Glen Canyon. They were the same hard limestones and sandstones encountered above in Cataract Canyon. Down the upper reach of what they would name Marble Canyon, from a place that Sumner said was "desolate enough to suit a love-sick poet," they looked with some uneasiness. Bradley talked to himself: "We have all learned to like mild rapids better than we do still water. But some of the party want them very mild."[11]

The sixty-five miles of Marble Canyon, which Powell named for the hard polished limestone of its walls and floor, have been historically one of the deadliest stretches on the river. Lodore and Cataract Canyons have capsized boats and ducked boatmen, the

Grand Canyon has swallowed people mysteriously, leaving their boat rocking in an eddy for searchers to find, but Marble Canyon has drowned them plainly and in the open. Here, twenty years after Powell's pioneer voyage, the expedition of Frank Mason Brown and Robert Brewster Stanton, designed with almost-Sam Adams optimism to survey a water-level railway line to the coast, came to grief twice. In the first wreck Brown himself died; in the second two of his men, Peter Hansbrough and Henry Richards, went down. After the second disaster the expedition was abandoned until later that same year, when Stanton returned, still determined to complete the survey. He did so, but only after he had had one more experience with Marble Canyon. On January 1, 1890, his photographer, Nims, fell off a ledge there and broke a leg. They had to climb the wall, walk thirty-five miles to Lee's Ferry, and bring a wagon back to meet Nims' stretcher before they could proceed.[12] Near the head of this same sixty-five miles of alternating fierce and calm water Bert Loper, one of the bona fide river rats, a skilled boatman but a man too old for his own adventurous spirit, went under in the summer of 1949 and never came up. One of the Marble Canyon rapids (Soap Creek) was never run until the Clyde Eddy Expedition of 1927, bowling down the river with a bear cub aboard for company, ran it in happy ignorance of where they were.

All across the great barren Marble Canyon Platform which stretches north of the river from the monoclinal eastern flank of the Kaibab to the angle of the Vermilion Cliffs, abrupt gorges come in, cut by runoff waters from the higher country. Badger Creek and Soap Creek and other lesser watercourses come in by canyons as deep as the river's own, and every junction is piled with the boulders of flash floods. Every junction is a rapid; the prevailing strike of the beds is upstream, a condition which is a maker of rapids as surely as hard rock and lateral gorges are. And the Colorado now is a great stream, but squeezed into a narrow frothing channel that reflects every summer shower by sharp rises. Between high and low water in parts of the canyon there is a vertical difference of a hundred feet. At low water the rocks are deadly, at high water the waves toss a boat like a chip. And they are waves of a peculiar ferocity, for they are not ocean waves, where the water remains in place and only the form passes on. Here the form remains and the water passes on, and it goes like fire engines, with a roar that trembles the rocks, and in flood the water itself is heavy with red silt.

They went with care, lining Badger Creek, portaging Soap Creek. Soaked to the hide all day, pounded by a pitiless sun, sick of the rancid bacon and the mouldy flour cakes and the inescapable dried apples, they camped and died a little exhausted death on the bank and in the morning went on past more rapids. Three times, because Powell remained cautious, they had to portage everything: it was only on the portages that they blessed the emptiness of the boats. At one portage they had to use again the dangerous three-ply lining technique, stringing all three boats out into the rapid and taking them in from the bottom, after which they could carry around the rest of the fall. The boats were badly battered. On August 7 Bradley had to put four new ribs into his, and recalk the whole hull. That was the day Powell and his brother climbed out to the rim, a half mile above the river, and set up instruments for the expected eclipse. Here too the scientific results were doomed to be disappointing. As they sat waiting, clouds matted over the whole sky, and it began to rain. To cap their day they got lost coming down the cliff and had to crouch soaking on a ledge all through a miserable night until daylight showed them a path down.

No observations on the eclipse, hence no longitude, a thing Powell was desperately anxious to determine. And no Sunday rest next day. Probably not even Bradley, considering the state of their rations, would have suggested it. On a muddy and rising river they ran, or rather portaged, a laborious three and a half miles and camped under the dome of an immense water-worn cave in a bend, a little dubious about their shelter because of the rising water, for high water obviously swept this cave like a broom. They could barely rustle enough firewood to cook supper.

Now they ran through a canyon of polished marble of many colors that even in their ragged and hungry state excited their imaginations. Bradley cocked an eye at the notion of collecting specimens and reluctantly gave it up as impractical. The Major found a marble pavement, polished like glass, that ran for more than a mile; the sun glinted on polished parts of the cliffs. Then a rainstorm showed them the polishing agent: within minutes of the first drops, muddy rills from the sandstone rims poured over the limestone walls, scouring them from rim to talus. At a bend where the river turned sharply to the east a wall glittered as if set with gems, and on coming nearer they found springs bursting from the cliffs high up and sheeting the rock in rainbows. Below was a garden of incredible green, moss and maidenhair and redbud and hackberry and ferns. They named it Vasey's Paradise, after their last year's botanist from Bloomington.

As they went on the walls grew higher, and still higher, and great buttresses thrust out into the channel to block the river into coves and twist it in whirlpools. But here the channel was wider, the river less swift, so that they could take a more leisurely look at the marble chambers and alcoves and caves. Through the gates of flaring canyons that came in from the right, draining the lofty table of the Kaibab westward, they saw the piney back of that noble plateau. Finally they reached another landmark, one that Lieutenant Ives had tried for but failed to reach in 1858[13] — the mouth of the River of Flax, the Colorado Chiquito of the Spaniards.

By this time Major Powell had determined that what he had called Ute Creek at the foot of the Vermilion Cliffs had been the Paria, had straightened out the rest of his geography, and knew the Little Colorado for what it was.[14] It was nothing much to excite any of them. Though at certain seasons of low water on the Little Colorado and high water on the main river the Little Colorado lies in clear sky-blue pools as lovely as the lime-impregnated waters of Havasu Creek in the little paradise near the foot of the Grand Canyon, the Powell party found it, in Bradley's words, "a loathesome little stream, so filthy and muddy it fairly stinks,"[15] and Sumner wrote it up for "as disgusting a stream as there is on the continent."[16] Their spirits were not cheered when they heard that they would have to stay here at least two days for the infuriating observations and the absolutely-necessary repairing of the boats.

Above them, where they camped below the cataclysmic Y of the canyons, the walls went up three thousand feet — the highest they had yet measured. From the rim Powell saw that to the westward they were even higher. Their campsite afforded no decent water, no game. It was "filthy with dust and alive with insects," and they killed three rattlesnakes the first afternoon. Anyone camping on the river learns to shake the scorpions out of his bedding and shoes before dressing in the morning, but Bradley (and others, he observed, were in the same fix) did not even have a pair of boots to catch scorpions in. For lack of footwear that would let him climb the cliffs, he went around camp barefoot, saving his one remaining pair of camp mocassins to put on when the sand got too hot or the rocks too sharp.

"Thank God the trip is nearly over," he wrote, making full records sitting at a stone table in the Little Colorado camp. "It is no place for a man in my circumstances but it will let me out of the Army, and for that I would almost agree to explore the River Styx." But the others had no such reward to sustain them. "The men are uneasy and discontented and eager to move on. If the Major does not do something soon I fear the consequences, but he is contented and seems to think that biscuit made of sour and musty flour and a few dried apples is ample to sustain a laboring man. If he can only study geology he will be happy without food or shelter but the rest of us are not afflicted with it to an alarming extent."[17]

Neither commander nor men appeared to understand the precise feelings of the other. The Major, as usual, confided only skeleton data to his field notes, but wrote up in his later *Report* his feelings at that stage. If he actually felt what he wrote, and there is little reason to doubt that he did, they were not quite the carefree geologizing preoccupations that Bradley supposed. Below the Colorado Chiquito lay the chasm, Ives' "Big Canyon,"[18] that had been a report on men's tongues for a good deal more than two hundred years without ever becoming known. Much more than the frowning gate of Lodore it seemed to him ominous, and for cause:

> We are now ready to start on our way down the Great Unknown. Our boats, tied to a common stake, are chafing each other, as they are tossed by the fretful river. They ride high and buoyant, for their loads are lighter than we could desire. We have but a month's rations remaining. The flour has been resifted through the mosquito-net sieve; the spoiled bacon has been dried, and the worst of it boiled; the few pounds of dried apples have been spread in the sun, and reshrunken to their normal bulk; the sugar has all melted, and gone on its way down the river; but we have a large sack of coffee. The lighting of the boats has this advantage: they will ride the waves better, and we shall have but little to carry when we make a portage.

We are three quarters of a mile in the depths of the earth, and the great river shrinks into insignificance, as it dashes its angry waves against the walls and cliffs, that rise to the world above; they are but puny ripples, and we but pigmies, running up and down the sands, or lost among the boulders.

We have an unknown distance yet to run; an unknown river yet to explore. What falls there are, we know not; what rocks beset the channel, we know not; what walls rise over the river, we know not. Ah, well! we may conjecture many things. The men talk as cheerfully as ever; jests are bandied about freely this morning; but to me the cheer is somber and the jests are ghastly.[19]

Either he was unconscious of the growing sullenness among the men, or for literary effect, writing at a later time, he suppressed that detail. Perhaps that famous passage with which he shoved off into the Grand Canyon reflects a little of both reasons.

An unknown distance, an unknown river. Actually 217 miles, the full length of the Grand Canyon from the Little Colorado to the Grand Wash Cliffs. And then easy water, according to both Jacob Hamblin [20] and Lieutenant Ives, to the mouth of the Virgin and the known world. This was what they faced, this last and most formidable leg of the exploration, as Sam Adams' crack-brained competing expedition collapsed, far back in Cedar Canyon on the Grand.

12. The Colorado: The River of Flax to the Virgin

THERE IS a rough physical law to the effect that the carrying power of water increases as the sixth power of its velocity, which is to say that a stream moving two miles an hour will carry particles sixty-four times as large as the same stream moving one mile an hour, and that one moving ten miles an hour will carry particles a million times as great.[1] A stream that in low water will deposit even its fine silt and sand, in high water will roll enormous boulders along its bed, and sometimes one can stand near the bank and see a rock that looks as big as a small house yield and sway with the force of the current.

Where the Colorado River entered the granite a few miles below the Little Colorado the channel was narrow, the river engorged, very deep, and very swift. It took hold of a boat irresistibly: the characteristic reaction of our diarists was awe. More times than once Bradley was led to report rapids as the worst of the trip so far, and all of them felt the gloom of that black inner gorge and the poverty of the narrow sky.[2] To add to undernourishment and exhaustion and strain they had nights of rain that caught them miserable and unprotected on bouldery shores, days of alternating sun and rain that first drenched them and then boiled them in temperatures of 115°. Rarely was there a decent camping place; they stopped where daylight or endurance ran out on them. With very little shore, the river did not even provide adequate firewood. Curling up on the edges of cliffs, among boulders, on wet spits of sand, they made out as they could. And along with their discomforts there was an increasing but unspoken fear.

Partly the lack of shores did it, the way the river sometimes took up all the space and left them no place for lining, no trail for a portage. Rapids that they feared to run they ran because they could do nothing else, and as they came plunging through the waves, tossed from one side to the other by the cushion of the water piling against great rocks, they often had no chance to inspect the river ahead, to search out channels, to guard against falls. They went with the recklessness of Sam Adams, not for lack of better sense but in sheer helplessness.

The pretense that it was a scientific expedition had worn thin. Every barometer they had was out of commission, so that they had lost track of their altitude and had no way of telling how much fall there was before the Virgin. Even an accurate view of where they had been was denied them, after Howland lost in a swamping his map of the river from the Little Colorado down, and all his notes with it. Anxiety closed around them like the dark rock, and looking up lateral gorges to the outer walls so high and far above, to the buttes and towers and enormous pediments and alcoves of the cliff-edged plateaus that now rose above them more than a vertical mile, they could add claustrophobia to their burdens, and the haunting speculation of what it would mean if they had to try to climb out.

Unrelieved labor, incessant strain and anxiety, continuing rain, a river that seemed every day to grow worse, and for food the same moldy bread, spoiled bacon, stewed apples, and for commander a man who they felt would risk all their lives for an extra hour of geologizing, an extra night of squinting at a star.

When they ran into the granite on the second day below the Little Colorado — one of the days that Bradley recorded as the wildest thus far — the *Emma Dean* was smashed under by a wave and ran swamped for half a mile before its crew got it into an eddy. Bradley and Walter Powell brought their boat through with the loss of an oar, the third escaped with a shaking up and a ducking. That night as they slept among boulders and on ledges so narrow that only Sumner and Major Powell found space wide enough to make a double bed, Bradley huddled off by himself and wrote up his secret diary in the rain. They had better lie quiet, he said, or one of them would be in the river before morning.

Some of them were in the river every day now. Hawkins capsized and lost his oars the next morning, and after only two and a half days in the Grand Canyon their supplies were again wet and spoiling. At the mouth of a beautiful clear creek coming in from the north they camped to saw out more oars and dry the food. That was Silver Creek, which Powell later, on a lecture tour, rechristened Bright Angel Creek to make a singularly happy contrast with the Dirty Devil above. The cutwater of the *Emma Dean* was broken and all of them were exhausted. Even Bradley was willing to lay over a day for a rest. Immediately Powell, seizing the opportunity, took off up the canyon to geologize.

As if to emphasize the need for haste, the Bright Angel layover was hard on the rations. There they finally threw away what remained of the bacon, so many times spoiled and dried and boiled and redried that they gagged at it. And Billy Hawkins, making biscuits on a rock, had the misfortune to let the saleratus get sawed off into the river by the line of one of the boats. From that time on they ate unleavened bread.

Below Bright Angel they got through one laborious day without accident. On the afternoon of the next a furious thunder shower drove them to what shelter they could find among the rocks, where they sat dripping and heard the thunder bounce from cliff to cliff and saw hundreds of flash-flood rivulets burst over the walls above them. The more their need for haste, the less haste they seemed able to make. "Hard work and little distance seems to be the characteristic of this canyon," Bradley wrote. Then on the 19th the *Emma Dean* swamped again, and Bradley's boat, sweeping to the rescue, struck on her cutwater with a jolt that started her nails. Two more oars went in that rapid, and all the boats now were so battered that they had to be calked every day. For the sixth day out of the last seven they lay down in soaking blankets. But that night when it cleared off, a great drying fire restored them. So bedraggled were they that they did not start until noon the next day. They were all looking ahead, watching for that break in the walls that might be the Grand Wash Cliffs.

It seemed as if they might have reached it, or neared it, for the walls did fall back a little and the rapids were further apart. In a half day's run, including a portage and two linings, they ran ten miles. The next day was again for Bradley "first for dashing wildness of any day we have seen or *will* see." Swept broadside down upon a rapid, Powell's boat rebounded from the cliff and was carried into a narrow slot with no shores to land on. Ahead a bend cut off the view. From around it came the "mad roar" that had taught them caution many times already. Here they could not be cautious if they would. Powell stood up, hanging to a strap that ran from gunwale to gunwale, trying to spot a channel through the long, winding chute of white water. Their luck held. All they got out of that one was a tremendously exhilarating ride for ten precious miles before the roar of another heavy fall below made them pull ashore to reconnoiter. By the time they had portaged that, they were out of the granite.

Their cheers had in them something of the hysteria of strain, and they did not stay cheerful long. Barely had they adjusted themselves to milder water when the river turned sharply from its north-by-west course and bored back almost straight east into the granite again. Overhead the clouds gathered blackly, and it rained.

Their hypnotized spirits now rose and fell with the river, and changed with its course. When, away back at the Little Colorado, they had discovered their latitude to be as low as that of Callville, they had been cheered, but the river taught them to wait and see, for it persisted in running back toward the north with them. Now it rubbed in the lesson of skepticism by taking them back into the hard rock they feared. "If it keeps on this way," Bradley wrote, "we shall be back where we started from, which would make us feel very much as I imagine the old hog felt when he moved the hollow log so that both ends came on the outside of the fence." [3]

Still, there was nothing they could do except to keep rooting at the log. They fought their way down to spend another night on the rocks, with a bad rapid facing them as soon as they should wake up, and its roar an uneasy sound in their dreams. But next day the unpredictable river switched again. After two hard miles the hated granite sank under toward its home at the earth's core. The rapids, though tremendous, seemed by Grand Canyon standards lighter.[4] On the afternoon when they ran out of the granite they made ten miles.

The following day they made twenty-two with great cheerfulness, and their cheer was doubled by the great marble cave in which the Major chose to camp — dry and spacious and out of the interminable rain. Around their fire they sat speculating on how far Grand Wash might be, for the Mormons whose notes on the river from Grand Wash to Callville were in the Major's pocket put the Wash no more than seventy or eighty miles below the mouth of the Little Colorado. On the dogleg river they had already gone more than one hundred twenty. They must be very close, perhaps within a day's running. Ahead, they convinced themselves, the river seemed to widen and the current to slack off. They examined their flour — one sack plus enough for a meal or two — and gauged the skimpy supply against the possible miles ahead. They were half naked, bearded, skinny, and their dreams were haunted by visions of gargantuan meals, but they knew they would make it now.

The river relented. On August 25 they made thirty-five marvelous miles, in spite of a hard portage around what they called Lava Falls, where a basalt flow had first dammed the canyon and then been cut clean through, and in spite of a near accident when the iron strap in the bow of one boat pulled loose and almost let the boat get away in a rapid. All the boats, clearly, were about as used up as the men. They drove themselves.

The opening of their last sack of flour was a solemn moment, and a warning. Down a violent stretch of river where lava made continuous but not major rapids they ran the battered boats recklessly, lining only once in thirty-five miles when they landed on the wrong side of a rapid and couldn't get across to run it safely. Another good omen: the dry abandoned dwellings and granaries of ancient Indians that they had been seeing among the cliffs ever since Glen Canyon gave way to signs of life. In an Indian garden they found squash big enough to eat, and stole a dozen to make green squash sauce, their first fresh vegetable food since the disastrous potato-top greens in Uinta Valley fifty days before. Though the nearly vertical walls of the inner gorge grew higher and higher, their two-day run of seventy miles put them close to two hundred miles below the Little Colorado. "A few days like this," Powell said, "and we are out of prison."

It was a prison even to him now, not a happy hunting ground of science. And the river knew better than they did. On the morning of August 27 it swung south, and since the dip of the beds was to the north, they rapidly ran into lower and lower formations. If it kept up this way they would be back in the granite. By nine o'clock they saw the dreaded rock, brown here instead of black, but unmistakable, rising up from the shoreline. They had to portage at the very entrance to the granite gorge. By eleven they came to a place that forced them ashore with sinking hearts.

Later river runners, with some justification, have disputed Powell's description of that rapid, both as to its violence and to its shape. [5] There can be no doubting the fact that it looked to them, in their demoralized and discouraged state, like the worst thing on the river. Sumner's journal calls it "a hell of foam"; Powell and Bradley agree in calling it the worst they had met. "The billows are huge," said Bradley, "and I fear our boats could not ride them if we could keep them off the rocks. The spectacle is appalling to us." [6]

It should have been. They had five days' rations remaining. Above the narrow inner gorge the outer walls stepped back in lofty and perhaps unclimbable cliffs. The nearest Mormon settlement was miles away to the north across unknown plateaus and deserts. To run the rapid was, as far as Powell could see, pure self-destruction. Above the pounding water rose abrupt granite cliffs. Trying the right bank, they could find no way either to portage or to line. Crossing over above the rapid, they tried the left, working along the craggy granite to try to get a view of the river below the first fall. The cliff shut off the water.

Telling about that day in his published *Report,* Powell records an adventure that neither his own daily notes nor the journals of Bradley and Sumner mention. He says that, intent upon seeing and appraising the rapid, he worked out upon the pinnacles and crags of the cliff and once more, as in Desolation Canyon, got himself "rimmed." He was four hundred feet above the boulder-strewn water, clinging to the rock with his one hand, when he called for help. He says that the men climbed close above him and dropped him a rope, but that he dared not let go to grab for it. Hanging grimly, unable even to advise them because he could not see his own position, he clung while two men hurried down the cliff and came back with a pair of the largest oars. Themselves working on a perilous edge, they reached out an oar and finally jammed it in a crevice beyond Powell so that they could pinch him in against the cliff and hold him there. Then they jammed the second oar below him, and carefully he turned himself until he could step on this oar and inch back to safety.

How they may have looked at one another, whether or not they may have cursed him to themselves for being maimed and a burden, how fully they may have laid their situation at his door, no one will ever know. Since the journals do not mention the episode at all, it may not even be true. It may be a piece of fiction suggested by his previous rimming and inserted into the narrative as peculiarly effective here.[7] Perhaps it is part of that impulse to self-dramatization that had led Powell to make speeches on top of Long's Peak, and sit on a spectacular crag above Flaming Gorge producing rhetoric for the Chicago *Tribune.* But even if the story is not true, it ought to be. There could have been no more striking symbolic summary of the fix the whole expedition was in than the spectacle of the maimed leader hanging perilously between advance and retreat, unable to move either way, on a crag of the hated granite.

Without getting a really good view, they spent another hour trying to see from the left-hand cliff, and in the afternoon crossed again to try the right, but without success.

After almost a full day of studying the situation, Powell could see no way except to let down over the first fall, run the rapid to the head of the second, and then pull like fury to the left to avoid a great rock against which the river poured a curving, boiling wall of water. It was not a plan that appealed to him; it appealed even less to some of the men. Bradley, who had reported rebelliousness before, reported it again: "There is discontent in camp tonight and I fear some of the party will take to the mountains but hope not."[8]

Crossing the river again and camping in the mouth of a lateral gorge, they had both certainties and uncertainties to contemplate as they chewed on their leathery unleavened bread. There were the alternative uncertainties of a fearful nest of rapids with an unknown river below, and a perhaps equally dangerous climb out some side gorge onto the plateau and across it to the Mormon settlements northward. And there were the desperate certainties of failing supplies, failing boats, failing strength, failing nerve. Sitting apart from the others and writing up his notes, Bradley called it "decidedly the darkest day of the trip."[9]

Of all the men who had accompanied Major Powell through a summer of natural history in the Colorado parks, a winter of studying Indians and topography from the base camp on White River, and more than three tense months in the canyons, O. G. Howland was best fitted by education and interests to be a companion for the commander. He was the oldest in the party, though at thirty-six, less than a year older than Powell, he was hardly decrepit to match his beard. Like Sumner, Hawkins, and his brother Seneca, he was technically entered on the expedition's roll as a hunter, but he was no buckskin savage. Since arriving in Denver in 1860 on the tide of the Colorado gold rush he had been a printer and editor of Byer's *Rocky Mountain News,* business agent for a Methodist Episcopal magazine known as the *Sunday School Casket,* member and later vice-president of the Denver Typographical Union Local No. 49, and secretary and member of the board of the Nonpareil Prospecting and Mining Company. Judged by his letters to the *News,* he was the most literate and articulate of the group. By Powell's own testimony, he was of a "faithful, genial nature." When Powell took a companion with him on his exploratory climbs around the canyon rims and up side gulches he almost always took his brother, Bradley, or the elder Howland. Bradley was the only member of the party over thirty, outside of Howland and Powell, and he had been an army non-com long enough to learn discipline.

But the same qualities that made Howland a companion and friend for Powell half unfitted him for the grueling adventure of the river. He had a certain scientific and literary curiosity, and part of his job was to map the river and make notes as they went, but his appetite for knowledge was nothing like Powell's omnivorous passion, and though he was an outdoor man and a sportsman he had not quite the hardihood or the youth of the hunters and Andy Hall. Also, he had been the unlucky one. His momentary error of sight or judgment had led to the wreck of the *No-Name,* the loss of a third of their provisions, and their present starving and desperate condition. The comparative meagerness of their scientific results could be traced to his misfortune in twice losing his maps and notes in swampings. Possibly the sense of personal failure troubled him. Just possibly Powell or his brother, under the increasing strain, may in some moment of irritation have thrown it up to him. Conceivably too, as Sumner and Hawkins many years after the fact asserted, the Major and Bill Dunn may have rubbed each other the wrong way, or trouble may have brewed between the moody Walter Powell and Dunn. Bradley's journal mentions no such cause of discontent, however, and he was not one to spare the Major when he thought Powell needed criticism. Sumner's journal is equally bare.

Put it down to strain, to the steady corrosion of strength and nerve. Lay it to the dark oppressive granite, to the repeated hope that they had run out of it for good and the each-time-greater anger and disappointment when the river switched them back into it. Put it down to the rapid they now faced without a clear chance to run, line, or portage. Put it down to a growing lack of confidence in Powell's judgment or the reliability of his scientific observations, to the gnawing need for a square meal or to the arrival at an ultimate ceiling of endurance. Whatever it is put down to, it was clear to Powell on the night of August 27 that the whole expedition was close to where he himself had been that afternoon on the cliff, unable to go forward or back.

That was even clearer when Howland came to him after supper and asked him to walk up the side canyon for a little talk. Howland had been talking things over with his brother and Bill Dunn. It was madness and suicide to try to go on. He proposed that the whole expedition abandon the river and make its way out to the Mormon settlements on the Virgin. If Powell would not take the whole party out, the Howlands and Dunn would go by themselves. They had had enough.

Powell had strong arguments. He knew that they could not be more than a few days' run from Grand Wash, he knew that the river had been falling so fast that it could not possibly have much further to fall to the level of Callville. But Howland had a stronger one. He had only to point to the furious string of rapids that blocked their way downriver. Even if past them there were calm water all the rest of the way to the Virgin, those were enough.

In the end they agreed not to say anything to the other men until Powell had had time to plot their position by dead reckoning to find out exactly where they were. It was a clear night; he got a meridian observation with the sextant and found that it agreed pretty closely with the plot. By airline, they could not be more than forty-five miles from the mouth of the Virgin, twenty miles from which there were Mormon towns. Moreover, for a good many miles above the Virgin the Mormon party under Jacob Hamblin had found low walls and no bad rapids on the Colorado. The eighty or ninety meandering miles of river still ahead might contain no more than a day or two of bad water.

He was several hours establishing to his own satisfaction that there was no possibility of serious error in his calculations. Then he woke Howland and spread the plot on the sand and showed him. This is how he told it later:

> We have another short talk about the morrow, and he lies down again; but for me there is no sleep. All night long, I pace up and down a little path, on a few yards of sand beach, along by the river. Is it wise to go on? I go to the boats again, to look at our rations. I feel satisfied that we can get over the danger immediately before us; what there may be below I know not. From our outlook yesterday, on the cliffs, the cañon seemed to make another great bend to the south, and this, from our experience heretofore, means more and higher granite walls. I am not sure that we can climb out of the cañon here, and, when at the top of the wall, I know enough of

> the country to be certain that it is a desert of rock and sand, between this and the nearest Mormon town, which, on the most direct line, must be seventy five miles away. True, the late rains have been favorable to us, should we go out, for the probabilities are that we shall find water still standing in holes, and, at one time, I almost conclude to leave the river. But for years I have been contemplating this trip. To leave the exploration unfinished, to say that there is a part of the cañon which I cannot explore, having already almost accomplished it, is more than I am willing to acknowledge, and I determine to go on.[10]

He woke Walter Powell and told him of the decision that must be made. Walter promised to stay with him. He woke Billy Hawkins, the irrepressible, and Andy Hall, the lighthearted, and Sumner, the hardy, and Bradley, the saturnine, and they promised the same. Though reduced, it would still be an expedition.

Breakfast on August 28 was "solemn as a funeral." In silence except for the pounding roar of the rapid, deep in the gloomy rock where the early sun could not reach, they ate Hawkins' flat biscuits and drank their coffee and avoided each others' eyes. They had finished eating when Powell asked his question. With five men behind him he could ask it bluntly. Did the three want to come along, or climb out?

Seneca Howland, left to himself, would have stuck, but neither he nor the other six could persuade his brother and Bill Dunn. They had all climbed enough on the walls to know the possibility of unbroken, unscalable cliffs stretching for miles. But they thought they could make their way out one of the side canyons, and they were sure they could kill game on the plateau. They were mountain men, the wilderness was their natural home. Listening to the arguments of the others, they shook their heads; in the end Seneca Howland dcided to stay with his brother.

They were given two rifles and a shotgun and invited to take their share of the miserable rations. It was to their credit, and evidence of friendliness between the two groups, that they refused. The three crossed the river with the others, helped them unload the leaky *Emma Dean,* which was to be abandoned, and assisted in portaging the two large boats over a thirty-foot rock and lining them down the first fall. Hawkins left a pan of biscuits on the rock for them. Sumner gave Howland his watch to deliver to his sister, Mrs. William

Byers, in Denver. Powell wrote a letter to his wife. The records of the expedition were, as Powell thought, divided, each party taking one complete copy. At the head of a two hundred yard rapid between the two falls each entreated the other to change its mind. They shook hands; there were tears. "They left us with good feelings," Bradley wrote, "though we deeply regret their loss for they are as fine fellows as I ever had the good fortune to meet."[11] Bradley was a grumbler, but he rose nobly to occasions.

So the parting at Separation Rapid was not quite Sam Adams' experience of collecting a purse and sending someone home as a "common nuisance," nor was it marked by the quarreling and accusation and blame that attended the breakup of Adams' volunteers. Neither was it what some unaccountably virulent enemies of Powell asserted later: a harsh discharge of three men at a place and in circumstances that might mean their death. Neither was it what some of Powell's defenders have tried to make it, a craven desertion by three cowards. It was a sad parting at the brink of two dangers, by men who respected one another.[12]

The original ten were now six, the four boats two. What had been rations for ten months was now rations for five days. What had been thrilling was grim. From up on the cliff the Howlands and Dunn watched as Powell stepped into the *Maid of the Canyon* and the men shoved off into the waves along the right-hand wall. The river seized them. They shot down a hollow, up a wave, past a rock half buried in the foaming water. The oarsmen pulled madly at the clumsy oars — a job of enormous difficulty in a boat leaping through waves at a speed of twenty miles an hour, tossed now up, now down, the water falling away suddenly so that the oarblade bites air, then surging up to bury the oar to the handle. To hit a hidden rock with an oar was to risk shattering it or having it driven into the oarsman's body; to catch a crab was to lose all chance of control. They rowed as the river had taught them to row, pulling hard for the tongue of the second fall. There the boat was all but snatched from under them. They shot down the fall and burst into the great back-cresting waves at its foot. Instantly they were full of water, but half swamped they still rowed like madmen, pulling across the current. The wild pile-up of water against the righthand rock caught them only partially. They raced up the sloping wall of water, fell away to the left, down into a hole, and were through into the diminishing tailwaves. The whole rapid had taken perhaps a minute. While they pulled for shore to bail out, the *Kitty Clyde's Sister* plunged through the tailwaves and was with them, safe. Powell afterward thought the rapid, in spite of its fearful look, no worse than others they had run. Bradley continued to think it the worst to date, until they met another one that afternoon.

Below the rapid, according to Powell's *Report,* they landed and fired off their guns in the hope that the three hunters would climb down and rejoin them. But they did not come, and the boats went on.[13] They had dangers enough of their own to occupy them. Powell's journal entry for the day of parting is indication of how even so serious an event had to take its place in the day's routine. His journal reads simply, "Boys left us. Ran rapid. Bradley boat. Make camp on left bank. Camp 44."[14]

In that one brief entry are contained not merely the schism that all but destroyed the expedition, but the incident that of all their summer's adventures was perhaps most hair-raising. "Bradley boat," the Major says. What he thus reminded himself of was a climactic little episode. As the wreck of the *No-Name* in Lodore initiated them to disaster and taught them caution, so Bradley's adventure below Separation Rapid ended their river dangers in desperation and cool skill. They had come a long way from the initial amateurishness and inattention to Bradley's complete adequacy to his job, from Powell's first caution to his final recklessness.

Like many another rapid, the big one (Lava Cliff) six and a half miles below Separation struck Bradley as the worst they had met on the river. The stage of water has such an unpredictable, even unbelievable effect upon specific rapids that there would be little chance of checking his judgment, even if that rapid were not now silted up at the head of Lake Mead.[15] But it was bad enough. Sumner referred to it as "another hell." Powell landed to look it over, and found that along one side a line could be taken up on the basalt cliff and the boats lined from above. But when he arrived back on the riverbank he found that the men had already started one boat, Bradley's, down toward the head of the fall. She was in fast water, too much in the sweep of the current for them to pull her back, and their line was not long enough to be taken up over the cliff. They took a bight around a rock and hung on while one went for more rope.

Meantime Bradley, in the very sag of the fall, found himself swinging at the end of a mighty pendulum. The current set in close and fierce against the basalt wall, and suspended as he was from above, he yawed in a wide arc out into the rapids and then was slammed back in against the cliff. Standing in the boat, he fended himself off with an oar, but the moment he stopped the inward swing the waves snatched him outward again. Powell saw him take quick looks down river, saw him look at the straining, worn line, saw him reach in his pocket for his knife.

Before he could cut the line the whole sternpost was jerked out of the boat, rope and cutwater flew thirty feet into the air, and the *Sister* was off like a horse from the starting line. Bradley dropped his knife and leaped to the steering oar, fighting to get her bow pointed downstream, for to go over broadside-on would be certain wreck. One stroke, two, three, and just as he hit the fall he turned her. She went clear under in a welter of white, came up on a huge crest, went down again and out of sight beyond some rocks. In half a breath she shot into the open, Bradley still standing, and swung into an eddy. Bradley waved his hat in triumph, but from where Powell stood it was impossible to see how badly the boat was damaged, and he feared both it and Bradley might go down into the whirlpool.

Powell shouted at his brother and Sumner to run along the cliff to help below. Then with Hawkins and Hall he leaped into the second boat, pushed off, and went over the falls any way the water took them, endways and sideways, blind with water, beaten almost out of the boat by waves. It was an act totally uncharacteristic, reckless beyond anything he had permitted himself or his men all the way down the river. It is as good documentation as any for the desperation of their case.

Bradley had to rescue them, capsized and strangling, and help them pull their boat to safety against the cliff. There was handshaking around to match that when the Howlands and Goodman were rescued from their island at Disaster Falls. Powell said nothing ever thrilled him so much as to see Bradley swing his hat from the spinning boat after running her through. It is clear from his various accounts of the trip that Bradley, more than any other member of the party, had his complete respect as a man of skill and courage. As for Bradley, his diary was getting used to superlatives. This ride, he said, "stands A No. 1 of the trip."

That was the last big roar from the river dragon. Two or three miles below that great rapid the river swung northwest. By nightfall they were out of the granite. By noon of the next day, after a swift uneventful run, they passed through the sudden portal in the Grand Wash Cliffs and saw rolling country, low walls, distant mountains.

Where they camped that night is not certain. To be appropriate, it should have been in the little loop that now, as part of Lake Mead, on the Nevada-Arizona boundary, is known as God's Pocket. They were in God's pocket sure enough. Their joy, Powell says, was almost ecstasy, though even in that relaxed and triumphant camp, in the clear night, with an unreal wide sky over them, they speculated a long time on how the Howlands and Dunn were faring, how they had managed on the cliffs, whether they might now be in the high plateau forest filling themselves with venison or wild mutton or whether they might be stuck in some gulch groping for a way up and out. They could say I-told-you-so; they could also, more generously, hope the others' luck had been equal to their own.

For there was no doubt that they were now "out of prison." On August 30 they scared away one band of naked Paiutes and talked to another family that Powell coaxed near by speaking Ute to them. From the Indians, however, they learned little and got no food, and so they pushed on. Just after the noon stop they saw four men pulling a seine in the river. They were a Mormon named Asa and his two sons and an Indian, and they were there on instructions from Church headquarters in Salt Lake City to watch the river for wreckage or bodies from the Powell Expedition, reported lost weeks ago in the depths of the Colorado canyons.

That was the first official notice Brigham Young ever paid to Major Powell. He would pay him more later; the two would become something like friends, and Brigham would draw on Powell for scientific information useful to his empire. His interest now was something more than mortuary, something more than merely humanitarian. For Powell's river party was in a way doing Brigham's business for him, exploring the heart of the country on whose fringes Brigham's colonists had scratched out precarious toeholds of settlement. If Asa and his sons and their Indian companion waiting in the glare of the red mudflats at the mouth of the Virgin saw no bodies floating by, they might at least intercept something else — records or wreckage — from which to piece together information about the canyons. They intercepted more than they expected, and yet their humanitarian and mortuary gesture was not to be entirely wasted either.

Nine men had plunged into the unknown from the last outpost of civilization in the Uinta Valley on the sixth of July, 1869. On August 30 six came out.

After the first exuberant greetings from the three-times-reported dead, after the sybaritic banquets of bread and butter and cheese and watermelons that Bishop Leithead sent down from St. Thomas, after the devouring of the first mail since leaving the Uinta Agency almost two months before, after the triumph and the congratulations, there remained the anticlimax of disbandment. Powell divided among his ragged volunteers the little money he had to spare, and gave them the two boats to continue on down. Of the four, Bradley and Sumner would leave the river at Yuma, and only Hawkins and Hall would run the Colorado's whole length to tidewater. For Powell's purposes, there was no use in going farther. Ives had surveyed up this far; steamboats had charted the full length of the lower river. As exploration, the expedition had ended at the Grand Wash Cliffs. Only the loyalty of five men and Powell's own resolution had kept it from ending in failure on the very brink of success, at Separation Rapid. What had been a tight and even tense organization, a desperate comradeship, a true expedition, had begun to crumble with the departure of the Howlands and Dunn. Now with the bond of danger gone it suddenly dissolved. Almost lamely, Powell and his brother shook hands with the other four and turned north with their Mormon hosts to St. Thomas and on over the Beaver Dam Mountains to St. George, the capital of Brigham Young's southern province. As they went they inquired of everyone they met for word of the three who had elected to fight their way out overland.

At St. Thomas there was no word, at Santa Clara no word, at St.

George, well into the edge of civilization and linked to Salt Lake by a carriage road and the Deseret Telegraph, still nothing. The church authorities sent out riders to outlying ranches and to the Paiutes of the plateaus, but they disappeared into that silence from which the Powells had themselves only just emerged. They waited, though they were wild to get home, and the Deseret Telegraph had sent out ahead of them messages that assured them a hero's welcome. Perhaps then more than any time earlier they felt the implacable emptiness through which they had labored for a hundred days. Other western explorations had met Indians, buffalo and antelope and elk, grizzlies; they had passed alertly through a wilderness that teemed with life. Their own had passed through a wasteland naked even of game, sometimes even of vegetation, and its trademark was the ancient and terrible stillness which was all they heard now, waiting in St. George. That stillness had not been broken a day later when they had to leave.

They were only two days on their way, somewhere up along the Mormon Trail that followed the abrupt eastern edge of the Great Basin, when word of Dunn and the Howlands caught up with them from St. George. The three had climbed the wall and made it to the forested top of the plateau. They had made it no farther. They lay out there now somewhere beside a waterpocket, stripped and filled with Shivwits arrows, victims of an Indian misunderstanding and of their own miscalculation of the algebra of chance.

And so back home to Normal on the palace cars, reading of their own exploits and the lonely death of their companions as they went. Now came the round of entertainments and the jubilance of congratulation from friends in Illinois, and now the many-times-repeated story of the adventure began to be sandpapered and smoothed in the telling around dinner tables and on the lecture platforms of Salt Lake, Detroit, Cincinnati, Wheaton, Chicago, Hennepin, Bloomington, towns that had once known Powell as an independent sort of boy interested in bugs and snakes, and cities that knew him now as a famous explorer. On the river Powell's persistent caution had infuriated Bradley and Sumner and the rest, but to the home folks and the jealously askance colleagues of Normal University he must have looked like a lucky gambler. Sam Bowles writing from the dude camp in Middle Park had been precisely right: the Powell expedition was fortunate in its leader. The exploration had been of a peculiar boldness. It had also been spectacularly successful, and its success had been made piquant by tragedy.

Major Powell came back to Illinois, and eventually on to Washington, a national hero, a club-car celebrity. People found him romantically maimed, awesomely resolute, winningly genial and enthusiastic, a persuasive talker. He showed none of the signs of self-importance or a swelled head; then and later he was what a colleague called him, a "notably magnetic man." The nation that had scarcely heard of him until Risdon announced his death went out of its way to notice and praise him now.

He had unlocked the last great unknown region in the country and made it his own, and in that region so simple and so empty of people, scientific knowledge lay on the surface like the moss agates and jasper geodes of some of its valleys, ready to be scooped up in the hand. Powell's mark was already on it. Its mountains and creeks and buttes bore names he and his men had given them. And his mark would be on it more, by his own determination and the national consent.

The Congress which had twice listened suspicious and unconvinced to his requests for help would shortly appropriate $10,000 to assist his continued geographical and topographical exploration of the Colorado River, and set him up in business in a western survey competing with those of Clarence King, F. V. Hayden, and Lieutenant Wheeler.

But there was one dissenter amid the chorus of applause. Almost as soon as the news of Powell's success started eastward along the wires, the *Omaha Republican* printed a complaint against "a recent explorer, who has expended nothing individually and incurred none of the hardships inseparably connected with the development of the west . . ." and "whose vision was so remarkably acute, that at the distance of three hundred miles from Green River, he could see the cañons of the Colorado in all their length and depth, and whose letters stated that he was the first to ascend Long's Peak, when it is a matter of public notoriety, that women and men had gone before him for the past ten years, the date of whose ascent was marked upon the place of his triumph." The much-publicized Colorado River exploration was a sell. "Through all the cañons," the correspondent said, "I have ascended and descended several times within the past three years." [16]

Like a feisty dog yapping on the fringes of a parade, Sam Adams was pursuing with senseless single-mindedness the shadow of his delusion. It was his idiot function to go on pursuing it. Major Powell, having catapulted himself into prominence by a piece of adventure, would devote the next ten years to justifying the adventure by the manifold work of revealing and opening his chosen part of the West. The exploration, spectacular though it was, was only a preliminary move, a means to an end. The end was new knowledge, and new knowledge would be the peculiar contribution of the United States Geographical and Geological Survey of the Rocky Mountain Region, J. W. Powell in Charge, which Congress voted into existence on July 12, 1870. It did not have that comprehensive title when it was created; if it had any official name at all, it was the "Geographical and Topographical Survey of the Colorado River of the West," and for part of its existence it was called the "Geological and Geographical Survey of the Territories, Second Division." The name does not matter: call it the Powell Survey. What matters is that its work was a continuity constantly enlarged but never interrupted for the next nine years.

What also matters is that Powell committed himself, enlisted himself at a strategic moment in history as a scientist in the service of the government. He was not yet a full-fledged federal employee, for until 1872 he continued to draw his salary from Illinois State Normal University, and until that year he maintained his official residence in Normal rather than in Washington. But in 1870 he put his foot in the door and got his eye fixed on what was beyond the door. His future was predictable from that point, because all his life his only direction had been forward.

Significantly, he committed himself to government science and the public service at almost the precise time when Henry Adams, after more than a year of trying to stomach the spectacle of Reconstruction politics, threw up his hands in disgust and abandoned a government that appalled him in favor of an academic life in which he had only a partial or tentative faith. Adams' disgust with Grant's

Washington was well earned. But so was Powell's allegiance. For Powell's involvement in Washington was not with its political maneuvering, though he found himself forced to learn that game too. His involvement was with the unopened West and with the instrumentalities of science that, centrally directed in the public interest, might be used to open it. And that was a part of Washington's function that within a year would excite the enthusiasm even of Henry Adams.

II
THE PLATEAU PROVINCE

1. Center and Frontier

IT IS EASY for an enthusiast in Western history to exaggerate the importance of the opening West in the years following the Civil War, and to forget how complex and perplexing the nation's other problems were during Grant's two terms. It was not only in the West that we suffered from growing pains. The Internal Revenue scandals, the Indian Bureau scandals, the Land Office scandals, the Crédit Mobilier scandal, the collapse of Jay Cooke's Northern Pacific, were convincing evidence of the importance of the West as the place of boodle, if nothing else. But it is essential to remember that Washington too, during the war and after, had acquired a new potency. Centralization bred by the crisis did not cease with the crisis. Not only was Washington preoccupied with the country's novel and uncomfortable position as a world power, but it was the source of policies, bureaus, and departments — and men — who controlled the West in its critical opening years.

Powell himself, from 1870 on, was a forceful part of that Washington which had formed during the war and which compacted itself in the dozen years afterward. He had a large hand in the creation of new central bureaus and in the formulation of new policies, none of which can be understood in purely Western terms. They must be fitted into a context in which the nation's capital and its concerns are central [1] — that capital which is vividly present in *The Education of Henry Adams* and in Adams' mordant novel *Democracy*, and in Mark Twain's and Charles Dudley Warner's *The Gilded Age*, and in the writings and the careers of Hamilton

Fish, Abram Hewitt, Carl Schurz. The interaction between Western interests and Washington power is sourly apparent in the *Reminiscences* of Senator William Stewart of Nevada, the sagebrush statesman for whom Mark Twain was briefly and unhappily secretary, and who may have sat for Twain's portrait of the Congressman: "the smallest mind and the selfishest soul and the cowardliest heart that God makes."[2] There is an astonishing amount of this new sense of centrality buried in the publications of the various government bureaus and the extraordinary collection of scientific men drawn capital-ward to staff them. It shines in the revolutionary sociology of Lester Ward, for a time one of Powell's employees and all his life one of Powell's friends. It is in the enormous, encompassing, encyclopedic learning and the crusty energy of Elliott Coues, also for a time one of Powell's employees. The cavalier familiarity that Raphael Pumpelly — another Powell employee — showed for the whole wide world reflected a man who knew where home base was.

Out of Washington and its centralizing set of mind, as much as out of the West and the Western temper, came institutions that have shaped the West and to a lesser degree the whole country: Geological Survey, National Park Service, Forest Service, Coast and Geodetic Survey, Weather Bureau, Bureau of Standards, Bureau of Mines, Reclamation Service, many of them proliferating out of the mitotic cell of the Smithsonian. Government science before the Civil War was largely, though not quite exclusively, Joseph Henry and Spencer Baird of the Smithsonian. Geology was a States' rights matter, topography and mapping were diversions to occupy the peacetime Army, time and weather were for the Navy to play with, and too much of private science was the occupation of amateurs of the kind that Powell himself started out to be. Postwar Washington permitted and encouraged the development of professionals and put them in charge of operations of incalculable potential. Less than twenty years after the war, Washington was one of the great scientific centers of the world. It was so for a multitude of causes, but partly because America had the virgin West for Science to open, and in Washington forged keys to open it with.

Henry Adams' heroine Madeline Lee, who went up to the capital "to see with her own eyes the action of primary forces, to touch with her own hand the massive machinery of society; to measure with her own mind the capacity of the motive power," [3] was after the motive power of politics, but she could quite as effectively have studied in the same years and the same place the motive power of American science.

That science was not merely becoming centralized; it was growing up with a rush. It was only a generation since the paleontological Munchausen, Albert Koch, had edified the nation with his theories, or since sober Professor Silliman of Yale had attempted to tie geological history to the Noachian deluge. It was less than fifty years since the Reverend Frederick Rapp had interpreted fossil footprints in a slab of limestone as the footprints of the Christ. There were still plenty (including Clarence King and his first master, Professor Whitney, now of Yale) who clung to their belief in catastrophism as the explanation of mountains. George Catlin would propose a theory of the origin of the Gulf Stream in this very year 1870 that would raise some scientific hair, and Joaquin Miller a little later would poetically imagine the formation of the Grand Canyon by the collapse of the crust over an underground river hundreds of miles long. In the *American Journal of Science* not too long before Washington began to collect and systematize scientific learning, a writer had explained the glacial drift in Velikovsky terms as having been caused by the rush of waters at a time when the earth's rotation stopped.

In 1870 plenty of speculation and plenty of pure nonsense passed for science. But in Washington, after the Civil War, there grew up a tough-minded group of men hard to fool, intent upon verification, and with unprecedented government support. At their backs they had the whole new West for a laboratory. Of that group and in that West John Wesley Powell was one of the first.

2. *Geography*

ONE OF MAJOR POWELL'S first services to geography was to explore a region previously little known. One of his next, after he

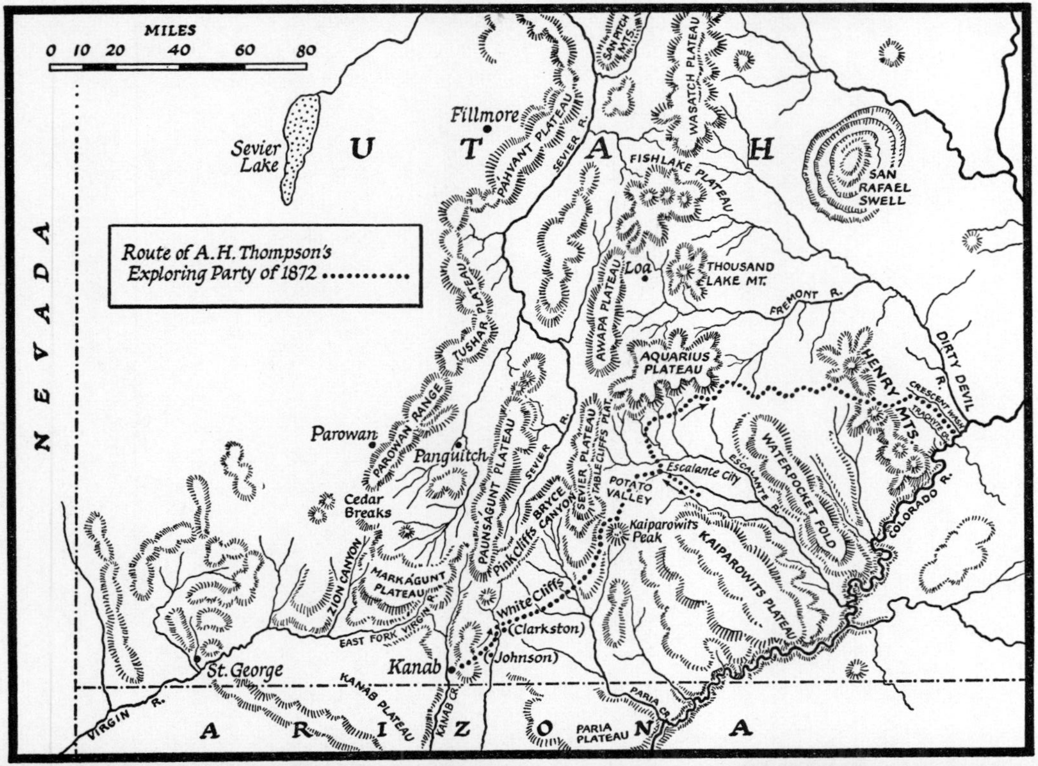
Route of A.H. Thompson's Exploring Party of 1872
MILES
0 10 20 40 60 80
NEVADA
UTAH
ARIZONA
Sevier Lake
Fillmore
PAHVANT PLATEAU
SEVIER R.
SAN PITCH MTS.
WASATCH PLATEAU
FISHLAKE PLATEAU
SAN RAFAEL SWELL
TUSHAR PLATEAU
Loa
THOUSAND LAKE MT.
FREMONT R.
AWAPA PLATEAU
AQUARIUS PLATEAU
HENRY MTS.
DIRTY DEVIL R.
CRESCENT WASH
TRACHYTE CR.
PAROWAN RANGE
Parowan
Panguitch
PAUNSAGUNT PLATEAU
SEVIER R.
SEVIER PLATEAU
TABLE CLIFFS PLAT.
Escalante City
POTATO VALLEY
ESCALANTE R.
WATERPOCKET FOLD
COLORADO R.
Cedar Breaks
BRYCE CANYON
Pink Cliffs
Kaiparowits Peak
KAIPAROWITS PLATEAU
ZION CANYON
MARKAGUNT PLATEAU
White Cliffs
(Clarkston)
EAST FORK VIRGIN R.
Kanab
(Johnson)
St. George
KANAB PLATEAU
KANAB CR.
VIRGIN R.
PARIA CR.
PARIA PLATEAU

obtained federal assistance for his expedition, was to divide the mountain West into three physiographic regions, which he called the Park Province, the Plateau Province, and the Great Basin Province.[1] The first included the Colorado and northern New Mexico ranges and the great parks between them. The second included the great region of flat-bedded plateaus and mesas stretching from the western slope of Colorado to the east rim of the Great Basin in Utah, and from approximately the 40th parallel to the Painted Desert. The third began at the Wasatch Mountains in Utah and their southern extensions, and took in all the tormented ranges and great valleys and dead sea bottoms from there to the Sierras.

It is the Plateau Province, comprising all of eastern and southern Utah, part of western Colorado, and part of northern New Mexico and Arizona, that concerns us, since it is what primarily concerned Powell. Its boundaries are precise on the north and west, less certain on east and south. Essentially the province follows an ancient shoreline of Mesozoic times, when the Great Basin, the Wasatch, and part of what is now Arizona were islands or parts of the mainland, and what is now the Plateau Province was a great loop of sea. The region of plateaus with which the Powell Survey was chiefly concerned reaches from the Uinta Mountains southwestward to the Colorado River. It is mainly in Utah but includes the slice of Arizona north of the Grand Canyon, and it laps over on the east into Colorado and on the west into Nevada. It is scenically the most spectacular and humanly the least usable of all our regions.[2]

Here geological and human history have at least a poetic similarity. Here the earth has had a slow, regular pulse. It rose and fell for millions of years under Carboniferous, Permian, Triassic oceans, under Cretaceous seas, under the fresh-water lakes of the Eocene, before it was heaved up and exposed to rain and frost and running water and the sandblast winds. Mountains were carved out of its great tables and domes, river systems cut into it and formed canyons, elevations were weathered and carried away. What had accumulated pebble by pebble and grain by grain, cemented with lime and silica, folding into itself the shells of sea life, scales of fishes, the compacted houses of corals, began to disintegrate again. Vast cyclic changes have left only traces. Though the geological record in the Plateau Province is probably as clear as it is anywhere on earth, the boundary between ignorance and knowledge, between speculation and certainty, is often no more than a line of ancient fracture almost obliterated, or an enigmatic unconformity between two layers of rock, or a slight but significant change from salt water to brackish water fossils.

Human history in that country is almost as tentative, and to our foreshortening eyes nearly as long. A vague sort of knowledge, with plenty of speculation to accompany it, reaches back to that all-but-Eozoic time when the Ho-ho-kam in the southwestern desert and the Anasazi among the plateaus built their mortared houses and granaries, and lived for certain years whose remoteness is measurable by the fading radioactivity of their dead campfires, and were driven out by certain causes including drouths known to us by the starved growth rings of ancient trees. Gradually, over several generations, we have sorted out a kind of stratigraphy of the plateau peoples: Basket-Maker I, Basket-Maker II, Post-Basket-Maker, Pre-Pueblo, Pueblo I, II, or III. We can distinguish among their artifacts and compare what we know of them with what we know of their cultural heirs, the Pueblos, including the Hopi and Zuñi. We can mark the unconformities between strata of human history, and knowledge broadens down, not quite from precedent to precedent, but from inference to inference, toward historical time. By the same sort of taxonomy that classifies and groups and separates fossils, we classify and group and separate peoples and their leavings, and read history of a kind from them. Though we may be often and for long periods on solid ground, we are never quite out of sight of the half-effaced shorelines of speculation. Knowledge extends in promontories and bays; or to put it vertically rather than horizontally, the strata from remote to recent never lie so unbroken that we cannot find some line of unconformity where the imagination must make a leap. There are so many horizons, geological and human, where the evidence is missing or incomplete.

Ever since the coming of white men, the region has gone through cyclic emergence and subsidence. It emerged hotly and briefly in the sixteenth century, when tales of golden cities, the antique and seductive Cibola, drew Coronado and Cárdenas northward through the wastes only to show them, at the extreme stretch of their journey, the appalling barrier of the Grand Canyon. It went through an uneasy up and down period from 1540 to 1781, when the death of Padre Garcés ended the great period of the *entradas* whose horizons were marked by Oñate, Kino, Garces himself, and Escalante.[3] What comes to us from that period of the *entradas* is a mixture of fact, fantasy, and folklore; the continent of knowledge is infirm and unstable. And from 1781 to the eighteen-twenties the region was submerged completely again. The Spanish maps used by Zebulon Pike in making his own chart of his 1806 explorations had a heavy mixture of speculation among their facts.

In some ways even less dependable is what comes to us from the era of the fur traders, that all-but-obliterated age when Jed Smith, General Ashley, Thomas Fitzpatrick, Jim Bridger, Kit Carson, and the other partisans, French, American, and British, spread like a thin abrupt lava over the West from the Marias to the Gila, and the Missouri to the Pacific. They spread very thin in the Plateau Province, where neither country nor climate was generally favorable for beaver except in the north, and only an impatient itch for travel justified the hardships. Fragmentary fossils, little more, remain from their passage — the ruins of Antoine Robidou's fort in the Uinta Valley, D. Julien's name on a canyon wall, James Ohio Pattie's embroidered Odyssey, the late-discovered narratives of Ashley and Jed Smith.[4] But there is no unconformity between the horizon of the trappers and that of John Charles Frémont, who with trapper aid became the Pathfinder for the thousands destined to sweep westward from the forties on, though in fact he was more Path-publicizer than Path-finder. In geological terms, if the trappers were Pleistocene, Frémont marks the transition to the Recent. At about this level, modern knowledge begins; it was enormously strengthened by the Pacific Railway Surveys of 1853 and after. But though both Frémont and the Railway Surveys pierced the Plateau Province, their real results were found elsewhere. Offering neither opportunity for settlement, promise of mineral wealth, nor routes for travel, the Plateau Province lay like an unknown and forbidding island across two thirds of the state of Utah and down into Arizona, between what would one day be Highway 30 and what would be Highway 66, or roughly between the line of the Union Pacific and that of the Santa Fe.

There was a thick crust of fable over this region, and as the country was lifted slowly into knowledge the layers of fable lifted with it, bending upward at the flanks like sedimentary strata along the axis of a great earth-flexure. It would take a long while for these to wear away; until they did, this could still be part of the Land of Gilpin. Lieutenant Gouverneur Warren, summarizing on his map of 1857 the aggregate of existing knowledge,[5] had to splash the word "Unexplored" across almost eight degrees of longitude, and leave a good part of the middle plateau country hatched in with mountains that represented less information than an unwillingness to leave the paper white.

The state of knowledge, or rather of ignorance, properly demanded blankness without even hachures. Ignorance covered the geography of the region, its topography, landforms, drainage, and scenery, its geological and orographic history, its inhabitants both vanished and extant, its products, resources, and potential usefulness. The few fixed points, the small amounts of verified information, were only enough to whet the appetite either of fabulist or scientist. To make this island a province of human knowledge, to reveal it clear and make it contribute to the sum of verified information, to extract from it what it could offer to the practice of legitimate inference, was a job that Powell individually began in the winter of 1868 and that the government-supported Powell Survey between 1870 and 1879 at least roughly completed. A chapter that had begun with the beginning of the century when Robert Livingston and James Monroe took a chance and bought vaguely-defined Louisiana from a harried French Empire,[6] ended approximately in 1872 when a party of Powell's men discovered and named the last unknown river and explored the last unknown mountains in the United States. From that time on, the Plateau Province has been an increasingly firm part of dry land. By the time they were through, Powell and his colleagues had given it a map, boundaries, many of its names. They had painstakingly worked out its geological history, and incidentally illuminated one whole division of the science. They had recorded it in drawings, paintings, and photographs. They had extracted from it a number of rules that became a kind of decalogue of dryland agriculture and dryland social institutions. They had even given it a rudimentary aesthetics, used it as a starting point for a curious and provocative inquiry into the sublime and beautiful, and strengthened the affinity that Turner and Ruskin had established between geology and art.

3. The Geographical and Geological Survey of the Rocky Mountain Region, J. W. Powell in Charge

AN AUTHORIZATION and a $10,000 appropriation granted casually for one year only by a Congress preoccupied with the Alabama Claims, Cuban insurrection, Fenian threats to invade Canada, tension between Southerners and Carpetbaggers, and Grant's expansionist adventure in Santo Domingo, did not automatically insure either the continuation or the scientific maturity of Powell's work. Not even a happy clerical error that removed his new survey from the jurisdiction of the Department of the Interior, where the Sundry Civil Bill of July 12, 1870, had put him, and subordinated him to the learned and non-political Smithsonian Institution,[1] could remove from his project the lingering look of the amateur. Only Powell's own intellectual maturing could do that, and that had not yet come, despite gratifying notoriety and publicity, a successful lecture tour, the jealousy of his Normal colleagues, and a greatly increased acquaintanceship in Washington, whence all power flowed.

Scientifically, Powell had not yet done anything. He had gathered data to correct an empty or inaccurate map, but he had produced neither map nor report of his own, and the scientific results of two expeditions to the Rockies and a hundred days on the river amounted to little more than an incomplete and crude reconnoissance marked by inadequately checked latitudes and longitudes, some tables of elevation and barometric fluctuation, some geological sections of the cliffs, and some boxes of miscellaneous collections, still mainly unclassified and unlabeled. He had published only letters to the newspapers, much more literary than scientific. The one short account of his river trip that he had so far written was intended for a book that would not even be published in the United States.[2]

For all that, the process of self-education never stopped in him. He learned in his sleep. He learned from every book, acquaintance, experience; facts stuck in his mind, and not like stray flies on fly-paper but like orderly iron filings around magnetic poles, or ions around anode and cathode in an electrolytic bath. Order was part of his very learning process, a function of his capacity to discriminate; and what he said later in tribute to Spencer Baird of the Smithsonian might even more truly have been said of himself: that in the world of modern science which was "almost buried under the debris of observation, the records of facts without meaning, the sands of fact that are ground from the rock of truth by the attrition of mind," he could "walk over the sands and see the diamonds." [3] But none of this was clear yet. There were numerous things John Wesley Powell had not caught on to. How to staff a scientific expedition, for example.

In both 1867 and 1868 he had signed up volunteers; if he wanted an expedition at all, he had no other choice. They were students, recent graduates, relatives, friends, members of the Natural History Society, bird watchers and botanizers willing to come along for the excitement. The river boatmen of 1869 were recruited about as haphazardly as Falstaff picked up his squad of ragamuffins, and they were equipped almost off the hedges. The one indispensable qualification of courage they all had, but though that would serve for purposes of exploration, it was not enough for purposes of scientific surveying. Yet now in 1870, authorized to continue the exploration of the Colorado River, and provided with backing and money and the chance to pack his expedition with brains and skill, Powell followed his old pattern of picking up local amateurs. Of all the people he would hire in the next four years, only three would be professionals. Two of those three, with help from developing amateurs, would remake the Survey.

To take charge of the topographical work Powell selected his brother-in-law Almon Thompson (a far better choice, actually, than most of the brother-in-law appointments of Grant's time) who had returned from acting as entomologist of the 1868 expedition to resume the superintendency of schools in Bloomington. From Bloomington also came Thompson's two assistants, Walter Graves, a cousin of the Howlands, and F. M. Bishop, a Union veteran and recent graduate of Normal. A third topographical assistant, S. V.

Jones, was principal of the Washburn, Illinois, schools, and a friend of Thompson's. As artist, Powell selected one of Thompson's remote relatives, a self-taught boy of seventeen named Frederick Dellenbaugh; as assistant photographer he hired his own young cousin, Clement Powell. The cook and handy man, Andy Hattan, was an army acquaintance; the second handy man, later assistant photographer and finally photographer, was a German immigrant named Jack Hillers, picked up by accident in Salt Lake City. The photographer, E. O. Beaman of New York, was the only real professional in that early crowd, and he turned out to be something less than first class. Powell passed over available trained geologists in favor of J. F. Steward, an amateur with whom he had hunted fossils in the trenches before Vicksburg.[4]

These, with a few pickups in the field, constituted the Powell Survey between 1870 and 1874. Though several of them were men of real ability and all but one gave devoted service, they would not have enriched *Who's Who*. Nepotism and an acquaintance among the schoolteachers of Illinois explained them all. There was not a real scientist in the lot except the leader, and he was unproved.

The amateurish condition is more apparent when one compares the Powell Survey with the other three surveys which since the end of the war had been established to produce information about the opening West. These were the United States Geological Survey of the Fortieth Parallel, the United States Geological and Geographical Survey of the Territories, and the Geographical Surveys West of the 100th Meridian, known, from their leaders, as the King, Hayden, and Wheeler Surveys.[5]

The Geological Survey of the Fortieth Parallel, promoted and directed by Henry Adams' meteoric friend Clarence King, under the supervision of the War Department, had in its party during 1870 not only King, who was a product of the Sheffield Scientific School, but Arnold and James Hague and S. F. Emmons, all of them far better trained than Powell or any of his group. There was no photographer that year, but for the three preceding years King had had the services of T. H. O'Sullivan, one of Matthew Brady's most spectacular combat photographers during the Civil War, and one of the great recorders of the frontier. That survey was small, select, and well heeled. It concentrated on economic geology, especially deposits of minerals, along a hundred-mile-wide strip centering on the 40th parallel, roughly the line of the Union and Central Pacific. It had certain eccentricities, such as the sybaritic camp life affected by its leader, but it was a highly competent outfit.

The Geological and Geographical Survey of the Territories, established like the King Survey in 1867, but under the Department of the Interior, was led by Dr. Ferdinand Vandeveer Hayden, a man of extraordinary and excitable energy, considerable imagination, some learning, and an experience on the western frontiers that had been consecutive from 1853, when he had explored the Dakota Badlands with F. B. Meek, the noted paleontologist. Hayden's 1870 group included a good geologist, J. J. Stevenson; a botanist, Cyrus Thomas, later a famous archaeologist; a zoologist, C. P. Carrington; a mineralogist, A. L. Lord; and an artist, Henry Elliott. It also included, for the first of several years, W. H. Jackson, whose frontier photographs over a long period, including the first pictures of Yellowstone and Mesa Verde, would earn him a reputation as one of the finest of his kind. In addition to his actual field party, Hayden could count on the collaboration of such eminent men as E. D. Cope, Joseph Leidy, and F. B. Meek to interpret his fossils, Leo Lesqueraux to oversee the paleobotany, and John Strong Newberry of Columbia University to act as consultant on the ancient lake bottoms of the West. Hayden's appropriation was more than twice that of Powell, his training and experience were much longer, his acquaintance reached everywhere, his publications and the publications that he controlled were extensive. Though his work seemed more impressive than it actually was, there is no doubt that his survey was in many ways the most imposing of the four. To Hayden, as much as to any other man, we owe the creation of Yellowstone National Park, which in 1872 became the foundation for all the future development of the park system.

Finally there was Lieutenant George M. Wheeler's Geographical Surveys West of the 100th Meridian, supported by the War Department, as was King's survey. Wheeler was not interested in geology; he didn't even take a geologist along until 1871, his third field season, when G. K. Gilbert and A. R. Marvine joined him. His interest was almost wholly topographical, looking toward a master atlas of the western states and territories. Later evidence would demonstrate that Wheeler's methods of mapping were inadequate and his results not always sound, but his survey was the direct inheritor of the prestige of the Corps of Topographical Engineers which had given the country most of its accurate information about the West. It did dabble in some of the all-purpose natural science that both Hayden and Powell had interested themselves in, and its actual and projected publication of maps looked impressive. It was sometimes accompanied, like Hayden's and King's parties, by a clanking escort of cavalry.

Among that company the Powell Survey was a shabby, latecome, and only semi-official Cinderella, but there is no indication that its director knew it, or if he knew it, cared. He was of a kind that goes about its business and keeps its end in view. His immediate end, as defined in the Sundry Civil Bill which created him, was "a geographical and topographical survey of the Colorado River of the West." At this stage he seems not to have had any ambitions beyond that. The tentativeness of his governmental connection is indicated by the fact that he still drew his salary from Illinois State Normal University rather than from his government appropriation. But it is pretty certain that his plans did not include much future time in the classroom. With his crowd of eager amateurs and teachers he would take out again into the West until the process of self-teaching would be complete. Some of his assistants would drop out, some would fail to develop, some would be replaced by key professionals. A few, notably Thompson, Hillers, and Powell himself, would acquire distinguished competence the hard way, in the field.

4. *Major Powell's Amateur Hour*

THE REAL BEGINNING of field work would have to wait a year, until the summer of 1871. First there was unfinished business, loose ends of the 1869 trip and plans for the next one. Powell might not know as much as he would know later, but he knew that even if all the records from 1869 had been preserved instead of being partly lost to the river or to the Shivwits, the scientific results would have been thin. Before he could claim anything more than an exploit he had to run the river again and really survey it. And because much of the difficulty of the first expedition had been caused by the necessity of carrying tons of food, he would not run the river again until he had located points at which it could be reached by supply trains.

The Green was no problem. There boats, men, and supplies would all be fresh, and the river could be reached at Brown's Hole, in the Uinta Valley, and at Gunnison's Crossing (Greenriver, Utah). And anyway the Green was comparatively well known. But below Gunnison's Crossing he knew of only two places of access, one at the Crossing of the Fathers in lower Glen Canyon, and the other only a few miles below, at the mouth of the Paria (Lee's Ferry). Another point ought to be found, preferably somewhere near the mouth of the Dirty Devil, at the foot of Cataract Canyon.

Privately assured by Garfield and Salmon P. Chase, both regents of the Smithsonian, that he could probably depend upon funds for more than the immediate year,[1] Major Powell dedicated 1870 to preparation. With Thompson in Bloomington he left the crudely meandered map and his own and Sumner's journals from the 1869 trip, and while Thompson studied those, Powell took two assistants, Walter Graves and Frank Bishop, and in mid-August made his fourth trip west.

Preparation involved not only supply routes but an understanding with the Indians. He could not count on and did not want the military escort that was standard equipment with most western scientific parties. With the White River Utes he had maintained friendship simply by being friendly and harmless; he would hope to continue that policy. But the murder of the Howlands and Dunn was a trouble, and he wanted to dig out the true facts. The story that had come out to St. George said that the three men had been shot for molesting a Shivwits squaw. That story he did not believe,[2] but whatever the cause of their death, he had to be assured of safety both from the Paiute bands and from the Navajo with whom the Mormons of southern Utah were conducting an erratic guerrilla war. Because his own interests coincided with those of the Mormons, he went to headquarters for advice, and came out from a conference with Brigham Young armed with a letter for Jacob Hamblin, the Mormon Leatherstocking, the Apostle to the Lamanites, head of the Southern Mission and pathfinder and peacemaker for all the southern Utah settlements. Either for geography or for Indians, he could hardly have done better; when he finally started out from the fort at Pipe Spring in Jacob's company he was in the best hands in Utah or Arizona.[3]

Hamblin knew the plateau and canyon country better than any man alive, for in the fifties when Brigham Young had projected an empire south and west and north from the New Jerusalem he had charged Hamblin with locating crossings of the hitherto impassable canyons across the southern frontier. Jacob had found a crossing below the Grand Wash Cliffs, at the lower end of the Grand Canyon, and another at the mouth of the Paria. He had been the first Anglo-American to use the Crossing of the Fathers, or Ute Ford, at the mouth of Padre Creek. He had navigated the lower Virgin and the Colorado from Grand Wash to Callville, had made his way across the wilderness of canyons south of the river and had visited the Hualpais, the Havasupais, the Hopi, the Navajo, the Coconinos. With them, as with the Santa Claras, Shivwits, Uinkarets, and Kaibabs north of the Colorado, his name was magic. It was magic also among his own people. A pious and orthodox Mormon with five wives, he had pioneered in Mountain Meadows, on the Santa Clara, and now at Kanab, below the Vermilion Cliffs, where an earlier village abandoned because of Navajo raids was about to be resettled. Though his ranch at Mountain Meadows was the nearest habitation to the scene of the Mountain Meadows Massacre, Jacob's name had never been tainted with complicity in that horror.[4] Pure, slow of speech and above anger, he was a rock of strength among the Mormon colonists and a bulwark against the Indians, whose languages he knew. A revelation had told him that if he never shed Indian blood no Indian would ever shed his; his life had been a demonstration of the dependability of God's midnight whisper. One of his wives was a Paiute.

Between them, Jacob and Powell were more effective than a

punitive expedition, more salutary than a company of soldiers. Accompanied by a group of Kaibab Indians including the chief Chuarruumpeak, they rode out of Pipe Spring, west of Kanab, in September, 1870, and headed southwest toward the plateau the Indians called Uinkaret, Place of Pines, dominated by the great lava-capped butte, twenty miles north of the Grand Canyon and sixty-odd from Kanab, that Powell would name Mount Trumbull in honor of his friend the senator from Illinois. There, just a week or two more than a year after his three men had died in the dark beside a waterpocket on the Shivwits Plateau, they camped near a band of Uinkarets and sent a runner to the Shivwits, farther west, to come to a council.

Before the Shivwits came, Powell half satisfied his purpose of finding a pack route to the lower Grand Canyon. The Uinkarets showed him a dangerous and difficult trail, the last stretch impassable for horses, down which Indian packers might take supplies in a pinch.[5]

Settlement of the Howland-Dunn affair awaited the arrival of the Shivwits. But by the evidence of all his words and actions, Powell was diverted from that almost from the moment he arrived. He found himself among Indians more primitive and untouched than any he had ever seen, as primitive probably as any left in the continental United States. Waiting for the Shivwits was no trouble; it was one long ethnological picnic.

He must have cursed his failure to bring a photographer, for he went out of his way to get the Indians' promise to be photographed the next year,[6] as he went out of his way to be interested in their life. "An eminently magnetic man," he worked his charm upon squaws and warriors and wise men as he had upon university regents or on editors encountered in Colorado parks. Knowing little Paiute, he made himself understood in Ute. Squaws showed him how they roasted seeds in wicker trays filled with hot coals, shaking the trays so dexterously that gradually roasted seeds collected at one side and coals at the other. Old women giggled, sitting with seed baskets between their knees and rolling out meal on mealing stones. Propped against trees, children wrapped in rabbit and wildcat skins stared from their wicker hoods. Even the young men were stimulated by the interest of Ka-pur-ats, One-

Arm-Off, to extraordinary showing off. They set up a wide-winged net and put on a rabbit drive to demonstrate their way of catching game, and that evening while they feasted on the result Powell induced them to tell aloud the story of Stone-Shirt, though it was not the proper ritual season. That was a diplomatic request: he had found that one of the surest signs of friendship was an Indian's willingness to talk about his religion. By the time the Shivwits arrived, Ka-pur-ats was almost as solid with the Uinkarets as Jacob himself. He had enriched his Paiute vocabulary and filled packs with rabbit-skin robes, papoose hoods, nets, seed baskets, and all the paraphernalia of the tribe, to be deposited ultimately in the Smithsonian.

In 1870 the day of the Indian as wild animal was by no means over. The hostiles of the plains were still unsubdued, the Custer Massacre and the Meeker Massacre and the Apache Wars and the brilliant and desperate campaign of Chief Joseph were still in the future, the subjugation of the Navajo at Canyon de Chelly still a recent memory. Wolves to be exterminated or curs to be kicked aside, verminous and beggarly and treacherous pests, Indians had had little enough of the consideration that Powell and Jacob gave them. Sam Garman's fastidious disgust with Antero's Utes was tenderfoot orthodoxy; the orthodoxy of the schooled frontiersman was of a bloodier kind.[7] Though the Shivwits and Uinkarets were probably too innocent to realize it, they were being given a revolutionary treatment. Jacob respected Indians and was respected by them because he granted them souls and gave even the Lamanite a chance at Heaven. Powell respected them, and earned their respect, because he accepted without question their right to be what they were, to hold to the beliefs and institutions natural to them. To approach a strange culture and a strange people without prejudice, suspicion, condescension, or fear is common enough among students now; it was not too common in 1870, and it made his councils with the Shivwits an unqualified success.

The Shivwits admitted freely enough that they had killed Powell's three men. But they had not understood who they were. The three had arrived worn out and hungry, and had been fed and shown the way to the Mormon towns. After them came a runner from another band saying these three must be the prospectors who had molested and then shot a squaw. The more the Shivwits talked over the story the white men had told of coming down the big water, the plainer it appeared that the three were liars. Eventually warriors followed the strangers and shot them with arrows as they lay asleep. But they would not have harmed them if they had known they were Ka-pur-ats' men.

This was the point at which frontier orthodoxy would have demanded at least a token punishment, possibly even a hanging or two. Instead, Powell smoked with the Shivwits — something, as he described it, slightly more difficult than hanging a few of them.

> Hamblin speaks their language well, and has a great influence over all the Indians in the region round about. He is a silent, reserved man, and when he speaks, it is in a slow, quiet way, that inspires great awe. His talk is so low that they must listen attentively to hear, and they sit around him in deathlike silence. When he finishes a measured sentence, the chief repeats it, and they all give a solemn grunt. But, first, I fill my pipe, light it, and take a few whiffs, then pass it to Hamblin; he smokes, and gives it to the man next, and so it goes around. When it has passed the chief, he takes out his own pipe, fills, and lights it, and passes it around after mine. I can smoke my own pipe in turn, but, when the Indian pipe comes around, I am nonplussed. It has a large stem, which has, at some time, been broken, and now there is a buckskin rag wound around it, and tied with sinew, so that the end of the stem is a huge mouthful, and looks like the burying ground of old dead spittle, venerable for a century. To gain time, I refill it, then engage in very earnest conversation, and, all unawares, I pass it to my neighbor unlighted.[8]

By such means must duplicity bend the processes of diplomacy. But with that small exception Powell's acceptance of the Indians and their point of view was complete. He read them no scoldings for their murderous ways, made no demands that the guilty be dragged forward for punishment, threatened no reprisals and asked no indemnity, required no assurances from the Shivwits beyond their word — and this despite the fact that the dead men had been his comrades and friends. He left his outfit scattered around without fear of their stealing, and nothing was stolen; he slept among the murderers without fear of harm, and none came to him. His experience with these Stone Age bands lost on an unvisited plateau not only whetted his appetite for discovery in regions of human geography already being rapidly obliterated, but reinforced his belief — which was Jacob's — that one who meant no harm could travel freely among Indians, at least within the territory of a single tribe, unarmed and unprotected, except when foolish or brutal white men stirred a tribe to revenge, when even the innocent could suffer. Perhaps Powell's maiming was a protection of sorts, and he spoke always with a straight tongue, and his introduction by Jacob gave him great status. But his chief qualification for dealing with the tribes was his conviction that a naked Paiute shivering under a tree on the Place of Pines belonged as surely on the map of mankind as a patroon sitting down to dinner in his house above the Hudson, or a Boston Brahmin crossing the Common toward the Athenaeum. He arrived at this conviction without effort and without the sentimentality of many Indian advocates and without in any way regarding his attitude as remarkable. It was simply a natural product of his thirst for knowing and the incorrigible orderliness of his mind, which was as ready to reduce the tribes of man to systems and categories as to arrange the stratigraphic series in a cliff.

To the ethnological goldmine on the plateaus Powell would return as he promised, with a photographer to record Uinkaret and Shivwits before civilization destroyed them. But he had other temptations now. Seventy-five miles by trail southeast of Kanab, at the angle where the Echo Cliffs crossed the Colorado and the Paria added its dry-season trickle to the river, was one of the crossings that Hamblin had pioneered. Several days' ride to the south and east across the river from there was Cárdenas' ancient province of Tusayan, home of those Indians whom the Mormons called the Moki or Moquis, and whom we call the Hopi, whose towns had been discovered by the Spaniards almost a century before Plymouth Rock but who had stubbornly maintained themselves intact, aloof, and little known. The legends that had formed a deposit over the whole Plateau Province encrusted them: they were the descendants of the "Aztecs" who had left houses and granaries and hewn footholds among the cliffs, and crumbling towns and irrigation systems along the desert rivers all through the Southwest. They were inheritors of the culture of the Nephites who according to the Book of Mormon had been driven northward by their dark brothers the Lamanites toward the Mormon Armageddon at the Hill Cumorah. They were descendants of those "white Indians," Welsh or otherwise, who have cropped up in American folklore from the beginning and have left among the Indians themselves the enigmatic story of the blue-eyed god.

As early as 1858 Jacob Hamblin and Thales Haskell had visited the Moki towns, escorting a Welsh Mormon named Durias Davis whose mission was to search for echoes of Welsh words in Moki mouths. Davis found none he could be sure of, but the three Hopis that Jacob took to Salt Lake for a visit of state in 1862 had barely hit town before some Welsh converts tried to make them admit they spoke Gaelic, and within seven years another Welsh Mormon, Llewellyn Harris, would start the Welsh legend all over again about the Zuñi. Verifiable knowledge makes its way slowly, and only under cultivation, but fable has burrs and feet and claws and wings and an indestructible sheath like weed-seed, and can be carried almost anywhere and take root without benefit of soil or water.

Whoever legend said they were, the Hopi were civilized Indians, town Indians, a kind Powell had not seen, and they were even more of a temptation than the primitive Paiutes. Jacob was going again this year to visit the Moki towns. One can almost watch Powell weigh this opportunity against the need of finding a way in to the mouth of the Dirty Devil. Though the route in was what he had primarily come to find, he let it go, and went with Jacob.

Joseph Henry, when Powell had first come to him back in 1867, had asked that Powell take advantage of the chance to study Indians on his western travels. The request could not have been made to a more responsive student. All of the western surveys except that of King studied the Indians to some extent; only Powell studied them with passion. So while Thompson back in Bloomington conned his maps and imagined that Powell was breaking a way in to the river, Powell was spending two delighted months among the Hopi, trading for artifacts, adding a Hopi vocabulary to his Ute and Paiute word lists and finding them related Shoshonean tongues. He watched the dances with which the Hopi marked every turn and change of the ceremonial year, recorded the intricate and devout ceremonial life, and listened to old men, living history books, tell the tribal myths.[9] It is doubtful that Congress in granting him funds had in mind that a "geographical and topographical survey" included this particular variety of field work, or that it knew it was authorizing Powell to sit in almost as an official Washington representative on the talks Jacob held with the chief men of Shapalauvi, Mishonghovi, Oraibi, Walpi, Tewa, all the seven stone towns overlooking from their beaked mesas the sweep of the Painted Desert.

It is quite as doubtful that Major Powell had any business in the peace conference that Jacob arranged with the Navajo over at Fort Defiance — not that he could have resisted taking part. At the beginning of November, 1870, he and Hamblin and their party crossed the Navajo and Apache country to the powwow. As part of the attempt to dissuade war parties of Navajo from crossing the Colorado, Powell spoke as if for Washington, explained the reservation system and the government annuities as changes that the Navajo must accept, reminded them of what they had already learned from the harsh schooling of Kit Carson: that resistance or continued raiding could only bring disaster to themselves. Those warnings were reinforced by the agent, Captain Bennett, and then Jacob spoke for peace. On November 5 he signed a non-aggression pact that outlawed raiding but welcomed the Navajo to the Mormon settlements on trading expeditions, and turned back toward the Moki towns and home, while Powell and his two men went on to the end of the stage line at Santa Fe.

One half-comic episode marked the end of his summer's work. At Oraibi he had made a friend of a Hopi, Tuleta, and had talked him into coming along back to Washington for a visit with the Great White Father. Hamblin had authority to take the Hopi chief Tuba and his wife back that fall to Salt Lake as good-will ambassadors, but exactly what Powell expected to do with an uninvited Hopi in Normal or Washington is not clear; perhaps stuff him and put him in the Smithsonian along with all the other artifacts he had collected. But the dependable Navajo saved him possible embarrassment. On the road between Fort Defiance and Santa Fe they stole Tuleta's horse. The party was in a hurry, and could wait only a day for Tuleta to find it. When he did not return, they went on. But Tuleta really wanted that visit to the Great Father. He borrowed another horse from somewhere and galloped after, arriving in Santa Fe a scant hour after Powell, Bishop, and Graves had climbed on the eastbound stage. Nobody in Santa Fe would believe that the chiefs in Washington had requested Tuleta's presence, and he had no paper to show, so he had a long ride home across New Mexico and Arizona to his primitive apartment house on Third Mesa.[10]

The way Powell's plans were scattering, more than hopeful Hopis were likely to get left behind. The route to the mouth of the Dirty Devil had got left behind too; the best Powell could do was engage Hamblin to try to find a way to it next summer. He also arranged that Kanab would be the headquarters for the survey party during the winter of 1871.

Kanab, as it turned out, would continue to be the principal base of operations for the Powell Survey, and the route to the mouth of the Dirty Devil would be located, but not until after two years of searching among the tangled headwaters of the Paria, Escalante, and Dirty Devil in the high rock country from Table Cliff across the Waterpocket Fold to the unknown cliffs and canyons south of the San Rafael Swell. And it would not be found by Jacob; that would be almost his only failure as Leatherstocking. A party of Powell's amateurs would do it for him.

5. *Exploration: Almon Thompson*

THOUGH ONLY LIMITED REPORTS were made of it at the time, and though for many years, through Powell's own fault,[1] its experiences and results were badly tangled with those of the 1869 expedition, few exploring journeys have actually been so thoroughly annotated as Powell's second trip down the Colorado. Powell, Thompson, Dellenbaugh, Bishop, Jones, Clem Powell, Steward, Beaman, and Hillers all kept diaries, and in addition Powell, Thompson, Jones, Bishop, and Steward made extensive field notes.

First Beaman, then Clem Powell, then for a short time James Fennemore, and finally Hillers took hundreds of photographs with the toilsome collodion plate cameras.[2] Clem Powell wrote letters to the Chicago *Tribune;* Dellenbaugh made sketches both scientific and scenic. Through lectures and newspaper writing he made himself a chronicler of the party, and his *A Canyon Voyage,* though not published until 1908, for a long time stood as the official story of the expedition.[3] Instead of a dramatic tale and a series of imperfect recollections, the second expedition brought back data.

It involved hardships nearly as great as those of the pioneer journey. Exhausting labor and malnutrition brought Jones and Steward into Kanab on stretchers, in the fall of 1871, and the whole company was afflicted with beriberi, scurvy, and the ache of old war wounds. And it was a tremendous adventure to the young men who participated in it. Yet somehow it doesn't make a story. It hasn't the thrill or the suspense, the fear, the fateful climax, the ending muted by tragedy; it doesn't come to us with either the terror or triumph of the first. The second passage down the river was not an exploration, but a survey; what rendered it scientifically important rendered it dramatically second-hand. Exploration like seduction puts a premium upon the virgin.

Before he ever started down it the second time, the river had lost much of its grip on Powell's restless imagination. He was already looking beyond it to the unmapped hinterland, the great problems of physical geology, most of all the anthropological exhibits, the tribes both extinct and extant that awaited study. Pulled in a half dozen directions at once, he could not pretend even to himself that he was conducting a field party with a single concentrated purpose. He began delegating responsibility when he left to Jacob Hamblin the job of locating a route to the Dirty Devil; he continued in 1871 by unloading much of the conduct of the river party onto his brother-in-law, universally referred to as the Prof, while he himself shot off on other business.

From the start at Green River on May 22, 1871, Powell left the geographical work entirely in Thompson's hands, but he himself commanded the party as far as the mouth of the Yampa, which they reached on June 25. By that time restlessness, anxiety about whether or not Jacob had found a way in, and worry about his wife, waiting in Salt Lake and six months pregnant, led him to row on ahead and go out overland to Salt Lake by way of the Uinta Agency. Thompson had the unenviable job of commanding the expedition while it waited in the heat and mosquitoes at the dreary mouth of the Uinta, and the equally unenviable one of leading it on down through Desolation and Gray Canyons at a snail's pace and in laboriously low water after Powell, who had returned to Uinta briefly, rode off south to investigate Jacob's reported failure to find a way from Kanab to the Dirty Devil's mouth.

At Gunnison's Crossing, having failed to find a route further south, Powell, Jacob, and two of Jacob's sons met the party on September 3 with supplies, and while Jacob went back to try the Dirty Devil yet again, Powell took command of the boats down through Labyrinth and Stillwater Canyons to the junction with the Grand, and on through Cataract Canyon. Where the Dirty Devil came in at the foot of Cataract, they found no traces of Jacob. Their food was very short, their photographic supplies used up. To save effort they cached one boat, the *Cañonita,* and again, as he had in 1869, Powell pressed down the easy water of Glen Canyon without having time for astronomical observations or examination of the barren country back from the walls. At the Crossing of the Fathers they encountered two packers, and Pardon Dodds, the former agent at Uinta, whom Jacob had sent to this point with rescue supplies.

Just here, on October 9, Powell elected to leave the river again, making up his mind so hastily that he would hardly wait for the men to write letters.[4] After he left, Thompson and his ailing crew ran the leaky boats down to the mouth of the Paria, where John D. Lee had settled one of his several wives. At this place which Lee called "Lonely Dell," later known as Lee's Ferry, the party spent the last days of October caching the boats and supplies, and after an irritable interval of uncertainty assembled in Kanab for the winter's topographical work.

In Kanab, as on the river, it was more Thompson's party than Major Powell's. Powell came back on November 30, 1871, escorting his wife and three-months-old daughter Mary, a Mormon nurse girl, and Mrs. Thompson and her dog Fuzz. Their camp was at Eight Mile Spring, their entertainment the dances in the Kanab branch ward house and an occasional jug of wine made in the Mormon "Dixie" around St. George. For a while, with the ladies, the baby, the dances, the contacts with gawky Mormon girls, leathery patriarchs, credulous and hardy young men, "aunties" with broods but without visible husbands, the Powell Expedition had a reasonably social time. They got to see Brigham when he made his annual visit. They kidded the Paiutes who squatted near town. They traded horses for blankets with the Navajo who rode in under the safe-conduct Jacob had arranged the year before. They met John D. Lee, rumored to have been the chief murderer at Mountain Meadows, and Isaac Haight, almost as deeply involved, and found both men so ordinary it was hard to believe that bloody fanaticism of 1857. Haight even made a hard forced march to bring them supplies when he thought they were stranded without food at Lonely Dell.

These were the diversions. The work of triangulation went on steadily from the nine-mile baseline they measured on the Kanab Desert, but with this topographical work Powell had little to do. He was already toying with the notion of returning to Washington to see about another appropriation, either for a survey of the valleys of the Sevier and the Virgin, or for the publication of the reports of their explorations up to now. Having once or twice sniffed the powder of that redoubt at the end of Pennsylvania Avenue, he could no more have stayed on the Kanab Desert while Congress met than he could have jumped the Grand Canyon. He asked Thompson if he would work for nothing for a year, if it proved necessary, while arrangements were made. Thompson was willing; he was a man who liked to get a job done. On the first of February, 1872, the Powells were gone.

With single-minded placidity the Prof carried forward the triangulation south to the Canyon, east to the Paria, west to the Beaver Dam Mountains. He worked through and around a good-sized gold rush set off by the stories of Riley and Bonnemort, two of his packers, that there was color in the Colorado sandbars, and when the excited outburst of ill-equipped fortune hunters ebbed as fast as it had risen, Thompson was still there serenely locating stations and plotting the map of the river. What had always been his expedition was his uninterruptedly until August, 1872, when

Powell finally returned after an irritatingly long and uncertain delay.

In that time the amateur party had hardened to its more enduring elements and made its enduring contributions. Beaman was gone, too lazy and too ambitious for personal gain to be of real use. Steward was gone for reasons of health. Bishop, bitter and humorless, had quit after he finished plotting the river map, but his bitterness sweetened as he made good friends among the Kanab Mormons, and shortly he would be marrying a Mormon girl in Salt Lake, joining the Church, and settling down to teach at the University of Deseret. Hattan, Clem Powell, Jones, Dellenbaugh, and Hillers remained; there was also a frail young photographer named Fennemore whom Powell had hired at Savage's [5] in Salt Lake to replace Beaman. And there were some local Mormons — Adairs, Hamblins, Johnsons. On May 30, 1872, having been continuously in the field for more than a year, Thompson and his party started from the little settlement of Johnson to make a fourth try at the Dirty Devil route. The *Cañonita* needed to be brought down with the other two boats at Lonely Dell and readied for the second leg of the river run, through Marble and Grand Canyons. While it was being brought down, its crew could photograph and examine the previously skimped reaches of Glen Canyon.

This trip was the Prof's personal triumph, for the methodical topographer succeeded where Powell, Hamblin, and Pardon Dodds had all failed. From Johnson northward to Swallow Park was an easy two days, with the flaming broken edges of the Paria Amphitheater beginning to show ahead on their right. The third day they struggled eastward across a plexus of canyons below the White Cliffs, passed the spot where a young Mormon named Elijah Averett had been killed by the Red Lake Utes six years before, and camped in the valley of the Paria. On the fourth day they worked up the Paria and its Henrieville Fork, crossed the divide between the bold jut of Table Cliff and Kaiparowits Peak, and found themselves in a valley sloping strongly south and east. This was what the Mormons called Potato or Spud Valley.[6] In it now is the remote little hamlet of Escalante.

Here they halted, hampered by rain and confused by the topography. Down the southwestern edge of the valley ran a line of bold cliffs, unbroken until they ended abruptly on the unseen rim of Glen Canyon opposite Navajo Mountain. These cliffs formed the eastern edge of a tableland that as Wild Horse Mesa would figure largely in the writings of a then-unborn hack writer named Zane Grey. Thompson would ink it on his map as the Kaiparowits Plateau. But the creek that headed here puzzled him. It should be the headwaters of the Dirty Devil, and it should flow down this valley and around the flank of the Dirty Devil or Unknown Mountains into the Colorado. But this creek canyoned so abruptly that they could not follow down its perpendicular slot, and though he rode ten miles south, with a wide view ahead, he saw not a trace of the Dirty Devil Mountains.

Next day he and Pardon Dodds climbed a southeast ridge and sat their horses looking out over one of those grand, lonely, colorful panoramas that the plateau country offers in abundance and that are seen nowhere else. Northward was what Thompson called, in ignorance, the Wasatch Mountains. It was so marked on Lieutenant Warren's map, though later exploration by Powell's parties would show that the Wasatch proper ended at Mount Nebo, ninety miles south of Salt Lake, and that what reached down into southern Utah was not a mountain range but a complex of very lofty plateaus.[7] He might have seen, with drifts of snow even yet unmelted on their cliffs, the southward thrusting edges of the Aquarius, Thousand Lake, perhaps even distant rims of the Fish Lake and the Wasatch Plateaus, basalt-topped, flame-edged where they were eroded into cliffs. Eastward, below the lower slopes of the Aquarius, was a painted waste of rock and sand, crossed by a comb of sugary-white. He saw chocolate strata sculptured like organ pipes, a crumbling talus of blue-green shale, gray cliffs streaked with yellow, fierce outbreaks of red. In that maze cliffs swung and meandered and appeared far off hazed with distance across hollow valleys of unmitigated stone. And across those badlands, forty miles by airline and looking like near neighbors, were what Thompson had been looking for: the peaks that Powell had seen from the river rim in 1869 and called the Unknown Mountains. There they were, gray-green peaks incongruous in this country of mesa and abrupt cliff, a range almost as high as the great timbered plateau northward, the surface looking at that distance like sage-colored velvet.

"Can see only three, or counting the little one, four," Thompson's journal says. "East of them can just see the tops of mountains thought to be Sierra la Sal, and further east the Sierra Abajo."[8]

Both ranges were close to a hundred and fifty miles away. But it was the stream which interested him most. He traced it down Potato Valley into its slotted canyon, and saw that after a little distance it turned straight eastward through the ridge, cutting into it with as little regard to topography as the Green cut into the Uintas at Flaming Gorge. From his point of vantage he saw it emerge on the eastern side and after about ten miles turn southeast in almost a straight line to the Colorado, joining it just a little above the mouth of the San Juan. This was the stream both Jacob and Dodds had tried laboriously to traverse, and failed because of the impassable narrow canyon of its lower reaches. On the outspread relief map below them Dodds showed Thompson a place where he had climbed out. He said that all the way down, whenever they could get a bearing, they had seen the Dirty Devil Mountains to the left and back of them.

It was clear now why they had all failed. Thompson put it down in his diary and then underlined it. *"Is not the Dirty Devil."* The stream that he now tentatively called Potato Creek was a tributary of the Colorado, all right, but one that both the 1869 and the 1871 river parties had entirely missed. Its mouth was not even shown on his own map.[9]

That was the last river added to the map of the United States. Thompson called it the Escalante after the first white man known to have crossed that wilderness, not quite a hundred years before. The gray-green peaks he thought of as the Dirty Devil Mountains were the last mountain range to go onto the map, also; the name they would finally bear was that of Powell's first and most helpful friend in Washington, Joseph Henry.

In some writings, Prof Thompson is given credit for the discovery of Bryce Canyon. The credit is probably not deserved, though his party could not have missed a distant view of the eroded edge of the Paunságunt Plateau as they came up to the Table Cliff divide from Clarkston. They passed close to Bryce, but neither Thompson's nor Dellenbaugh's nor Clem Powell's diary makes any special mention of the canyon, and their route would seem to have swung them south and east of it, across the open end of the Paria Amphitheater in which Bryce is a detail.

But there seems no doubt that the Prof's party was the first across the back of the Aquarius, and that was Darien enough. To reach the headwaters of the Dirty Devil from Potato Valley they had to swing far north across the mountain. As they worked their way up a creek and out onto the back of that noble tableland that Captain Dutton later said should be described in blank verse, even the laconic Thompson was diverted from topography to scenery.

> There are five lakes in sight from a point above camp. The aspens grow very thick. Pine and fir trees also. Found the bear-berry in blossom. Strawberries just in bloom. . . . Traveled 10 miles by 12M over an open country with groves of aspen and pine. . . . The landscape from the divide which we came over is beautiful. . . . Creeks every mile or two. Often groves of aspen and pine and clear meadows. Is a perfect paradise for the ranchers. . . .[10]

It is a perfect paradise for anybody — still is. The present road from Escalante to Bicknell across the southern shoulder that Thompson was traversing in 1872 is the only one. Until 1929 the town of Boulder on its roof got mail by packmule. The Hell's Backbone Trail that branches off to serve Boulder now would bring the lights of most drivers clear to the roof of their mouths. Until jeeps started taking fishing and hunting parties in about 1946 there had never been a wheeled vehicle on much of its northern end. Wooded clear across its 11,500 foot top, studded with a hundred lakes, it offers from any part of its periphery not only the charm of its own mountain scenery and climate, but views to take the breath: southeastward to the Henry Mountains on the edge of the Colorado; southwestward over the desert to the knife-edge of the Kaiparowits; northeastward across the toothed comb of the Waterpocket Fold to Thousand Lake Mountain climbing from its red base courses to its crest of dark lava and darker spruce.

From the salient angle of the plateau the party worked down a branch of Pleasant Creek, scared up a band of Paiutes who were finally induced to come back and smoke a pipe and give directions, passed over a divide, and reached the headwaters of Pine Alcove (now Bullfrog) Creek, on the slope of the Dirty Devil or Henry Mountains. For several days they climbed among the peaks, one of which Thompson named Mount Ellen for his wife, before they circled the north end of what would be called Mount Pennell, sorted out Trachyte Creek and Crescent Wash, both running in deep canyons, from the true drainage of the Dirty Devil, and just before noon on June 22 passed down the long-sought waterway to the Colorado. The trip had taken them close to a month; they had been in completely unexplored country much of that time.

At the river the party split. Dellenbaugh, Hillers, Johnson, and Fennemore ran the *Cañonita* down to Lee's Ferry, and Thompson returned with the others back across the Waterpocket Fold and the high, cool, beautiful whaleback of the Aquarius to Potato Valley, where Clem Powell and a supply train had been awaiting them. On July 7, 1872, they were back in Kanab.

That trip was Thompson's most spectacular, though probably not his most important, contribution. During August and September he gave up the command again to Major Powell, who had during the six months of his absence from the party negotiated an appropriation for the fiscal year 1872–73, bought a house on M Street in Washington, scotched some bogus claims for federal compensation by Captain Sam Adams, resigned from Normal University and arranged the sale of his house in Bloomington, and confirmed himself in the resolution to make his career in the survey of this part of the West.

In what they reported as exceedingly high water the boat party ran the Marble and Grand Canyons from Lee's Ferry to the mouth of Kanab Wash. By the time they arrived there on September 7, they were badly battered and pretty shaky, and after a consultation with Thompson Powell decided to leave the river.

Probably they lost something by not going on down, but not a great deal. Ives had mapped the south side of the lower Grand Canyon, and Thompson was sure he could map the north side as well by land as by water. The packers who brought food in at Kanab Wash brought news from Jacob Hamblin that the Shivwits were angry again and threatening to kill Powell's party if it came through. The brief gold rush to the Colorado's sandbars had destroyed the goodwill that Jacob and the Major had generated. And there may even have been in the back of the Major's mind the memory of Lava Falls, or of the rapid where the Howlands and Dunn had given up. He might have remembered the wild water where Bradley's boat jerked its sternpost loose and shot down like a chip with tough little Bradley desperately hurling his weight against the sweep. The water now was higher than it had been then; all the rapids, though they held fewer dangers from rocks, were of an unbelievable violence. The talus and shore needed for lining were gone in some places; the water foamed against nearly vertical cliffs. Shivwits, high water, used-up boats, tired men, fear of the river, or plain good sense — or a combination of these — ended the adventuring at Kanab Wash on September 9, 1872. Not a single diary indicates regret.

From that point on, while Powell turned his restless attention to the Southern Paiutes (he would spend much of the next year as a special commissioner for the Bureau of Indian Affairs, investigating the condition of the Utah and Nevada tribes) Thompson took over the field work again. With Jones, Dellenbaugh, and later a recruit named John Renshawe, he plotted and drew the map incorporating their explorations from Green River to the mouth of the White, and later with other assistants the successive atlas sheets covering the country from the Grand Canyon northward into the plateaus and westward to the Great Basin where they could be hooked onto the atlas sheets of the King and Wheeler Surveys. It was Thompson who ran Powell's errands, distributed government goods to the Paiutes as Powell got more and more involved with the Indian Bureau, stalled off Powell's creditors, cussed out his brother-in-law in downright language when Powell left him stranded without funds or instructions. His map was a good map; for its time it was an exceptional one. For some parts of the region it covered it is still, after eighty years, the only map available. The geographies and atlases and government map makers still draw on sheets that Thompson, Dellenbaugh, and Renshawe finished in a tent in Kanab in the winter of 1873. Though Thompson later, as a geographer of the Powell Survey and of the United States Geological Survey, would prepare many more maps, covering almost the whole Plateau Province clear to Fort Wingate in New Mexico, none would have so much of himself in them, and none would reflect so real a pioneering.

6. *Physiography: Birth of a Science*

THE DELEGATION of powers that was forced upon Powell by his own incapacity to keep out of ever newer and wider activities did not end with Hamblin and Thompson. The Powell Survey was not five years old before its director had turned over to assistants practically all the geological studies he had blocked out for himself. Before he was through, he had delegated himself almost completely out of the Plateau Province and out of the science of geology. But what he let go of there, he seized elsewhere; what geology lost, ethnology and Indian policy and public land policy and the structure of government science gained. The ripples started by his first plunge into the West in 1867 widened to include the whole nation. And his distribution of the work of his survey was one of the surest signs that he had outgrown the amateurism and localism of his first years. He was too intelligent a man to delegate to an incompetent a job that really excited him, and when he had turned over a task to a capable assistant he knew enough to let him alone. As he was carried out of arm's reach of his center he split his survey among three men, each of whom left a mark upon the history of American science and the history of the West.

One of them was his acidulous but dependable brother-in-law, the second was Grove Karl Gilbert, and the third was Captain Clarence E. Dutton of the Ordnance Corps, U.S. Army. Thompson, as we have seen, inherited and completed the job of exploration and mapping. Gilbert took over some of the great physiographic problems, especially as they were revealed in the Henry Mountains and in the Great Basin. Dutton became the interpreter of the Grand Canyon of the Colorado and of the High Plateaus that stepped back northward from the Vermilion Cliffs into central Utah.

In an odd way Gilbert and Dutton were like opposed or complementary sides of Powell himself; they were extensions of him, a right hand and a left, a cool observer and an enthusiast. The three worked together in a collaboration so close that none of them knew precisely which one had suggested a particular idea.[1] During the years they worked together, they were probably the most brilliant geological team in the business. But however close the collaboration and the friendship, and however brilliant the contributions of the two assistants, there is no overlooking the fact that Powell's greater experience and bolder generalizing imagination provided Gilbert and Dutton with many of their basic concepts, built them a foundation, gave them their stance. The combined work of the three over many years represents a substitute, a richer substitute undoubtedly, for the comprehensive work on the Plateau Province that Powell had first planned to do by himself. To that co-operative effort Powell gave early and much, and what he gave illustrates, like his choice of collaborators, that the Major at least in the years of the early eighteen-seventies was an unstable mixture of scientist and enthusiast, observer and adventurer, realist and romantic.

What he found time to say on geological matters he said in two books, the *Report on the Exploration of the Colorado River of the West and Its Tributaries,* published in 1875, and the *Report on the Geology of the Eastern Portion of the Uinta Mountains,* published in the next year. He wrote them during the winters in Washington, out of the notes and observations of every summer since 1868, working on them in the spare time of days devoted to planning the next field season, promoting appropriations, making friends of Congressmen by gifts of photographic packets, reading papers and delivering lectures, and presiding over meetings of the Washington Philosophical Society. The latter half of the *Exploration* and all of the *Uinta Mountains* are sober geological discussion of great importance; the first half of the *Exploration,* though of equal importance, is to some extent a work of the imagination.

A day-by-day account of the first run down the Colorado, it contains some peculiar suppressions, alterations, and additions of fact that would be thoroughly justified in fiction or in a book of popular travel, but that have a sinful and hangdog look in a scientific monograph. Moreover, the *Exploration* so consistently and effectively exploits the dramatic elements of the trip that it is impossible to read it except as a tense adventure story.

By the side of an impersonal factual record such as that, say, of Lieutenant Emory, parts of Powell's *Exploration* seem lush and sensational. Other sections have a bare intensity that is the product of considerable literary skill. In still other passages, such as that climactic scene in which he reports getting rimmed on the granite above Separation Rapid, there is some reason to suspect that he is romancing with facts, or at least transposing them. There was a good bit of John C. Frémont in Major Powell. When he wrote the *Exploration* he had his eye partly on scientific results and the scientific reader, partly on the persuasive power the narrative might have on appropriations committees, and partly on the public impression he would make. It is hard to say which motivation worked on him most, but it is possible to risk a guess.

The facts are that the *Exploration,* not published until almost six years after the completion of the first voyage, draws upon a considerable number of observations made not by that expedition but by the second. It uses a good many place names conferred by the second expedition as if they were conferred by the first, and some that were, like Bright Angel Creek, invented between voyages to adorn a tale. Yet the *Exploration* mentions the second trip only in an oblique reference in Chapter IX, and it gives no credit to and makes no mention of any member of the second expedition except Thompson, whose journal of the exploration to the mouth of the Dirty Devil in 1872 is reproduced as part of the report.[2]

Presumably the second river trip was unmentioned because of Powell's avowed intention to report only original explorations. He never tried to conceal the fact that there had been a second voyage, for his preliminary report of 1874 [3] discusses it, and his preface to the *Exploration* itself, as well as the title page, indicates that the river was explored "in 1869, 1870, 1871, and 1872." It was perhaps ungracious not to give even a passing mention to the men who had served him faithfully for two years or more, but the omission is further evidence of how little the second voyage really enlisted Powell's own interest. Still, it did add and did clarify a good many things. He put them in without bothering to complicate his story, or name their true date and source, and got himself into something embarrassingly close to manipulation of the facts.

Stranger even than his failure to credit the second expedition is the alteration of dates in Chapter X. This is made up principally of the story of Powell's trip with Jacob to visit the Uinkarets and Shivwits. But onto the record of that journey of 1870 he tacked the record of another, down the Parúnuweap Canyon from the roof of the Markágunt Plateau into what is now Zion National Park — a piece of original exploration like the others, *but made in 1872,* not in 1870 when Powell said it was. He could not have made that mistake unwittingly. There were too many ways he could have been reminded; the events themselves were recent and important to him. His was not the kind of mind in which the observations made on original explorations floated like unattached weeds. Undoubtedly he deliberately altered the date of the Zion exploration to bring into something more like unity the scattered explorations of his party — and just possibly to insure priority for his visit to Zion, since Lieutenant Wheeler's parties were working in the same region in 1871 and 1872, and Wheeler was an empire builder eager to claim everything he could.[4]

The literary reason is almost certainly the proper one. The whole first half of the *Exploration* indicates a literary intent. Those empurpled descriptions written from a crag above the Gate of Lodore and from the camp at the mouth of the Yampa are transplanted little altered from the Chicago *Tribune,* and there are plenty more like them. Though the journal and field notes on which the *Exploration* is presumably based are singularly curt and bare, the *Exploration* through a good part of its length has the tone of the *Tribune* letters, the tone of the nineteenth-century literary traveler with an expanded and throbbing capacity for sensations.

Powell's literary style was always self-conscious, whether in his flowery beginnings or in his later years when his prose became crabbed and riddling and salted with coined words of his own. His young taste ran to the romantic poets; on the second river expedition he brought along volumes of Scott, Tennyson, and Longfellow, and through Brown's Hole and on other calm stretches he read them aloud to the crews of the lashed boats floating together. In the *Exploration* his writing is marked by effusiveness, poetic inversions and contractions, sweeping and panoramic effects, the exploitation of every chance for dramatics, but also by precision of line and considerable associative imagination. And he had justification for a high tone. He was in truth engaged in a hazardous and exciting voyage, and the country through which he passed was calculated to stir the superlatives out of almost anyone.[5] Heightened or not, the *Exploration* is an extraordinarily thrilling story, good enough to have been reprinted twice from its official format and to have had several magazine versions.[6]

This fact of magazine publication is the main reason for the "literary" and "unscientific" tone of the first half of the book. Major

Powell was no more capable of writing a single-purpose manuscript than he was of conducting a single-purpose field expedition. The publication of the *Exploration* in 1875 involved a complexity of double-duty deals, in which both text and illustrations were called upon to serve several purposes.

Inquiries from magazine editors had come early after his return in 1869, but though he was always in need of money, and though he very energetically undertook the sale of stereographs and views in partnership with Thompson and Hillers,[7] it was several years before he tried to write anything. When he did, he seems to have been jogged into it by his ex-photographer Beaman, who during 1873 was peddling his own reminiscences of the second voyage. Beaman had never been a favorite with the party. They had all considered him lazy, and Clem Powell, his assistant, found him unwilling to teach what he knew. Whether he quit before he was fired or was fired before he quit in Kanab early in 1872 is a tossup,[8] but he had gone down to the Moki towns on his own and taken pictures, and now he had a book of his experiences there and on the river.

On March 6, 1873, H. O. Houghton of H. O. Houghton and Company, Boston, wrote to Powell expressing interest in Powell's book, some chapters of which had evidently been submitted to him for publication.[9] In the same letter he indicated that his firm had just turned down Beaman's book, a fact which would have pleased Powell, quite apart from his feelings about Beaman, because to have an account of the second expedition published — and by the least reliable member of the party — before any account of the original exploration appeared, must have seemed an unhappy chance. The possibility that Beaman might succeed before he placed his own manuscript seems to have spurred Powell to activity. His manuscript was still with Houghton and Company early in April,[10] but within less than a week it was in the hands of Henry M. Alden of Harper's. Alden on April 12 cautiously asked for a full manuscript, or a plan thereof, before making a decision,[11] but definitely requested two articles for *Harper's Magazine*, one on the canyons and one on the "Aztec" civilization of the Southwest, at fifteen dollars per page.

Nothing came of that, neither book nor articles. Either Powell had no time then to write them, or decided to wait until he could satisfy the request that both Houghton and Alden had made for a full-sized manuscript. On April 13 Alden returned the manuscript[12] and photographs and Powell apparently did nothing more about them for over a year, leaving the field to Beaman. Beaman's book eventually landed in *Appleton's Journal,* which printed it in seven installments during April and May, 1874. Its appearance may have had something to do with Powell's decision to omit all mention of the second expedition from his own book.

But it did not discourage him from trying to publish in a popular journal. On July 17, 1874, he signed an elaborate contract[13] with Richard Watson Gilder of *Scribner's* which did credit both to Gilder's eye for publishing innovations and Powell's knack of carrying water on both shoulders. Scribner's agreed to pay Major Powell $500 for three or four articles plus twelve engravings on wood which Powell was to supply. But in addition to these twelve pictures, *Scribner's,* at that moment moving to revolutionize the art of magazine illustration, would spend $2000 for others, which after use in the magazine would become Powell's property. By this stroke the Major not only made himself a modest sum, but he assured himself a spectacular spread in the magazine, and obtained besides an excellent collection of illustrations for his projected report.

So the scientific report was first written as a popular adventure story of original exploration and illustrated lavishly for a popular magazine. It was written, moreover, after Beaman had already published a highly-colored account, so that there may have been some inclination to outdo what had already been made public. To some such combination of motives are due the persistent heightenings and dramatizings that make the *Exploration* exciting reading but weaken its accuracy: the tendency (the opposite of what Bradley had grumbled at) to overestimate the drop of rapids, to dwell ominously on the dangers ahead, to "touch up."

As if to make amends for literary license in the first part, the second half of the *Exploration* is a sober treatise entitled "The Physical Features of the Valley of the Colorado." It was serialized too, but not in a general magazine: *The Popular Science Monthly* was not popular in that sense.

Some river historians, notably Stanton and Chalfant and Julius Stone, have taken a good deal of delight in pointing out inaccuracies or distortions of fact in Powell's account. Some of their criticism is legitimate, some a part of that curious jealousy which seems to persuade every man who ever ran the Colorado that he invented it. The distortions are there, most of them traceable to this literary motive and the complex circumstances under which his all-purpose narrative was written and published. But it is not possible to accuse Major Powell of the ordinary sort of inaccuracy-through-ignorance that fills the travel writing of his time or any other. He was no nature faker. He did not distort natural laws or misinterpret natural scenery. In his own way he was part of that inevitable slow movement toward realism whose local literary beginnings in John Hay and Edward Eggleston were almost precisely contemporary with his own beginnings as a scientist. Writer and scientist in that tradition do not differ so widely: Powell's method of observing natural phenomena did not differ in kind from Mark Twain's — especially that Mark Twain who lampooned so mercilessly the romantic inaccuracies of Fenimore Cooper. But both Powell and Twain, realists and even factualists, might on occasion be led to follow Twain's own advice to Kipling: "Young man, first get your facts and then do with them what you will." In literature, if not in science, an unintentional lie is worse than a deliberate one.

The element of the spectacular in Powell's story is therefore not remarkable. He had shown before then that he was a vigorous and sharply intelligent young man on the make, with a considerable instinctive and some trained knowledge of the arts of self promotion. But the *Exploration* is the last real demonstration of any such motive — a kind of last fling, a farewell to his *Wanderjahre.* After 1876 he delegated both his geological speculations and his scenic and dramatic enthusiasms and settled down to organize government science. But first he firmly clinched the reputation as a geologist that the second half of his first book had established.

Many of the generalizations that Powell made in the *Exploration* and in the *Uinta Mountains* have at this date an air of the obvious; yet when he made them they were either new or newly emphatic. His homemade education fitted him to grasp the obvious and state it without embarrassment — he had not been educated into scholarly caution and that squidlike tendency to retreat, squirting ink, which sophisticated learning often displays. He was intellectually a plunger, not a retreater. As it turned out, the obvious clearly stated, and combined with new observations, was sometimes close to revolutionary. And the obvious in the Plateau Province was so much more obvious than it was anywhere else that it demanded statement and at the same time presented incontrovertible proofs.

As a single example, consider his remarks on the behavior of streams. He observed that often they paid no attention to the terrain through which they ran. The Yampa, the Green, the Escalante, with valleys at hand to run through, chose instead to cut straight into massive ridges or mountain ranges. Since water does not run uphill, he had to conclude that these rivers were older than the mountains, and that as the mountains rose across their path they rose slowly enough to be cut like a log held against a revolving saw. Out of that simple observation arose a whole complex of ideas: that mountains were relatively ephemeral earth features, that nature abhorred an elevation almost as fiercely as it was said to abhor a vacuum, and persistently cut it down and carried it away; that in this case at least, and probably in most, earth movements were slow, not catastrophic as Dana and King and some other geologists held; and in particular that drainage upon this slowly altering earth-surface could be divided into three classes which he called *antecedent, consequent,* and *superimposed.* In the first, a previously existing river such as the Green cut through a rising mountain range as fast as the range rose, and held its course; in the second, an obstruction that rose too fast ponded the rivers, or diverted them to new channels established by the new topography; in the third, a drainage produced by the topography of one age held its course while erosion leveled and obliterated all those elevations and valleys it had been born among, so that the rivers were "superimposed" upon an entirely different topography exposed underneath.

These general classifications seem simple and obvious enough; they have become the alphabet of the study of drainage, in the Plateau Province or anywhere else.

Working from the same observed facts, Powell made certain generalizations about erosion, which he instantly recognized as the prime agent in the land forms of the region. He put together things already well known: That the corrasion of a stream's bed was relatively swift, and increased with the declivity by a much more than arithmetical ratio. That the weathering away of elevated country proceeded much more slowly, so that a stream would cut a deep, narrow canyon before its walls or the surface of the country back from them would be much affected by erosion. That the erosion of low country was near a minimum, and that this minimum was always being approached. He called it the "base level of erosion" and gave another fundamental concept to the science. He noted the way in which cliffs were eaten back by the weathering out of soft layers and the caving in of the undermined hard strata, and he gave it a name; the recession of cliffs. Dutton would elaborate the idea, and point out among other things that the profile of such a retreating cliff would, once established, remain constant. But the original observation and the rubric were Powell's.

The characteristic flat crest lines and the vertical cliff-edges of butte and mesa and plateau Powell noted as the product of horizontal strata and arid climate, and he isolated a good many of the effects of climate upon the processes of erosion. His conclusions began to reach outside the area of the obvious when he insisted that this region, where the rivers had cut gorges sometimes more than a mile deep, and where weathering had demonstrably swept away thousands of feet of solid rock from a territory totaling thousands of square miles, was actually not a region of maximum erosion, but one of minimum. With an incorrigible lust to put things into categories, he classified the types of mountain and plateau structure found in the Plateau Province and found that some of them had never been revealed or studied elsewhere, and had no relation to the Appalachian structure and the tight plication that the textbooks thought characteristic of all mountains. These mountains — the Uintas, say — were not folded and tangled; they were simply a great arch, like an asymmetrical Quonset hut, carved and furrowed by the erosional processes eager to reduce it to a plain again. The plateaus of the Grand Canyon region and northward were sometimes arches, or half arches, and sometimes flat blocks sheared upward along fault lines. Sometimes the shear of a fault broke into a series of step faults, and sometimes into a simple monoclinal fold. He arrived at the conclusion that there was no essential difference between fault and monocline, and his evidence was so plain, revealed along bare exposed fronts that could be traced for dozens of miles, that there was no disputing it. These generalizations too Gilbert and Dutton would amplify, document, and elaborate, but not alter. From the time of their publication, first in the *American Journal of Science*[14] and later in the *Exploration* and the *Uinta Mountains,* they were part of the basic textbook of geology.

Though he collected fossils, Powell was no paleontologist; though he took geological sections, he was no stratigrapher; though he had a lively and even excited interest in the historical geology of the Plateau Province, what most took his eye and his imagination was the land forms, the plateaus, mesas, buttes, canyons, cliffs, the fantastic erosional remains that simply by their shapes and their positions on a denuded plain told of the forces that had created them. Quite alone, his generalizations about earth movements (with his support of uniformitarianism when it was still widely disputed), about the character of rivers and the forms of earth sculpture and the laws that govern erosion, would more than justify his years of work in the West. In his two monographs, according to Emmons,[15] was born the modern science of physical geology.

7. Geology: Grove Karl Gilbert

IN THE YEARS of the Powell Survey between 1874 and 1879, and later in the eighties when the United States Geological Survey was growing into a major federal bureau, Grove Karl Gilbert was Major Powell's right hand. Geological ideas that Powell touched and left, sketched and passed on from, Gilbert grappled with and exhausted. Powell's broad principles were divided, subdivided, reduced to that near-mathematical certainty that was Gilbert's ideal. A genial, kindly, much-loved man, he was in his own way as brilliantly speculative as Powell, and as far removed from a laboratory drudge, but he operated on some other kind of fuel. He built a bridge of equations where Powell leaped by intuition, and he tidied things up as he went so that everything was solid behind him — a thing that could not always be said for the Major.

The chapter on erosion in his *Geology of the Henry Mountains* does not alter Powell's systematic observations, but it systematizes them further and develops them so fully that that chapter needs practically no revision even today. Neither does his study of those mountains which had been a Powell Survey discovery in geographical terms and which Gilbert made into a discovery of another kind. He described and dissected them so precisely and exactly that they have been known ever since as the classic type of a special kind of mountain structure. Gilbert called them "laccolites" but others corrected his Greek to "laccoliths." These are "bubble mountains," formed of strata domed upward by lava masses from beneath, the layers of sedimentary rock interleaved by sheets of lava and penetrated by dikes. Marvine, Holmes, and others had speculated on some such structure;[1] Gilbert demonstrated it not only for the Henrys but for the La Sals, the Abajo, and Navajo Mountain.

The Geology of the Henry Mountains appeared as a Powell Survey monograph in 1877, at a time when, as we shall see, Powell needed every evidence of scientific accomplishment his survey could muster if he was to induce Congress to prolong its life. Much later, after his own assistants and other geologists had taken some of the bloom from the subject, Gilbert produced a second report, this one on Lake Bonneville,[2] and this like his first was so careful, so thorough, so perceptive of those lost or buried or effaced traces by which geological history must be known that it became at once a landmark. The Pleistocene lake that used to spread deep water across much of the western Utah and eastern Nevada desert has needed little study since. But it is worth noting that at the foundation of Gilbert's reconstruction of the extent, history, drainage, climate, and character of the extinct lake are Powell's rules of erosion, modified and extended to the habits of lakes rather than rivers, and traceable by shore cliffs, beach terraces, embankments, spits, and bars instead of by canyons, cliffs of erosion, alluvial fans, and cameo buttes. The basic laws are still to some extent Powell's, and the focus of attention is still, as with Powell, the land forms, the sculpture of the earth, and the processes by which it is created.

Like several of Major Powell's later professional colleagues, Gilbert [3] was borrowed, not developed, by the Survey. After graduation from the University of Rochester and a general scientific apprenticeship in Ward's Natural History Establishment, that fantastic business house, still extant, which provided and will still provide anything from trays of fossils to live black widows, from platypus eggs to relief maps, from laboratory insects to articulated skeletons of men or mastodons, he had worked briefly for the Ohio State Geological Survey and developed an acquaintance with the habits of living lakes that he later used effectively in the study of a dead one. In 1871, with his friend Archibald Marvine, he had gone out with Lieutenant Wheeler's Geographical Surveys West of the 100th Meridian.

He had not been happy with Wheeler, for Wheeler dragged his geologists from place to place on a leash, covering enormous stretches of country in very hasty reconnoissance so that they barely got to sniff an exciting problem before their noses were dragged away from it. They were not scientists, but assistants to topographers. Late in 1872 Gilbert's path crossed that of the Powell party when Wheeler's outfit camped near Kanab, and though Powell was not there at the time, being busy about some Paiute investigations, Gilbert visited with Clem Powell and others, and bought a Navajo rug from Nellie Thompson.[4] Apparently he met the Major in Washington, where community of interests and mutual membership in scientific societies would have thrown them together naturally, in that winter or the next. In November, 1874, just after his marriage, Gilbert accepted Powell's offer of a job, and moved at once out of a restricting, frustrating, military organization into complete freedom.

Under Powell, once the two of them decided on an area for field study, Gilbert went as he pleased, stayed until the budget or the weather chased him home, studied what he wanted, lingered where he wished, returned if he felt like it for another visit or another whole field season. The freedom with which he was allowed to work, and the liberality with which Powell gave away his most illuminating ideas,[5] cemented a personal friendship that was as close as any in either man's life. As ranking geologist and for a time as acting director of the United States Geological Survey,

Gilbert loyally subordinated his personal wishes and his own studies to help Powell in one or another promotional scheme. At the end of the eighteen-seventies and again at the end of the eighteen-eighties, as we shall see in later chapters, Powell focused most of his incredible energy on the political fight to establish scientific laws and policies for the administration of the Public Domain. While he did so, his bureaus were expected to run themselves. Translated, this means that Powell's assistants, notably Gilbert, took over. He let himself, though among geologists he was quite as respected as his chief and more universally liked, become a tail to Powell's kite. When Powell died it was Gilbert who acted as his executor and Gilbert who was his first and most respectful biographer.[6] The only thing he did not do that he might have been expected to do was to succeed the Major in one of his several administrative jobs.

Actually it was pure kindness that Powell did not urge one of these positions on him. Gilbert was a scholar, not a promoter or an administrator. He disliked politics and hated even scientific controversy so much that with evidence enough to hang a man he corrected him hesitantly and apologetically and gave him every opportunity to save face. There was no better loved man in all of Washington's scientific company. But though he outlived Powell by sixteen years, his productivity in those years was not so great as many would have expected of him — perhaps because with all his virtues he needed the galvanizing influence of his one-armed friend and collaborator. His monographs, though greatly admired by geologists and less in need of modernization or revision than the work of any geologist of his time, make tough reading for the unenlightened.

8. *Geological Aesthetics: Clarence Edward Dutton*

NOT SO THE WRITINGS of Powell's left hand, Captain Dutton. A Yale classmate of O. C. Marsh, two years ahead of Clarence King, he had been like King a college athlete and like King he was attractive, charming, many-sided. An aptitude for mathematics had led him after the war to take a permanent commission in the Ordnance Corps, but he had a literary flair too. As an undergraduate he had won the Yale Literary Prize; his reading all his life was so various and extensive that he called himself omnibiblical. During his years in Washington he developed a considerable reputation as a public lecturer, and there is plenty of testimony to the charm and instructiveness of his conversation.[1] Altogether he was a somewhat less sybaritic and less spectacular King.

He arrived at geology by a process almost as circuitous as Powell's own. Trained for the ministry, diverted to the army, he found himself at the war's end stationed at the Watervliet Arsenal in West Troy, New York. There was nothing much for a peacetime officer to do; his wounds were healed, he was young and vigorous and interested in many things. Before long he got to studying the Bessemer Steel Works; his first scientific paper dealt with the chemistry of the Bessemer process and the mysterious and debated differences between iron and steel. But the influence of the local wise men touched him too: James Hall and R. P. Whitfield of Albany's paleontological museum gave him a competing interest in geology. By 1871, when after two transfers he landed in Washington, geology had won, and most of the members of the Washington Philosophical Society with whom he associated — Henry and Baird of the Smithsonian, Hilgard of the Coast Survey, Newcomb, Hall, and Harkness of the Naval Observatory, Woodward and Billings of the Medical Department, Powell and Hayden of the Western surveys — confirmed his scientific bent. By 1874 Powell was sufficiently impressed with his capacities to urge him to take a field party west. In the next year the Major and Joseph Henry maneuvered a special act of Congress that released Dutton from the army for detached duty with the Powell Survey.[2] In that work he spent at least part of every year for the next fifteen.

There is every evidence that Powell looked upon Dutton as his geological heir; like Gilbert, Dutton built upon the same base of Powell generalizations and Powell specialties. But the country into which his work led him, plus his earlier flirtation with chemistry, threw him a little to one side. Erosion and land-forms interested him — they had to, in that country — and he did his share toward amplifying and documenting Powell's doctrine of antecedent, consequent, and superimposed drainage, his recession of cliffs, his homology between faults and monoclines, and his theory of plural erosion cycles postulated on nature's tendency to approach a base level of erosion. These ideas were not so much his own as part of the common store. When he dealt with erosion, he started from Gilbert's brilliant chapter in the *Henry Mountains*. When he classified structural forms he followed Powell's *Uinta Mountains* and his "Physical Features of the Valley of the Colorado." But when he became interested in the earth movements which caused the displacements of the Plateau Province, he speculated further and more brilliantly than Powell did.

Powell had used the plain observable facts of the province, with their implications, to reshape the science of physiography. Dutton used them to establish Herschel's neglected theory of isostasy, which postulated the slow sinking of sea bottoms loaded with sediment and the corresponding rise of eroded land masses, with bending and fracturing along the margins or coastlines. Yet in his speculations about the creaking difficult adjustments by which the earth maintains its equilibrium Dutton was still drawing on the collaborative work of the survey. Powell had marked the homology between faults and monoclines, discounted the still prevalent theories of catastrophism, classified the basic structures of the great upraised and down-thrown blocks of plateaus, valleys, and mountains. Gilbert had proposed, probably for the first time in this country, the idea of an earth which was plastic without being necessarily fluid. Dutton, corroborating the beliefs of his old friend James Hall, took the step beyond.

His interests consistently led him to abstruse problems. Knowing blast furnaces from West Troy, he turned his attention to nature's own blast furnaces. Volcanism was his most abiding interest — volcanism and the earth movements which accompanied it. As early as 1880, pondering the lava flows of southern Utah, he was coming to the conclusion that volcanic loci were not funnels down into a molten core of the earth, but relatively shallow and limited cysts, and even then he was groping for the source of volcanic heat, though it was not until thirty years later that he satisfied himself he had found it in radioactivity.[3] Before he was through, he had studied extinct volcanoes in Utah, Arizona, New Mexico, and Oregon, and had spent several months among the calderas of Hawaii. He had made the most exhaustive study of the Charleston earthquake of 1884, and had reported to Congress on the quake-threatened right of way of the proposed Nicaraguan Canal. He had examined volcanic rocks microscopically and chemically and in the field, and had made adjustments in Richthofen's theory of the order of extrusive lavas. Part of his work, like Gilbert's, was done with the Powell Survey, part with its successor. When the Western surveys were consolidated in 1879 into the United States Geological Survey, with Clarence King as the first director, Dutton continued under King and the new bureau the precise work he had been doing under the Powell Survey, and when Powell succeeded King in the spring of 1881 Dutton was still at it. It is the part of his work which grew directly out of Powell's delegation of his own interests that gives Dutton a special position; and it is not his geological contributions, which were great, but his literary flair, which would seem quite irrelevant, that has kept his name fresh. Gilbert was perhaps a more important geologist, but Dutton is better known, because he was the first literary tourist in a country where tourist travel has become the number one business.

To the traveler from east or west — and most tourist travel comes from those directions — the Plateau Province presents difficulties. It is easy to skirt the region, hard to cross it, for from Bear Lake at its northern border to the Vermilion Cliffs along the south, Utah has a spine like a Stegosaurus. The northern half of the spine is the Wasatch, true mountains whose gorges used to spill glaciers into the waters of Lake Bonneville. The southern half is a triple chain of lofty plateaus separated by broad but profound valleys. The plateau chains overlap with the end of the Wasatch at Mount Nebo, near the modern town of Nephi, and gradually widen toward the south like a three-fingered hand. The western chain, from north to south, is composed of the Páhvant (Sigurd Mountain), the Tushar (Beaver Mountain), and the Markágunt, which terminates in the cliffs and temples of Zion National Park; these three form the eastern wall of the Great

Basin and mark the ancient Mesozoic shoreline. The traveler between Salt Lake City and Los Angeles on Highway 91 skirts it from Levan nearly to St. George. The plateaus are deceptively high; the Tushar goes up above twelve thousand feet, and many others are well above eleven thousand, higher than many major mountain ranges. Roads across from chain to chain are opportunistic jogs through the few passes or laborious grapevines across the roofs. East of the Páhvant-Tushar-Markágunt chain the land falls away into the green garden-valleys of the Sevier and the Sanpete settled by Danish converts to Mormonism in the fifties and sixties. Eastward, walling the valleys, tower the flat crests of the Sevier and Paunságunt Plateaus, and across those and down again is Grass Valley tipping southward past the Koosharem Paiute reservation and along Otter Creek to its junction with the East Fork of the Sevier at the head of East Fork Canyon which splits the Sevier Plateau to its base. Straight across Grass Valley the struggling traveler is confronted with the eleven-thousand-foot rampart of the Fish Lake Plateau, which is linked southward with the Awapa, which in turn steps up to the last of this chain, the Aquarius, with its outliers Thousand Lake Mountain and Table Mountain.

These "High Plateaus" constitute a special and clearly marked division of the Plateau Province. The route by which Gunnison and later Frémont crossed them — Gunnison to his death — in 1853 remains undeveloped either as road or railroad.[4] The tourist routes flow along lines of less resistance and come westward through the Wasatch at Salt Lake or Ogden; or around the southern end of the Plateau Province by Highway 66 and the Santa Fe, south of the Grand Canyon; or out through a break in the Great Basin wall along the Virgin River. The High Plateaus are only a part of the barrier, for eastward from the Wasatch, Thousand Lake, or Aquarius Plateaus one looks out across Castle Valley and the San Rafael Swell and the desert badlands, the emptiest part of America, that separate them from the Green River. Westward, Páhvant and Tushar and Markágunt overlook the twisted ranges and the whirlwind-haunted alkali valleys of the Great Basin. Southward, Markágunt, Paunságunt, and Aquarius break off in plunging cliffs to the lower platforms, and these rise steadily southward into the Paria, Kaibab, and Kanab Plateaus across which the Colorado has cut Marble Canyon and most of the Grand Canyon. The geography which made its exploration difficult and late continues to make its development even for tourist travel an enormous undertaking. Powell himself, though on several occasions he supported moves to make the Grand Canyon a national park, thought the difficulties of access and the lack of adequate water supplies might prove insuperable.

Intimately linked, by geological history, scenery, and at least rudimentary communications with the Grand Canyon, the High Plateaus have a character of their own. Tucked away in the cliffs and canyons of those remarkable mountains that are not mountains at all but greatly elevated rolling plains, are two national parks and three national monuments. Of the parks, Zion is carved in the southwestern flank of the Markágunt by one fork of the Virgin River, and Zion National Monument is carved by the other. (The first description of both of these was in Powell's *Exploration.*) Bryce Canyon is a horseshoe amphitheater gaudily eroded back into the strawberry-ice-cream colors of the Pink Cliffs crowning the Paunságunt. Capitol Reef National Monument is a stretch on the upper Frémont or Dirty Devil River, where the Waterpocket Fold turns up a domed wall of white Jurassic sandstone between the Aquarius and Thousand Lake Plateaus. Cedar Breaks is another amphitheater on the western rim of the Markágunt, above ten thousand feet, where an even more colorful but less bizarre Bryce has been chewed and dissolved out of the Pink Cliffs.

Add to these the other reservations in the rest of the Plateau Province — the Arches National Monument near Moab, the Natural Bridges in White Canyon under the Bear's Ears Plateau, the Hovenweep in the barren canyons of San Juan County, the Rainbow Natural Bridge on the flank of Navajo Mountain near the junction of the Colorado and the San Juan, and the Grand Canyon itself, the granddaddy of all spectacles, that divides the northern and southern parts of the Plateau Province — and it is clear that as a tourist attraction this part of the world justifies every superlative of the chambers of commerce. Culturally it is a kind of Ozarks, an isolated and wonderful pocket in industrial America, but that is another story. Traffic flows in and out of its better-advertised reservations, and fishermen and hunters come in from a thousand miles away in season and find their way up into the high marvelous weather of the Tushar or Fish Lake or Aquarius or Markágunt. But hundreds of square miles of country that anywhere else would be thought superlative lie unmarked and unadvertised, and the parts of the Plateau Province that asphalt has not reached are not greatly different from what they were when Gilbert, Thompson, and Dutton worked through them in the seventies.

Much of the region will never have anything to offer but scenery. But scenery it has in superlative degree and extravagant forms. High Plateaus, Grand Canyon, or sandrock wilderness, the scenery is no raw material exported by a colonial dependency, but the finished product. It is not merely finished, but unparalleled; not merely superlative, but utterly new. What the Plateau Province at large and the Grand Canyon in particular presented the country in the way of scenery was an innovation as surely as Gilbert's laccolithic mountains were a geological innovation, or the laws of physical geology that Powell derived from the cloven and eroded strata. Strangest and newest of our regions, last to be opened and last known, the northern part of the Plateau Province compelled new sensibilities and new aesthetic perceptions as well as new geological laws. It was Dutton's distinction (and pleasure), while Powell in the eighteen-eighties acquired more and more power and more and more responsibility as the simultaneous head of two great and growing Washington bureaus, and while he solidified his position as the organizer and champion of government-sponsored science, to take over and elucidate the strange region Powell had opened.

The tourist and nature lover occupied a good large corner of Dutton. He never quite made up his mind whether he was literary traveler or sober scientific analyst: the temptations were essentially equal. He escaped his dilemma by being both, and in his reports a rich and embroidered nineteenth-century traveler's prose flows around bastions of geological fact as some of the lava coulees on the Uinkaret flow around gables of sedimentary strata. The literary tendency is progressive; it is apparent in *The Geology of the High Plateaus of Utah* (1880) and dominant in *The Tertiary His-*

tory of the Grand Canyon District (1882). With hardly an apology, Dutton forsook the "severe ascetic style" of science when he came to deal with the Grand Canyon. The Grand Canyon was beyond the reach of superlatives, it compelled effusion of a kind. The result is a scientific monograph of great geological importance which contains whole chapters as ebullient as the writing of John Muir, and deviates constantly into speculations so far from geological that they sound more like Ruskin than Lyell.

Dutton loved a grand view, a sweeping panorama. In the verbal landscape-painting into which he was constantly tempted it is easy to see the influence of that school which, painting from nature and with careful attention to the rocky bones of the earth, still threw over its pictures a romantic and exciting aura. That Turneresque philosophy was illustrated by no one better than by Thomas Moran, who for a time traveled with Dutton's party in the canyon country. It was, in fact, the method of a growing Western landscape school of which Moran was perhaps the greatest exemplar. What Moran loved to paint — the big, spectacular, colorful view — Dutton loved to describe. He took his stance like a painter and he composed like a painter, and his drift, like Moran's, was constantly away from the meticulous and toward the suggestive. Consider:

> From the southwest salient of the Markágunt we behold one of those sublime spectacles which characterize the loftiest standpoints of the Plateau Province. Even to the mere tourist there are few panoramas so broad and grand; but to the geologist there comes with all the visible grandeur a deep significance. The radius of vision is from 80 to 100 miles. We stand upon the great cliff of Tertiary beds which meanders to the eastward till lost in the distance, sculptured into strange and even startling forms, and lit up with colors so rich and glowing that they awaken enthusiasm in the most apathetic. To the southward the profile of the country drops down by a succession of terraces formed by lower and lower formations which come to the daylight as those which overlie them are successively terminated in lines of cliffs, each formation rising gently to the southward to recover a portion of the lost altitude until it is cut off by its own escarpment. Thirty miles away the last descent falls upon the Carboniferous, which slowly rises with an unbroken slope to the brink of the Grand Cañon.

> But the great abyss is not discernible, for the curvature of the earth hides it from sight. Standing among evergreens, knee-deep in succulent grass and a wealth of Alpine blossoms, fanned by chill, moist breezes, we look over terraces decked with towers and temples and gashed with cañons to the desert which stretches away beyond the southern horizon, blank, lifeless, and glowing with torrid heat. To the southwestward the Basin Ranges toss up their angry waves in characteristic confusion, sierra behind sierra, till the hazy distance hides them as with a veil. Due south Mount Trumbull is well in view, with its throng of black basaltic cones looking down into the Grand Cañon. To the southeast the Kaibab rears its noble palisade and smooth crest line, stretching southward until it dips below the horizon more than a hundred miles away. . . .[5]

That is relatively precise and relatively restrained nineteenth-century nature writing. By the time Dutton came to describe the same scene two years later something had changed.

> Before the observer who stands upon a southern salient of the Markágunt Plateau is spread out a magnificent spectacle. The altitude is nearly 11,000 feet above the sea, and the radius of vision reaches to the southward nearly a hundred miles. In the extreme distance is the calm of the desert platform, its surface mottled with indistinct lights and shades, too remote to disclose their meaning. Against the southeastern horizon is projected the pale blue escarpment of the Kaibab, which stretches away to the south until the curvature of the earth carries it out of sight. To the southward rise in merest outline, and devoid of all visible details, the dark mass of Mount Trumbull and the waving cones of the Uinkaret. . . .[6]

What was precise in the first description has been hazed over by an act not so much of the eye as of the imagination — or perhaps what was reported too precisely before has been newly seen and more accurately rendered. The distant desert is now "mottled with indistinct lights and shades," the Kaibab has acquired the romantic blue of distance, the Grand Canyon which was drawn in before is omitted now, because it cannot be seen, and the cones of the Uinkaret, distinct before, now shimmer with haze and heat. In the first passage Dutton supplied details which he knew but could not see; in the second he described only what the eye observed, with all its uncertainties. That change in temper presents a nice problem not only in scientific reporting but in art criticism;

the first passage, diagrammatic and precise, is actually an improvement on nature. The second, for all its romantic haze and blurring, is the more realistic; it is closer to what the eye sees. And yet it is also, by normal standards either of science or of art, the more atmospheric and "literary."

Like a Japanese painter, the observer of the Grand Canyon must deal with an atmosphere which is a fact, whatever its romantic connotations. The eighteenth-century English landscapists who wore gauze spectacles while painting could have taken off their glasses at the canyon:

> Those who are familiar with western scenery have, no doubt, been impressed with the peculiar character of its haze — or atmosphere, in the artistic sense of the word — and have noted its more prominent qualities. When the air is free from common smoke it has a pale blue color which is quite unlike the neutral gray of the east. It is always apparently more dense when we look towards the sun than when we look away from it, and this difference in the two directions, respectively, is a maximum near sunrise and sunset. This property is universal, but its peculiarities in the Plateau Province become conspicuous when the strong rich colors of the rocks are seen through it. The very air is then visible. We see it, palpably, as a tenuous fluid, and the rocks beyond it do not appear to be colored blue as they do in other regions, but reveal themselves clothed in colors of their own. The Grand Cañon is ever full of this haze. It fills it to the brim. Its apparent density, as elsewhere, is varied according to the direction in which it is viewed and the position of the sun; but it seems also to be denser and more concentrated than elsewhere. This is really a delusion arising from the fact that the enormous magnitude of the chasm and of its component masses dwarfs the distances; we are really looking through miles of atmosphere under the impression that they are only so many furlongs. This apparent concentration of haze, however, greatly intensifies all the beautiful or mysterious optical defects which are dependent upon the intervention of the atmosphere.[7]

Thus far the analyst. On his heels comes the man of sensibility, as subjective as a Muir or Burroughs:

> Whenever the brink of the chasm is reached the chances are that the sun is high and these abnormal effects in full force. The cañon is asleep. Or it is under a spell of enchantment which gives its bewildering mazes an aspect still more bewildering. Throughout

> the long summer forenoon the charm which binds it grows in potency. At midday the clouds begin to gather, first in fleecy flecks, then in cumuli, and throw their shadows into the gulf. At once the scene changes. The slumber of the chasm is disturbed. The temples and cloisters seem to raise themselves half awake to greet the passing shadow. Their wilted, drooping, flattened faces expand into relief. The long promontories reach out from the distant wall as if to catch a moment's refreshment from the shade. The colors begin to glow; the haze loses its opaque density and becomes more tenuous. The shadows pass, and the chasm relapses into its dull sleep again. Thus through the midday hours it lies in fitful slumber, overcome by the blinding glare and withering heat, yet responsive to every fluctuation of light and shadow like a delicate organism.[8]

Call it, with some justice, an example of that pathetic fallacy that Ruskin thought the resource of second and third rate poets. Recognize it as part of the same rather effusive school of nature writing to which Powell himself, in his literary moments, subscribed. But compare it with the effusions of others on the Grand Canyon, with the "God-finding," [9] the extravagance, the gasping, the clutching of the overburdened heart. It is part of both the romantic and the tourist creeds to be overcome by grand scenery. Compare Henry Van Dyke's iambics[10] in which timorous Dawn trips through the pines of the Kaibab and half expiring on the brink, pants for more light like the dying Goethe. Compare John Gould Fletcher's secondhand Thunder Spirit sulking in the depths,[11] or Harriet Monroe's Earth, a victim of fluvial rape, lying "stricken to the heart, her masks and draperies torn away, confessing her eternal passion to the absolving sun." [12] Dutton was as little likely to address apostrophes to the river, that "sullen, laboring slave of Gravitation," as he was to believe with Joaquin Miller that the canyon had been formed by the collapse of the crust over an underground stream.[13] And Fletcher's poetic summation of the canyon, the message he saw written all over it "in bright invisible words, 'It is finished,' " would have made Dutton smile.

The physical structures of the earth, Powell had taught them all, were ephemeral. The primordial river draining the great lake of Eocene times had established its course and held it across rising blocks of country, gouging its channel deeper as the land rose.

Its walls had weathered back, and the walls of every side canyon and gulch had weathered back, under the tiny blows of rain and sand and wind. Ten thousand feet of rock that still showed in the terraces stepping up to the lava-capped High Plateaus had once stretched unbroken over the whole Plateau Province and had been swept away. The Grand Canyon itself was but one phase of a new denudation that would eventually sweep away the Marble Canyon Platform, and the Kaibab, Uinkaret, Kanab, Shivwits, the Coconino Plateau reaching southward, and level them down toward the ancient peneplain of dark Archaean schist that Powell's boatmen had hated and feared. And at some immeasurably remote time beyond human caring the whole uneasy region might sink again beneath the sea and begin the cycle all over again by the slow deposition of new marls, shales, limestones, sandstones, deltaic conglomerates, perhaps with a fossil poet pressed and silicified between the leaves of rock.

It was so far from finished that it would have no end, as for human purposes it had never had a beginning. From one of the points of vantage that he liked, up on the eastern rim of the Wasatch Plateau, Dutton had looked down across the San Rafael Swell and seen how erosion, starting at a high central dome, had eaten that dome down until it was now a depression, and had eaten back into the surrounding country until now the swell was a hollow ringed with concentric lines of receding cliffs — an immense, rainbow-colored intaglio. He had studied the buttes on the Kanab Desert and knew them to be other remnants of the same denudation, this time in the form of isolated cameos. He had followed the tracks of erosion in the retreating tiers of cliffs, and in the great amphitheaters like that of the Paria eaten back into the edges of the High Plateaus. Intaglio, cameo, cliff-line, amphitheater, they were all evidences of endless cyclic change. Perhaps for that reason Dutton found no gods or thunder spirits in the canyon, but only itself, self-created, protean, and immortal.

What marks Captain Dutton off from the temperate pedestrians of science is a temperamental habit of metaphor, which revealed itself not only in his literary effusions but in a consistent playfulness and informality. He wrote to Clarence King about catching earth-faults *in flagrante delicto,* and described the behavior of certain volcanoes in orgastic similes.[14] Where Major Powell delighted in Scott and Longfellow and the Standard Poets, and sometimes read them aloud to edify his men, Dutton admired Mark Twain. There was no echo in him of Powell's quaint formality of address: he called King and Powell familiarly by their last names even though they were his official superiors and in a time when official correspondence even between close friends was sprinkled with Obedient Servants and Beg-to-Remains. Some of the poet's iconoclasm was in him, making him stretch beyond known laws in search of the geological mysteries, and forcing him, upon provocation, to burst the bounds of the formal scientific monograph. A man is all of a piece. Dutton was of a metaphorical, associative, speculative kind. He was lured as surely into aesthetic as into geological speculations, and there is ample evidence that Powell delighted in his ungeological deviations, having been tempted in that way himself.

Scenic illusions such as those caused by the haze, or the apparent diminution of scale where everything was enormous, intrigued Dutton. He labored to achieve an "abiding sense" of a cliff a half mile high. Looking at the dark rim of the Sevier Plateau above Richfield in the Sevier Valley of Utah, he wondered why a nearly vertical wall over a mile high above the valley was not more impressive, and eventually blamed the lack of detail or emphasis or variety in the forms: a row of peaks that high and abrupt would have been as spectacular as the Tetons from Jackson Hole. Or he asked himself (and his geological reader) why a forest such as the Kaibab, composed primarily of coniferous trees, should strike him and all his party as the loveliest place any of them had ever visited, and went digging into all the possible causes. Several million tourists since Dutton's time have found that climax forest as charming as he described it, but perhaps have not wondered quite so seriously why.

For the characteristic forms and colors of the Plateau Province there were no precedents, and he was compelled toward architectural terminology and architectural speculations, for the angular vertical-and-horizontal lines of the country aped human architecture in startling ways.[15] The parallel, Dutton insisted, was no mere suggestion, but a "vivid resemblance," and it was revealed not occasionally but everywhere, and with a curious persistence because of the way in which individual strata maintained their profiles under weathering. In any one place the piled effect might be bewildering — Baroque on Doric and Byzantine on Baroque and Churrigueresque on Byzantine, magenta on chocolate on yellow on pink — but the consistency with which any group of strata produced the same forms was very striking. The massive sandstone layer that Dutton knew as the White Wall [16] changes from sugar-white in Zion and the Capitol Reef to salmon-color in Glen Canyon, but most of the strata maintain their coloring over scores or hundreds of miles. And even the White Wall is always vividly recognizable. In Zion or Capitol Reef, in Glen or Split Mountain Canyons, in Navajo Mountain, on the Colob Plateau, it is always massive, cross-bedded, intricately filagreed by weathering; and it always erodes into domes, caves, baldheads, arches. What Powell and Dutton called the Shinárump series [17] has always the gray, mingled, banded colors, the erosional statuary like a continuous frieze in high relief, above a flowing slope of chocolate and variegated shales. Wherever the Eocene Pink Cliffs are exposed, they are layered in pink and yellow and white, and carved into statuary even more fantastic than the frieze of the Organ Rock or the Shinárump. For endless miles, in all the formations, the forms are as repetitive as if carved to a master plan, the strata level or nearly so, the thickness and colors persistent or changing only by imperceptible degrees.

Dutton first taught the world to look at that country and see it as it was. He corrected the common belief that the canyons were impressive because they were deep and narrow. The grandest views in all the Grand Canyon are those from such observation posts as Point Sublime, where the chasm is widest and a just proportion of width to depth is obtained. He was a student of form, as of color, and he dismissed the alpine, craggy forms among which the romantic imagination has loved to wander since Childe Harold showed it how. Those alpine forms, which are "only big and rough," do not appear in the Plateau Province. The forms that do appear have no counterparts among those which have shaped and trained our appreciation. What shall we make, he asks, of the Temples of the Virgin?

Directly in front of us a complex of white towers, springing from a central pile, mounts upwards to the clouds. Out of their midst, and high over all, rises a dome-like mass, which dominates the entire landscape. It is almost pure white, with brilliant streaks of carmine descending its vertical walls. At the summit it is truncated, and a flat tablet is laid upon the top, showing its edge of deep red. It is impossible to liken this object to any familiar shape, for it resembles none. Yet its shape is far from being indefinite; on the contrary, it has a definiteness and individuality which extort an exclamation of surprise when first beheld. There is no name provided for such an object, nor is it worth while to invent one. Call it a dome; not because it has the ordinary shape of such a structure, but because it performs the function of a dome.

The towers which surround it are of inferior mass and altitude, but each of them is a study of fine form and architectural effect. They are white above, and change to a strong, rich red below. Dome and towers are planted upon a substructure no less admirable. Its plan is indefinite, but its profiles are perfectly systematic. A curtain wall 1400 feet high descends vertically from the eaves of the temples and is succeeded by a steep slope of ever-widening base courses leading down to the esplanade below. The curtain wall is decorated with a lavish display of vertical moldings, and the ridges, eaves, and mitered angles are fretted with serrated cusps. This ornamentation is suggestive rather than precise, but it is nonetheless effective. It is repetitive, not symmetrical. But though exact symmetry is wanting, nature has here brought home to us the truth that symmetry is only one of an infinite range of devices by which beauty can be materialized.

And finer forms are in the quarry
Than ever Angelo evoked.[18]

It is useful to have an open mind, especially in a new country or among new ideas. Not all had it, among the western-survey men. Dr. Hayden, for one, found the forms of the northern plateau country at first startling and then tiresome. For anyone, as Dutton said, the Plateau Province was "a great innovation in modern ideas of scenery," which required long study for its understanding, and whose full appreciation was "a special culture."

The lover of nature, whose perceptions have been trained in the Alps, in Italy, Germany, or New England, in the Appalachians or Cordilleras, in Scotland or Colorado, would enter this strange region with a shock, and dwell there for a time with a sense of oppression,

> and perhaps with horror. Whatsoever things he had learned to regard as beautiful and noble he would seldom or never see, and whatsoever he might see would appear to him as anything but beautiful and noble. Whatsoever might be bold or striking would at first seem only grotesque. The colors would be the very ones he had learned to shun as tawdry and bizarre. The tones and shades, modest and tender, subdued yet rich, in which his fancy had always taken special delight, would be the ones which are conspicuously absent. But time would bring a gradual change. Some day he would suddenly become conscious that outlines which at first seemed harsh and trivial have grace and meaning; that forms which seemed grotesque are full of dignity; that magnitudes which had added enormity to coarseness have become replete with strength and even majesty; that colors which had been esteemed unrefined, immodest, and glaring, are as expressive, tender, changeful, and capacious of effects as any others. Great innovations, whether in art or literature, in science or in nature, seldom take the world by storm. They must be understood before they can be estimated, and must be cultivated before they can be understood.[19]

Strange words in a geological monograph. Strange monograph, divided about equally between geology and nature description, salted with aesthetic speculation and illustrated like an art book by two of the painters who most helped to expand the nation's appreciation to include the strange forms and colors of the West.[20] Scattered all over that Plateau Province whose description Dutton had inherited from Powell were forms which "if planted upon the plains of Central Europe, would have influenced modern art as profoundly as Fusiyama has influenced the decorative art of Japan." Being innovations, and newly discovered, they were powerless until cultivation released them into the aesthetic consciousness. Whether they have yet been so liberated, and whether the forms and colors of the plateau country strike most of us even yet as anything more than bizarre, is an open question.

Nevertheless the cultivation does go forward, if only through the activity of a cult of enthusiasts. And a surprising number of those who fall under the spell of that country find Dutton's *Tertiary History* a bible, a wise book surviving from an earlier time. The delegation of authority which Powell made was a real delegation: Dutton is almost as much the *genius loci* of the Grand Canyon as Muir is of Yosemite. And though it is Powell's monument to which the tourists walk after dinner to watch the sunset from the South Rim, it is with Dutton's eyes, as often as not, that they see.

9. *Pictures of a New World: Moran, Holmes, Hillers*

LET US SAY that when peace threw open the West that had lain neglected from 1861 to 1865, the regions beyond the Missouri were still, to most Americans, the same Idea they had been before. That idea was complex; it took in both desert and garden, sterile wilderness and happy hunting ground, danger and adventure and opportunity, sanctuary and exile. In any of its phases it was big, grandiose, fabulous. It stunned the imagination or detonated words of prophecy. It was Ophir, it was Canaan, it was New Jerusalem, it was the high road to Asia. The interior West which was at first leaped over — Great Plains, Rockies, Plateau Province, Great Basin — had its own gaudy claims on the popular imagination which were later in being corrected by observation. This West too was fable. Between 1846, when the western part of it came into American possession and the eastern part became not a frontier but an interior, and the end of the eighteen-seventies, when the realities had been partly assayed, its history was in many ways a transition from fable to fact.

Before the nation in any numbers took out to Oregon or California or the Zion in the desert, following whatever dream of wealth or empire or heaven on earth worked upon them, there were reasonably accurate reports on what lay along the western trails. The quality of wonder did not notably distort the records of Lewis and Clark, Zebulon Pike, or Dr. James, who wrote up the Long Expedition. Scientists, explorers, fur traders — Bradbury, Brackenridge, Nuttall, Bonneville, even Schoolcraft, even Catlin, wrote essentially what they saw. Actualities were very specific in Gregg's *Commerce of the Prairies*. Maximilian of Neuwied came into the upper Missouri country in 1833 with a zeal for fact that would have done credit to a

German candidate for a Ph.D. Sportsmen, buffalo hunters, historians on a holiday, artists such as Seymour, Miller, Bodmer, Catlin, coursed the West for forty years between Lewis and Clark and the Mexican War, and though they did not hit it all and did not learn everything about what they hit, they did bring back in words and pictures (and flora, fauna, artifacts, tame Indians) a good deal of uncolored fact.

Yet something happened to the facts they returned with. They went into the maw of that great machine that at once creates and obeys public opinion, and they came out something else. In the popular mind the West stayed fabulous, partly because many of its very facts were fabulous. Who could resist the persuasion of the Comstock or Central City or the Yellowstone? What convert yearning toward Zion could contravene the evidence of the desert blossoming as the rose? Fantasy won also because ideas are like dye thrown into moving water, and American minds two or three generations later and thousands of miles away could be tinged with the coloring of a Rousseau or a Chateaubriand, the German romantics or Samuel Taylor Coleridge. It won because what people wanted was not facts at all, but corroboration of legendry and lore. Though the reports of sober scientific gentlemen circulated, the prints of Mr. Currier and Mr. Ives circulated much better, and these were art, not fact, and were painted by men who had not been there. Look at the Currier and Ives print called "The Last Warwhoop," "One Rubbed Out," or any of that marvelous series, and remind yourself that this pictures Kansas. Fantasy, plus the exciting fact of buffalo and Pawnees, made Kansas a near-delirium in the imaginations of thousands of young Americans a hundred years ago. The reaction, plus certain exterminations, has shrunk it now until in the mind of the hurrying tourist it is flat, dull, blistering, drouthy, dusty, uncouth, the abode of the clodhopper and the cyclone. Both versions of that region are almost pure fiction.

Some variant of the same strain of ideas that led William Gilpin to aggrandize the political and economic future of the West, distort its climate and resources, and falsify its natives misled many kinds of Americans — novelists, travelers, painters, reporters, speculators, railroad or Mormon proselytizers among Europe's poor — into doing the same. The best copy was sensational copy. As art or promotion one does not quarrel with this. Some of the Currier and Ives prints are spectacularly good, far better than any buyer had a right to expect for fifteen cents. It is only as geographical, historical, or sociological *record* that these pictures and the journalism and dime-novel literature that matched them are impeachable. There was too little factual corrective, too little allowance for swiftly changing times, and trouble ensued when people ignorant of the West and needing to know a lot about it mistook imagination for observation and art for life.

The romanticizing of the West as the final and culminating home of the American Dream, of free land, of individual liberty, of adventure, action, drama, color, left us a great deal of charming literature, from the journey of Moncacht-Apé to Hopalong Cassidy; and some delightful pictures, and some colorful notions about the Red Man, and these even yet exert a remarkable influence on the West's notion of itself and on the notions of others about it.[1] Dime novel, pulp magazine, comic book, radio and television and movie, horse and tomahawk opera, have perpetuated it as the abiding place of the picturesque: it is appropriate that two of the most active suburbs of Hollywood which produce westerns are at Sedona, in Oak Creek Canyon in Arizona, and at Kanab, Powell's old headquarters under the Vermilion Cliffs — both in the heart of the Plateau Province, the last home of romance. It is perhaps unkind to observe that the romanticizing of the West also led to acute political and economic and agricultural blunders, to the sour failure of projects and lives, to the vast and avoidable waste of some resources and the monopolization of others, and to a long delay in the reconciling of institutions to realities.

The attempt to prevent the spread of misconceptions about the West would enlist a great amount of Powell's energies during many years. He and his survey supplied some of the essential factual correctives, not the least in the pictures they made and distributed. Yet here too, though he was a thorough and convinced scientist and a believer in facts, Powell was a child of his own time, touched by the excitement and wonder of new country and new knowledge. He was committed to the philosophy of progress and perfectibility, he had on occasion played the public hero just a little, he affected the romantic poets. It would be misleading to call him a completely objective realist. He liked a dash to things; he also liked things accurately stated. Hence his choice of illustrators.

If he had deliberately tried, he could not have found two men farther apart in their artistic intentions than Thomas Moran and William Henry Holmes, or two who better satisfied the opposed drives of his own nature. With an odd insistence they emphasize the double quality of Powell's own mind. Like Gilbert and Dutton, they reflect him.

In 1871 *Scribner's Monthly* was a brand new magazine looking for brand new ways of attracting a public. One of the inescapable devices, used by every other magazine as well, was to cater to popular interest in the West, with the result that early volumes of *Scribner's* are salted with articles on trans-Mississippi topics. Another device was to follow the lead of *Harper's Weekly* and specialize in striking illustration. Often it could combine the two, as when in May and June of 1871 it ran two articles on "The Wonders of the Yellowstone" by N. P. Langford, who had visited that little-known region with a party of Montana dignitaries the summer before. Langford's articles appeared while Powell and Thompson were running the second river expedition down the Green.

Every part of the West has been at some time a county of Cocaigne, a province of Canaan. Langford's articles, like Powell's explorations, were factual corrective; though they dealt with wonders, they helped make the Yellowstone a verifiable part of Montana and Wyoming. They had further important effects: they were the opening move in the agitation that would within a year result in the reservation of Yellowstone National Park and the beginning of that philosophy of conservation which has led us to set aside twelve million acres of the public domain as national playgrounds and shrines. And finally, they were the means of introducing to the West the young artist who in the opinion of some became its greatest landscape painter.

When he was called upon to help illustrate the Langford articles, Thomas Moran was compelled to do what dozens of other illustrators were doing all the time — produce on-the-spot drawings without ever having been near the spot. He drew some "singular pictures, from description,"[2] of Langford's wonders, including one of the Grand Canyon of the Yellowstone in which the chasm appears about four feet wide and four miles deep, and several of mud volcanoes in which the cones look as if they had been cut out of sheet metal with tin shears. None of the woodcuts engraved from his drawings should have made him famous, and yet in a way they did. Langford's descriptions of the clean wilderness and of scenery on the grandest scale made him itch to get out and paint these things from life, for in training and inclination he was Turner superimposed upon Bierstadt. As it happened, Langford's first article plus Moran's imaginary illustrations caught the eye of the alert Ferdinand Vandeveer Hayden, director of the Geological and Geographical Survey of the Territories. Hayden's staff artist, Henry Elliott, had little of Moran's obvious skill, and could stand reinforcement. Moreover, though Hayden had planned to continue in 1871 his survey of southern Wyoming, overlapping the northern edge of Powell's territory, he could adjust himself to circumstance when publicity was involved. Yellowstone, with Langford, General Washburn, and others writing about it, was very much in the news. So Hayden turned his whole party northward, and he invited Thomas Moran to come along. Almost by the time his singular Yellowstone woodcuts were in print, Moran was on his way to the Yellowstone in person.[3]

It was a party almost as well staffed with artists as with the military. Besides the painters Elliott and Moran, there were three photographers along. W. H. Jackson, Hayden's official cameraman for many years, was one. The others were J. Crissman of Bozeman and J. T. Hine of the Army Engineers expedition which accompanied Hayden's group part of the way. But not all the artists brought back records. The unhappy Crissman lost his camera over the edge of the Yellowstone Canyon. Hine, after making many negatives, carried them back to Chicago just in time to have them destroyed in the Chicago fire. Elliott got a good many sketches, some of which, undistinguished and unremembered, may be seen in Hayden's *Annual Report* for 1871. But the prize artistic products of that summer were Jackson's photographs and Moran's sketches and water colors. With Elliott's cruder efforts, they are the first pictorial record of the Yellowstone country. In the winter following, when Hayden and his colleagues were vigorously agitating for the creation of a national park, it was the pictures, both real and phony, that converted reluctant Congressmen. Four hundred copies of Langford's articles with the Moran woodcuts were distributed to Congress; Jackson's photographs and Moran's water colors from life were spread before suddenly galvanized committees. Yellowstone became the first national park by act of Congress on March 1, 1872.

In the summer of 1872 Moran did not visit the West, but worked at oils based upon his 1871 sketches, especially on his enormous "Grand Canyon of the Yellowstone." Then, as later, he used photographs to corroborate his own observation, and the results of his work from life, when compared with the *Scribner's* pictures, are instructive evidence that it pays to know what you are painting. The Grand Canyon has widened out from its gothic narrowness, has acquired magnitude and space; the sunny colors which are its greatest beauty have perhaps never been so successfully captured. This picture alone would have been a big step toward the creation of the new palette that the West demanded. The process that is triumphantly concluded in Moran's "Yellowstone" was one that had begun forty years before in the water colors of Alfred Jacob Miller, when the painter's eye first began to adjust to prairies that were not green meadows, mountains whose rocks were other than the Appalachian granite, scrub growth whose shades were those of gray and brown and yellow, earth which showed its oxidized bones, and air without the gray wool of humidity across its distances. The new descriptive vocabulary that Captain Dutton helped to provide in his *Tertiary History* was matched in advance by the new palette of Moran.

So much credit accrued to Hayden from the Yellowstone Park lobby and from Moran's spectacular paintings that he was eager for further association. He could not have been insensible, either, of the enormous public acclaim that had come to Powell by virtue of his Colorado River adventure, and to Clarence King because of his exposure in 1871 of the spectacular diamond swindle based upon a salted mine in the Uintas. And Powell and King, each with a survey in the field, were Hayden's rivals for publicity, appropriations, and credit for the scientific survey of the West. Moran was the best stick he had to hit the competition with. "There is no doubt," he wrote Moran in August, 1872, "that your reputation is made. Still you must do much to nurse it. The more you get, the greater care. . . . The next picture you paint must be the Tetons. I have arranged for a small party to take you from Fort Hall up Snake River, thence to the Yellowstone, etc. . . . Put in your best strokes this summer so as to be ready for a big campaign next summer. . . ."[4]

But Hayden's plans were disrupted by an order from the Secretary of the Interior instructing him to make a survey of Colorado, where mining strikes and the beginnings of agriculture and the steady spread of settlement had made knowledge of the local resources necessary. Moran therefore did not visit the Tetons — he did not see them for some years, and never from the east side. Instead, he struck off on a tack of his own by accepting a commission to illustrate three articles in William Cullen Bryant's ornate picture-and-text report on the nation, to be called *Picturesque America*.[5]

As it turned out, the changed plans of Hayden and Moran permitted further association, for in May of 1873 Moran and his writer, W. H. Rideing, accompanied one of Hayden's parties from Estes Park southward, and out of that hasty trip came sketches for fourteen woodcuts illustrating "The Rocky Mountains." The standard landmarks are all there — Pikes Peak, Garden of the Gods, Estes Park, Long's Peak, and that Mountain of the Holy Cross whose cruciform snowbanks excited the awe of the seventies.[6] These are by no means the first pictures of the Rockies. The very earliest Western artist, Samuel Seymour, had painted them from the camps of the Long Expedition in 1820; R. H. Kern, John Mix Stanley, Baron von Egloffstein, and other official artists with exploring expeditions had been across them; and since the war Alfred Mathews, Theodore Davis, Joseph Becker, and other illustrators had added their bit.[7] Nevertheless Moran's pictures are important, and simply as pictures of authentic Rocky Mountain scenery they excel their predecessors. Their reproduction in *Picturesque America,* in Hayden's 1874 *Annual Report,* and later in the Santa Fe Railroad's tourist bait, *The Rocky Mountain Tourist,* made Moran something like an official interpreter of the Rockies as he already was of the Yellowstone.

In this same summer of 1873 he extended his authority to still other regions. Most of June he spent working his way westward along the Union Pacific; the second of his *Picturesque America* articles, "The Plains and the Sierras," has a heavy coverage of orthodox wonders sketched between the Laramie Plains and Ogden: the bluffs above Green River, Castle Rock and Monument Rock, Devil's Gate and Devil's Slide. He drew essentially what the porter still calls passengers to the window to see.

While Moran was sketching the Rockies and the Wyoming Plateau, Powell had been back and forth from Washington on the business of a special Commission to investigate conditions among the Southern Paiutes and other tribes. With George W. Ingalls, recently appointed Agent for the Southwestern Paiutes, he came to Salt Lake on May 6, 1873, for conferences with Indian delegations, and to examine charges of fraud and malfeasance in the Indian Service of the area. By the end of the conferences the scandal seemed important enough to be carried personally back to Washington. Powell carried it, and in July brought back instructions — and an expense account from the Bureau of Indian Affairs — directing him and Ingalls to inquire into the condition of all the Indians in the area, to make a census and prepare a report on conditions and needs. He would be on that business most of the fall, but his path crossed Moran's at Salt Lake City in July.

Whether Moran had planned to break his trip at Ogden or whether the encounter there with Major Powell changed his plans is not clear. Very probably he and Powell met accidentally. At any rate he did not go on directly from Ogden to the coast. Instead, Prof Thompson, running his topographical survey out from Kanab, got a telegram from Powell saying that Thomas Moran and another artist named Colburn wanted to accompany a party into the country around the Grand Canyon.[8] Colburn was not an artist, but the writer assigned to do the piece on the Colorado Canyons for *Picturesque America.* He and Moran arrived in Kanab on July 30, 1873, and were taken on two pack trips, one with Powell's photographer Jack Hillers to Mount Trumbull and one with Powell himself, when he came through on Indian business, onto the Kaibab. After starting them off on the Kaibab trip on August 14, Thompson's journal does not mention them again. To the methodical Thompson they were probably an interruption and a nuisance.

But to Powell, who could smell the possibilities of a situation and appraise men more quickly than his brother-in-law, Moran's arrival was a stroke of luck. The real benefits of the association did not lie in the six woodcuts which appeared the next year in *Picturesque America,* though those were pleasant enough. The real benefits, for Moran as for Powell, would come in the future. Though Moran's pictures would appear in Hayden's publications in 1874 and again in 1878, he was never part of Hayden's survey again. For the next seven years, insofar as he was an illustrator for the Western surveys at all, he was a Powell man, and he helped to illustrate four of the most important Powell Survey reports. Moran himself got from the Grand Canyon trip essentially the same thing that he had got from his Yellowstone trip two years before — sketches from which one of his most famous landscapes would later come. A companion piece to his "Grand Canyon of the Yellowstone," his "Grand Chasm of the Colorado" would draw the same eventual price from the Congress of the United States — $10,000 — and become a Washington fixture, a trophy brought back from the wild West to match the Crow lodges and the Sioux war bonnets and the titanotherium bones of the National Museum.

Both the Yellowstone and the Grand Canyon pictures emphasize what should not be forgotten, that Moran was anything but a realistic painter, despite his careful observation and his use of photographs to corroborate the evidence of his eyes. Realism was for him a means to an end, not an intention or a philosophy. An idealizer of landscape, he had learned from Turner how to blur as well as how to reproduce details. His temperament matched Captain Dutton's; he proceeded from facts but attempted to transcend them. An artist's business, he said, was "to produce for the spectator of his pictures the impression produced by nature on himself." [9] He said further, "I place no value upon literal transcripts from nature. My personal scope is not realistic; all my tendencies are toward idealization. . . . Topography in art is valueless. The motive or incentive for my Grand Canyon of the Yellowstone was the gorgeous display of color that impressed itself upon me . . . and while I desired to tell truly of nature, I did not wish to realize the scene literally but to preserve and convey its true impression. Every form introduced into the picture is within view from a given point, but the relation of the separate parts are not always preserved. For instance, the precipitous rocks on the right were really at my back when I stood at that point, yet in their present position they are strictly true to pictorial nature; and so correct is the whole representation that every member of the expedition with which I was connected declared that he knew the exact spot which had been reproduced. . . . The rocks in the foreground are so carefully drawn that a geologist could determine their precise nature. I treated them so in order to serve my purpose."[10]

In allowing himself to be cavalier with fact so long as he remained faithful to "pictorial nature," Moran left room for the heightening of the literal record. His illustrations for Powell's *Exploration of the Colorado River of the West,* done on Powell's personal commission and used first in *Scribner's,* are doubly tainted as exact history. They are not only redrawn and touched up from photographs, but the photographs themselves were taken on the second expedition, not on the first.

There have been literalists to object — such literalists as Julius Stone.[11] As illustration, few of Moran's pictures deserve the ridicule that Stone heaped upon them. Some — "The Start from Green River Station," "The Gate of Lodore," "Repairing Boats at Gunnison's Butte," and most notably "The Spanish Bayonet in Marble Canyon" — are superb. And if Moran even this late in his career sometimes darkened and narrowed his gorges for ominous effect, that effect was precisely in tune with the desperation of the expedition whose adventure he was illustrating. One of the pictures attacked by Stone as being utterly false to the facts is a nearly literal reproduction of one of Hillers' photographs, in which what is really a promontory is made by the camera angle to look like an island monument. The principal addition Moran made was to put a full moon behind it in a direction impossible in nature. That distortion does not seem a serious one. As for the more sensational *Scribner's* illustrations, including one of Powell dangling one-armed from Bradley's underwear, one called "Running a Rapid," and one in which the men flee the blazing campground in Lodore, none of those was by Moran, and Powell carried none of them over into the official *Report.* Considering that Powell's story was itself a combination of adventure yarn and scientific record, it is hard to see how illustration could have been more appropriately performed than by Moran's heightening of Hillers' literal photographs.

Reality was bound to be filtered through several media anyway, because even after the perfection of photographic techniques it was a long time before facsimile methods of reproduction brought the photograph unmodified before the reader of a magazine. The stereograph was a parlor standby in the eighteen-seventies, but magazine illustration was still by lithograph or wood engraving made from an artist's sketch, or a double transfer from photograph to drawing to woodcut. Even a good painter like Moran was at the mercy of the craftsmen who interpreted him on woodblock or stone.

At least until someone discovers the original drawings, it is fair to judge Moran's work for Powell primarily as documentary illustration. The twenty-nine woodcuts that decorate Powell's *Exploration* (1875), the three in *The Geology of the Black Hills of Dakota* (1880), and the nine in Dutton's *Tertiary History of the Grand Canyon District* (1882) draw far more often upon photographs than upon personal observation, and even the fine large painting, "The Transept" reproduced in the atlas to the *Tertiary History,* is based on a sketch by W. H. Holmes. In his long life, Moran found the Grand Canyon one of the two most satisfactory places to live and paint, but his significant painting of it from nature was done outside the Survey. His illustrations for Powell, craftsmanly as they are, have certain petrified mannerisms: his skies are almost always stormy, and he never outgrew the decorative meticulously drawn foreground. Picture after picture moves backward from some carefully realistic detail, too often the leaning snag of a tree, or has its distances accented by the conventional flying birds. Yet even in these secondhand pictures limited by the conventions of magazine art, and without the color that makes his finest landscapes striking, Moran has both grace and strength. He was an artist, a good one; and though the galleries may neglect him and the historians of art pass him with a polite or a condescending paragraph, and though his mountains may be a little overgrand, his canyons overawesome, his skies unnecessarily dramatic, his art is recognizably of this earth and this West.

Though Moran was much closer to Powell than to Hayden, and worked with him over a much longer time, he actually derived more help for his own career from Hayden than from the Major. The Yellowstone pictures which Hayden made possible brought him his first fame as a Western artist, and the publication in 1876 of fifteen chromolithographs of his Yellowstone water colors, with a text by Hayden, gave the art-book public and those curious about the West one of the most beautiful books ever to come out of the Western explorations.[12] No such gem came out of his work with the Powell Survey. Though Powell's group also produced, in Dutton's *Tertiary History* and its atlas, two of the most beautiful of western books, and certainly the most beautiful of the official publications, Moran's part in them was secondary. In the main, these two volumes were the happy climax to the artistic career of William Henry Holmes, a painter whose whole function was to make the literal transcriptions from nature that Moran avoided, and to glorify the topography that Moran thought valueless in art.

There is a false spring in the Washington year, according to Henry Adams, when "a delicate mist hangs over Arlington, and softens even the harsh white glare of the Capitol; the struggle of existence seems to abate; Lent throws its calm shadow over society; and youthful diplomats, unconscious of their danger, are lured into asking foolish girls to marry them; the blood thaws in the heart and flows out into the veins, like the rills of sparkling water that trickle from every lump of ice or snow, as though all the ice and snow on earth, and all the hardness of heart, all the heresy and schism, all the works of the devil, had yielded to the force of love and to the fresh warmth of innocent, lamb-like, confiding virtue. In such a world there should be no guile — but there is a great deal of it notwithstanding. Indeed, at no other season is there so much. This is the season when the two whited sepulchres at either end of the Avenue reek with the thick atmosphere of bargain and sale. The old is going; the new is coming. Wealth, office, power are at auction. Who bids highest: who hates with most venom? who intrigues with most skill? who has done the dirtiest, the meanest, the darkest, and the most, political work? He shall have his reward."[13]

That was the Washington that Major Powell, from the time of his first hesitant visit in 1867, had to deal with. He would have to deal with it through all his official life, and he would be scarred by the experience. But things were easier if you had no political favors to ask. Then Washington could seem like a kind of fairyland where all the trees were sugar plum (or pork) trees and the very offices were made of gingerbread. William Henry Holmes, with no notion in his head in coming to Washington in 1871 except to study art, never had to feel the dangers of the Avenue he trod. Like a dutiful tourist, he went one day to the Smithsonian; a man of sensibility, he was attracted by a gorgeous stuffed tropical bird at the entrance; an artist, he got out his pencil and sketched it. His sketch was noticed by a Costa Rican scientist who led him upstairs to see a new book on Central American birds, and there they ran into Professor F. B. Meek, Hayden's paleontologist friend, who hired Holmes on the spot to draw fossils. Somewhat later, Hayden saw his fossil drawings and asked him to go along on the 1872 expedition to the Yellowstone, taking the place vacated by Moran.[14] Thus in a few casual strokes Washington's growing scientific group, as closely knit as a university faculty and far more powerful, could divert art to the purposes of science and sketch the outlines of a career.

On that 1872 expedition Holmes made what must be the earliest drawings of the spectacular Teton range, as well as many of the Wind River Mountains and of the Yellowstone. He also, with characteristic intensity, took up the study of geology, and he continued that study in subsequent seasons after Hayden moved the Survey to Colorado in 1873. His drawing was itself a part of his geological studies, for from the beginning he showed something close to genius for reproducing the very textures and the characteristic fracture planes and erosional forms of rocks. Moran's rocks in his painting of the Yellowstone Canyon could be read by a geologist but were there for other reasons; in Holmes' drawings all the rocks are there to be read by geologists and topographers. He was making the sort of topographical sketches that Egloffstein had made for Ives and Beckwith as an aid to the mappers,[15] but where Egloffstein was either merely literal or markedly inaccurate, Holmes managed to be pictorial and often striking. He made panoramas in great numbers and with great speed. They have such a persuasive look of reality that stratification can be read as far away as the drawing can be seen, and anyone familiar with the country reproduced has an instant shock of recognition. By 1873 Hayden's *Annual Report* had begun to add praise for Holmes' drawings to the customary accolade for Jackson's photographs. By 1874 Hayden had made Holmes an assistant geologist, and by 1875, the year when

Powell's *Exploration* finally appeared, he was in charge of a division, exploring the little-known San Juan region in the southeastern corner of Powell's Plateau Province.

Since Holmes does not figure in the art histories or the galleries at all, he must be viewed entirely in the government publications for which he drew. His sketches are in all the Hayden Survey *Annual Reports* from 1872 to 1878, and in the first two volumes of Hayden's *Bulletin*.[16] There are sketches from life of the cliff dwellings in the San Juan country, supplementing the famous photographs that Jackson took on the 1874 trip when he discovered Mesa Verde. There are profiles and sketches of geological features in Colorado, Wyoming, Utah, and there are literally dozens of the spectacular panoramas at which Holmes excelled — great sweeps of the Front Range, the Wind Rivers, the Tetons, the Gallatin Range, La Sal and Abajo, the Sage Plain, Montezuma Canyon. With equal facility he caught the essential structure of both alpine mountains and the long horizontally bedded plateaus. Ruskin, who insisted on a landscapist's knowledge of the anatomy of the earth, would have found Holmes letter-perfect in this at least.

With the 1876 season the survey of Colorado was completed, and Hayden's parties drifted back toward northern Wyoming. By 1878, the last year of the Hayden Survey, Holmes was a full-fledged geologist, and it was his geological report on the Yellowstone that really summed up Hayden's work there. With the folder of unbound atlas sheets that accompanied this last of Hayden's reports are three marvelous Holmes panoramas, two of the Wind Rivers near the headwaters of the Green, and one of the Tetons from Gros Ventre Butte. They seem so actual that the eye instinctively searches out climbing routes on their slopes. Though they are as far as possible from that idealization of landscape practiced by Moran, and though they lie somewhere close to both photograph and diagram, and though their purpose is the most utilitarian sort of scientific illustration, as utilitarian as the drawing of fossils, yet it is impossible not to feel that somehow they manage also to be art.

Dr. Hayden's work was scattered and disorganized, and he claimed more credit than was due him, but he did make very great contributions during his twenty-five years in the West. Not the least of these, as he noted himself, was the collection of more than two thousand negatives that Jackson had amassed by 1875. Jackson's pictures had done much, Hayden said, "to secure truthfulness in the representation of mountain and other scenery," of which, "twenty years ago, hardly more than caricatures existed."[17] And what could be said about his photographer — or about Hillers of the Powell Survey and O'Sullivan of the King and Wheeler Surveys — could be said of Moran and even more positively of Holmes. It is true that his sketches did not have a popular sale as photographs did, and true that he did not appear in the magazines, the galleries, or the Philadelphia Centennial and the other expositions as Moran did. He was limited strictly by the circulation of the government reports in which he appeared. But in his way he clarified the West more than any of them. A Holmes panorama cuts through the haze, it is clear to the farthest distance as no photograph ever is. By almost imperceptible tricks of contrast it emphasizes lines of stratification and the profiles of erosional forms. More impressively than any Western artist, even Moran, he captured the plastic qualities of rock. Look at his sketches: the architecture of his sedimentaries is instantly recognizable, his granite could be nothing else, his lava is frozen motion.

When the consolidation of the Western surveys into the United States Geological Survey in 1879 left Holmes out of a job, he promptly turned back to the art studies that had been interrupted by the encounter with the tropical bird in the Smithsonian. During the winter of 1879–80 he hobnobbed in Europe's art capitals with Frank Duveneck and other American painters, but by the summer of 1880 he was wanted again for the sort of job he did better than anyone else. Dutton wanted him to draw the Grand Canyon, and with his usual promptness Clarence King appointed Holmes an assistant geologist with the United States Geological Survey and packed him off for Kanab on July 3, 1880.[18]

Holmes thus joined the Powell Survey after it had ceased to exist, for it, like Hayden's, Wheeler's, and King's, had been disbanded by the consolidation. The definitive work on the Grand Canyon that Powell might have done was being done by a collaborator, would be illustrated by a Hayden man, and would be published by a bureau with which Powell then had technically nothing to do, though he would become its head the next year. Nevertheless this book was the true culmination of the geological work Powell had begun in 1867, and it was pure good fortune that Holmes was available to illustrate it. There could have been no happier combination than Dutton and Holmes, a poetic and speculative geologist and an artist with geological training and a genius for the literal. As soon as he saw what Holmes was doing from the Kaibab rims, Dutton wrote in raptures to King.[19] He had every reason to.

Only three artists had been before Holmes into the canyon country. To the first, Baron von Egloffstein, artist and topographer with the Ives Expedition of 1857, Dutton attributed much of the common misconception of the canyon, for Egloffstein so exaggerated verticality and narrowness, and so restricted the range of view in his pictures, that "never was a great subject more artistically misrepresented or more charmingly belittled." [20] The second, John E. Weyss, was with Wheeler in 1871 and 1872, but his pictures were not reproduced until the publication of Wheeler's *Geographical Report* in 1889, and anyway his sketches represent not the Grand Canyon proper, but its environs: the Crossing of the Fathers, the mouth of the Paria, the Valley of the Virgin.[21] The third artist, Moran, had worked only briefly in the field up to this time, and had depended mainly upon Hillers' photographs. Holmes is thus, both for the extent of his coverage and the authenticity of his pictures, the most important early artist of the Grand Canyon. Though there are nine Moran woodcuts in the *Tertiary History* and one painting, "The Transept," in the atlas, and though the volumes also contain some of Hillers' photographs badly reproduced by Heliotype, Holmes is the real illustrator of Dutton's monograph.

It is his illustrations, woodcuts, photoengravings, and chromolithographs that make the *Tertiary History* the most beautiful book produced by any of the surveys. The nine panoramas that Holmes made for the atlas are even finer; they must represent the highest point to which geological or topographical illustration ever reached in this country. The folio size gives them breadth and space commensurate with their subject. Holmes' marvelous plastic sense gives them both form and perspective. The lithographing and printing are probably the best that even Julius Bien, for years the chief lithographer of maps and illustrations for all the surveys, ever turned out. To open the *Tertiary History* atlas to any of its double-page panoramas is to step to the edge of forty miles of outdoors. I can think of no pictures of the Grand Canyon, literal or idealized, which have so much of the canyon's own precision and stillness. Yet these are drawn to illustrate the recession of cliffs, the character of the Great Denudation, the lava dykes in the walls, the architecture of buttes and amphitheaters.

For Holmes, though he was never properly a part of the Powell Survey, the Survey did something that Hayden had never done. It gave him scenery worthy of his highest powers, and reproduction on a scale and of a quality unrivaled even in the lavish government publications, which were uniformly ahead of most commercial books of the eighteen-eighties. This was Holmes' real triumph as artistic geologist and geological artist. He did many fine sketches and panoramas for Gilbert's *Lake Bonneville,* but publication was long delayed, and before it came Holmes was deep in another interest, archaeology, drifting away from the making of pictures and toward administration and museum work. Never again would he sketch such superb views as he had sketched from the rims of the canyon, from the desert below the Vermilion Cliffs at Short Creek, from the Kaibab overlooking the barren Marble Canyon Platform, from Vulcan's Throne at the mouth of the Toroweap.

From the end of 1880 on, Holmes devoted himself to editing the final publications of the Hayden Survey, overseeing all illustration for the Geological Survey publications, studying primitive art in the Smithsonian and in the field. He left Washington to become head curator of Chicago's Field Museum, returned to take a similar post at the National Museum in Washington, left that to succeed Powell as head of the Bureau of Ethnology in 1902, and left that to direct the new National Gallery. Energetic, austere, a little forbidding, he was a sound representative of that multi-purpose American type which the times seemed to turn out in great numbers, the type to which Powell, Dutton, King, Pumpelly, Coues, Ward, Nathaniel Shaler, and even F. V. Hayden belonged. All his life he managed in some way to combine science and art, but the art was gradually pushed backward and away from his primary interests. The minutiae of science that would have maddened most artists never bothered him at all. Joseph Pennell, one of Holmes' Washington acquaintances and himself a great illustrator, threw up his hands over him. Once, Pennell says, in trying for a job on the Survey, "I was given a sort of profile map which Holmes had made in pencil and told to copy it in ink. Holmes said he had made it with the thermometer away below zero, thawing the lead pencil, or himself, over a fire between his legs as he drew. I felt like telling him, as I used to be told, 'there is no merit in that.' . . . I took the map and improved it, and I did not get on the Survey. But how Holmes, who could make the most stunning direct watercolors, should have preferred this sort of drudgery was beyond me mentally as well as artistically." [22]

Possibly it was the geologist in Holmes who liked that sort of drudgery. Possibly it was some stubborn disinclination to "improve" nature that kept him a scientific artist, a glorified illustrator. But at least once, when there was no cause for improving on nature because nature was superlative, once when pure geology was art, he made such pictures as no one has made since, and contributed to the clarification of the Plateau Province something in the line of Powell's own ambition: art without falsification.

10. Names

ON THE FACE of the Plateau Province, as the region slowly emerged into definition, certain people had left names,[1] and others later had kept or altered them as whim, misunderstanding, and mispronunciation directed. Some of the names were as old as the tribes the white men encountered there, Paiute and Hopi and Navajo. Some were echoes of the florid piety of the Spaniards who made the *entradas* in search of souls or gold, or the New Mexicans who drove mules to California from Santa Fe and Taos. Thus there was in the heart of the plateau country a Virgin River, and on it a town La Verkin whose name the inhabitants themselves did not understand,[2] and there were the La Sal and Abajo Mountains, and the great river named for its red muddy water the Colorado, and El Vado de los Padres and the San Rafael, and names like Escalante and Spanish Fork that later men gave in memory of the Spaniards' passing.

Covering these was another layer, itself half effaced because never written down on maps, but sometimes persistent in the plateaus and even more in the beaver-heaven Uintas and Wasatch. The Seedskeedee-agie of the fur brigades had become the Green,[3] and Jedediah Smith's attempt to call the Virgin the Adams River had not succeeded, but Black's Fork and Ham's Fork and the Duchesne, Ashley Creek and Brown's Hole, the Provo and the Ogden and the Malad, recalled that time.

And on top of those was still another layer, complicated by the fact that the Mormons who gave these labels were both frontier farmers and zealots. In the nomenclature of Mormondom, Pleasant Valley and Richfield and Bountiful alternate with St. Joseph, St. Thomas, and St. George, who are no saints in the Catholic calendar but pioneer leaders of colonies, Latter-day Saints. The great men of Zion are on the map in Brigham City and Heber City and Knightsville, and between and among these are scattered those dense but hollow names, smooth outside with use, packed with associations like internal crystals, that come from the Bible or the Book of Mormon — names that are like Lehi and Manti and Hebron, Nephi and Moroni and Moab.

These are not all. Every exploration that traversed this country left names behind it, either those it gave or those given later in its memory. Frémont's name rests on a peak in the Wind Rivers, an island in Great Salt Lake, a town in Wayne County, Utah, a river heading in the Fish Lake Plateau. Lieutenant Gunnison has been given a river in western Colorado, a butte near where he crossed the Green, and a town in the Sevier Valley close to where he and seven of his party died at the hands of the Páhvant Utes. Stansbury, Simpson, Ives, Beckwith, Berthoud, are all there, either in the Plateau Province or on its borders. The highest peak in the Uintas and in Utah bears Clarence King's name. On other Uinta peaks are the names of Marsh, Emmons, and Hayden. All the survey parties down to the most recent have found something upon which they could confer the precision of named identity. Major Powell, because he was the first into many parts of the province and because he or his men worked in it for two decades, left more names than any but the Mormon settlers. Not only the map itself but dozens of its labels are his or his parties' doing.

His own name he did not give to anything — few explorers are that bald — but others did it for him: to a peak in the Colorado Rockies, to a national forest, to a whistle stop on the Santa Fe east of Needles, to the valley near Meeker where he wintered in 1868–69, to an island plateau in the Grand Canyon. But if he refused to aggrandize himself, Powell showed just as little inclination to pay off obligations by naming. Of all the names he suggested, only three honor people in any way his patrons. These are Mounts Trumbull and Logan on the Uinkaret, named for two Illinois senators, and the Henry Mountains, named for Professor Henry of the Smithsonian. It does not seem to have been Powell who made the mistake of naming two peaks on the Tushar, near Beaver, Utah, Mount Belknap and Mount Delano after two of Grant's most venal cabinet members. More likely it was Thompson or Dutton, neither of whom could have had any axe to grind. Powell named Gunnison Butte after his exploring predecessor, and someone, probably Gilbert or Dutton, honored Hilgard of the Naval Observatory with a peak between the Fish Lake and Wasatch Plateaus. Another nearby was named for Archibald Marvine, early dead, who had been Gilbert's geological companion on the Wheeler Survey.

Powell also took pains to honor his immediate associates and assistants. Every member of the Powell Survey except Walter Graves and Walter Powell seems to have been immortalized in some topographical feature of the High Plateaus or the Grand Canyon. Originally Powell named Navajo Mountain for the Howlands, but the name did not stick; the Howlands and Dunn are both commemorated instead in buttes in the Grand Canyon. Billy Hawkins gets both a butte in the Grand Canyon and a peak at the head of Beaver Dam Creek, west of St. George. Clem Powell, Andy Hattan, and Jack Hillers all have buttes, and Hillers in addition has his name attached to one of the peaks in the Henrys. Frank Bishop got a creek in the Uintas. Points in the Kaibab division of the Grand Canyon were named for Bradley, Jones, Sumner, Willie Johnson, Dutton, and Thompson. Dutton's name also rests on a Kaibab spring and a side canyon, as well as a peak on the Paunságunt Plateau. Thomas Moran got Moran Point, a mere tidbit beside the noble peak in the Tetons named for him earlier by Hayden. James Pilling, Powell's secretary, has a cascade in Kanab Canyon and "Uncle Jim Point" in the Grand Canyon. The two Powell Survey women remain on the map too, Emma Powell as Mount Emma on the Uinkaret and Nellie Thompson as Mount Ellen in the Henrys. Even Professor Harvey DeMotte of Illinois Wesleyan, who worked in the area only part of the summer of 1872, left his name on DeMotte Park in the Kaibab. Gilbert named the smallest of the Henry Mountains for Holmes, who had earlier acquired a peak in the Gallatin range in Montana. Gilbert seems not to be represented in the plateau country proper, but he appears on a mountain in the Uintas. And the Smithsonian Institution, whose support was indispensable to Powell for many years, received its thanks when Dutton called a peculiarly perfect cameo outlier of the Vermilion Cliffs Smithsonian Butte.

Illinois saved the Union during the war, it is said, by producing Lincoln and Grant. It dominated the Union for some years after the war, partly because Grant had a habit of appointing cronies and relatives to high places. One of the more ironic minor evidences of Illinois dominance in those years is the cluster of Illinois names that the Powell Survey fixed irremovably to the map of Utah, a state inhabited by Mormons whom the citizens of Illinois had in 1846 driven brutally into the wilderness.

Men, big or little, Illini or otherwise, provided only one of many sources of map names. Most of the modes and fashions of naming discussed by George R. Stewart in his admirable *Names on the Land* are present. Powell's own taste ran strongly to the descriptive. All down the length of the river from Green River to the Virgin he applied names to the reaches of the canyon and to notable features of the topography. The second expedition named a good many things that the first had missed, and altered some that the first had given (Craggy Canyon became Split Mountain Canyon, Coal Canyon became Gray Canyon) but the character of the naming remained consistent. Flaming Gorge, Horseshoe Canyon, Island Park, Desolation Canyon, Cataract Canyon, Lava Falls, and many more of Powell's names are purely descriptive. So, but with a special twist, are names such as Dirty Devil and Bright Angel, the first given on the spur of the moment from a remark of one of the men, the other contrived later to make a contrast.

All the names that Powell gave to major canyons on Green and Colorado have stuck. He named Marble Canyon from the polished limestone of its walls, and he restored to the Grand Canyon its enduring name, turning away from Ives' choice of "Big Canyon." Occasionally, as at Ashley Falls, where he found Ashley's name painted on a rock, and at Gunnison's Butte, where he recognized historical tracks, he named something for a predecessor. Sometimes, as at Disaster Falls, he commemorated an event. Once, and that at the suggestion of Andy Hall, he gave a name for a literary allusion — the name "Lodore" that so disgusted Jack Sumner as un-American. Once also, deferring to Steward, he bowed to the diabolism common in our placenames, and called a nasty stretch of the Green "Hell's Half Mile."

In his way, Powell was one of our better namers. He had a flair for the picturesque, and his descriptive terms are sometimes extremely apt, as in Split Mountain Canyon, Flaming Gorge, and the Vermilion Cliffs. He did not plaster politicians across the map, he had no weakness for the cute. Some notion of propriety preserved him from extravagance except in the happy contrast of Dirty Devil and Bright Angel. One gathers that he expected the names he put down to last, unlike Gilbert, whose preface to the *Henry Mountains* facetiously apologizes to Howell, Steward, Newberry, Marvine, Peale, Holmes, Geikie, Jukes, Scrope, and Dana for putting their names on insignificant details. The affront will never, he says, "be repeated by the future denizens of the region. The herders who build their hut at the base of the Newberry Arch are sure to call it 'the Cedar Knoll'; the Jukes Butte will be dubbed 'Pilot Knob,' and the Scrope, 'Rocky Point.' "[4] Gilbert was not entirely wrong. Even the beautifully named Aquarius Plateau is known locally as Boulder Mountain, the Tushar is called Beaver Mountain, and the Páhvant Sigurd Mountain.

Usage is freakish. Sometimes local names last, sometimes those of the explorer and surveyor, sometimes both. Powell's have shown a strong tendency to survive, and so, though they have been subjected to acid debate, have Dutton's.[5]

Down the vast 217-mile avenue of the Grand Canyon, that "mountain-range-in-a-ditch" any of whose subordinate buttes is larger than the mass of any mountain east of the Rockies, Dutton left a legacy of names. The honoring of Survey members took care of a good many features, and the descriptive habit which has dotted our western parks with Inspiration Points took care of some more. The tourist who slakes his thirst at Hidden Spring, or walks out for the view to Cape Royal, Cape Final, or Point Sublime, is orienting himself by names that Dutton put there. But the major features of the canyon, the great amphitheaters and side gorges and buttes, demanded something extra.

He might have used Indian names. But there were no existing Indian names for many of the things needing labels, and Dutton disliked Indian names anyway. He appears never to have learned Paiute, and he did not yield to the arguments of Fred Dellenbaugh that he make the Indians his source.[6] The map shows plenty of Indian names, and has since the very first sheets that Thompson produced — Shinumo, Kwagunt, Kaibab, Paria, Kanab, Uinkaret, Shivwits — but these were adopted earlier by the Mormons or by Powell. Dutton turned away from adding more, and began the series of oriental and architectural names that since the eighties have persisted and even spread.

The fixed binoculars at the lookout points will, for a dime, bring you close up to the Hindoo Amphitheater, the Ottoman Amphitheater, Vishnu's Temple, Shiva's Temple, the Temples of Isis and Osiris, the Transept, the Cloisters. They will show you the Tower of Set, named by Moran on Dutton's example, and Vulcan's Throne down on the Toroweap, and Wotan's Throne and Krishna Shrine and Rama Shrine. Besides the ones given in Dutton's time there is a host of Apollo Temples, Venus Temples, Jupiter Temples — and fading badly as inspiration strains itself, King Arthur Castle and Guenevere Castle and Holy Grail Temple. Dutton named East Temple and West Temple in Zion, where a religious flavor was inevitable both because of the architecture of the canyon and because of the character of the Mormon settlers. The religious and architectural parallel was compulsive in the Grand Canyon too, for the similarity of the buttes to pagodas with widening eaves, to temples "every inch carved," to the angular, massive, intricately decorated buildings of Asia is extraordinarily impressive. Perhaps the true objection is not to the original series, which was discriminating, but to later elaborations, which have spread the contagion over Bryce, Zion, Cedar

Breaks, and the rest of the canyon country. Yet the architectural names are all but inevitable; every explorer was compelled to them; every part of the Plateau Province bears them. Even the pioneers feeling their way down the Waterpocket Fold looked at the domes of white sandstone crowning the red cliffs and they named one red butte Cathedral Rock and the ridge itself the Capitol Reef from its resemblance to the dome of the Capitol in Washington.

Look at Vishnu's Temple. If you don't call it something like Vishnu's Temple what would you call it? Kwagunt Peak? Ivanpah Butte? The Indians had no architecture to match the imaginativeness of their religion or the majesty of these forms. Thunder Hogan would hardly do. You might take some elaborate descriptive phrase such as the Utes used for the country around the junction of Grand and Green, and try to cram "Tooḿ-pin-wu-near̍-tu-weap̍" on your map. Or you might seize upon some translation and call your butte "Standing Rock." But you would not have helped yourself much. Ute and Paiute do not strike us as especially euphonious tongues. Paiute mythical heroes are called Só-kus Waí-un-nats, or something worse; their chiefs labor under names like Chuarruumpeak or Naraguts; some native placenames are said to be too obscene for translation onto any polite map.[7]

Perhaps Dutton did as well as another might have. Bizarre topography may justify exotic or even eccentric names. The "temple" habit that spread to Bryce repeats the Isis and Osiris motif, and Bryce throws in to boot a Wall Street, a Silent City, a Cathedral. In places it goes cute, as in Peekaboo Canyon. But what should one do for names in a geological funhouse? In the Grand Canyon, at least, Dutton's names are like his superlatives of description — admissible because they cannot be avoided.

Later surveys of the river have had less unnamed country to work with and less imagination to turn loose. Since 1923 the fashion has been strictly practical. As plans for reclamation dams have crept down the canyons, surveyors' instead of explorers' language has come with them. Now on the detailed maps you will find every previously unnamed gulch and wash labeled for its distance from the head of the survey, which for the Grand Canyon division was Lee's Ferry.

Now they are Six Mile Wash and One Hundred and Thirty Mile

Canyon and Two Hundred Mile Rapid. At their very worst, Powell and Dutton did not name by transit or plane table or chain. Bright Angel Creek and Sockdolager Rapid, or for that matter Shiva's Temple and the Ottoman Amphitheater, seem livelier than Hundred and Ten Mile Point or 38° 40′ Spring.

11. The Lunatic Fringe: Samuel Adams Again

THIS WAS THE continuing job of the Powell Survey — the careful accumulation of fact on many scientific fronts and the interpretation of fact without inordinate subjective distortion. As geography, geology, paleontology, ethnology, drainage, climate, resources of soil and water and timber and minerals, the Plateau Province emerged into the area of knowledge. Of the four Western surveys of the seventies, that of Powell was the most intensive. Hayden and Wheeler wandered hectically all over the West, with results that showed their haste and their lack of system. King, as systematic as Powell, had chosen to survey a hundred-mile cross section along the route of the Pacific Railroad from the Rockies to the Sierra, with reference principally to its mineralogy. Powell devoted himself to a region and attempted to bring it cleanly into focus through a multiple study of its large problems.

Out of the studies of Powell and his collaborators came records: reports, photographs, sketches, geological sections, and the maps that were as essential to geology, Powell said, as a house was to housekeeping. Because the ideal of thoroughness made publication slow, not all the results of the Survey were immediately available, but through the seventies a growing body of accurate and careful information on Powell's chosen region began to appear. Contained in these maps and reports and in the field notes of the survey parties were not only geological, ethnological, and hydrographic data and the generalizations derivable from them, but the foreshadowings of larger generalizations that would eventually mature as broad proposals of policy. Something like organizing genius went into the

Powell Survey. The apparent excitability and tendency to run in many directions at once which so irritated Thompson began to show itself for what it really was: a masterful capacity to keep many knowledges in mind, to group and retain facts by clusters and yet make them all contribute to a larger and more comprehensive whole. It was as if he forced every scrap of knowledge acquired in years of study by himself and his collaborators to contribute ultimately to a purpose so clear that it looks — though it apparently was not — foreseen.

As we shall see, Powell did not impose his view of the West, either his facts or his deductions or his policies, upon a glad and unresisting nation. The powers of darkness ultimately descended on him like disturbed yellow jackets. Those who resisted facts did not give ground without loud cries and protestations. Take their maddest representative, Captain Sam Adams. Powell was hardly on his way home after the successful traverse of the canyons before Adams was belittling his exploit in the press. Within two months he had hurried to submit a long report of his own activities to Secretary of War Belknap (who had not asked for it), listing the resources of the Colorado basin, which in Adams' version, as in William Gilpin's, sounded dimly and wonderfully like a combination of Canaan and Ophir. The report included Adams' diary of the harebrained plunge down the Blue and Grand, carefully edited and rewritten and with distances, altitudes, and other invented data filled in to make it scientifically accurate. Belknap turned the document over to General Humphreys, Chief of the Corps of Engineers, who found that though "useful to the public," Adams' information could not be of material value to the War Department, and hence should not be rewarded.[1]

A rebuff from the War Department stopped Adams no more than logic or reason had ever stopped him. Within four months he had persuaded Representative George W. Julian to introduce a House resolution granting $20,000 for his services in exploring and opening the Colorado.[2]

The course of Adams' various moves for governmental compensation through the houses of Congress is like the course of his boats down the Blue — a succession of rapids and upsets and undaunted renewals. Julian's resolution was lost in committee for two years, but shortly after Powell had returned to Washington in February,

1872, from Kanab, where he had left Thompson triangulating the area north of the Grand Canyon, he received a letter from Representative R. M. McCormick of Arizona, asking his opinion of Adams' claims. Somehow the indomitable Captain had blown the breath of life into them again, and got the question reopened before the Committee on Claims. General Humphreys was also questioned again, and replied as before that he did not favor compensation. Powell wrote a letter to McCormick itemizing his contacts with Adams. That letter, documented and incontrovertible, should have sent Adams in splinters to the Gulf.[3] But Adams did not splinter readily. He was more like a bag of wind, and now, like a windbag held under water, he kept popping resistantly to the surface. Between 1870 and 1877 his case appears in an even half dozen Senate and House documents, and for a time it even seemed as if his efforts to "bring the true facts to the country" — and be compensated therefore — would be successful. On May 20, 1876, seven years after he had stormed off from Green River to take his "authorization" to the more pliable citizens of Breckenridge, and four years after Powell had completely discredited him, the House Committee on Claims recommended that Captain Adams be given $3750 in compensation.[4]

But circumstances were unkind to Adams — as he wrote to Austin Blair of the Claims Committee in 1873, even ten copies of the Sunday *Herald* containing his last communication on the Colorado had been stolen from him. "It appears as if there was to be no end to the efforts to keep the facts from the country." Apparently there was not. Now the Claims Committee's recommendation was not accepted; on January 11, 1878, Senator Cockrell of Missouri submitted a report for the Senate Committee on Claims denying Adams compensation on the ground that whatever services he might have rendered had been unauthorized.

That about cooked Adams' goose. He ebbed away from Washington muttering about "as revolting a system of ingratitude and injustice as has ever been conceived and carried out by corrupt officials, who have singled me out as their marked victim." Eventually he settled in his home town of Beaver, Pennsylvania, and went back to the practice of law. When he died at Beaver Falls in 1915 at the age of eighty-seven he was the oldest member of the Pennsylvania bar, and probably the craziest. But he went to his grave protesting and perhaps believing the tale of his wrongs and the fantasy of his discoveries in the West, and his obituary in the Beaver *Evening Tribune* indicates that to the end he found some who would believe him:

> ". . . he spent a number of years exploring the Colorado River, being sent unofficially by Secretary Stanton, who died before Mr. Adams returned, and his claim from the government was never adjusted.
>
> For a short time he was employed by one of the Government Departments in Washington, resigning to stump the County for Horace Greeley in 1872 [go west, young man, by the Colorado water-level route]. He then engaged in the coal business in Somerset County, Pa., and later devoted much time to the invention and perfection of the Portable Oil Driller, but owing to encroachment upon his patents he failed to reap any reward from his efforts." [5]

Poor Sam Adams was doomed never to reap the rewards, whether for patents or exploration. He was a preposterous, twelve-gauge, hundred-proof, kiln-dried, officially notarized fool, or else he was one of the most wildly incompetent scoundrels who ever lived. But fool or scoundrel, he was a symptom. In his resistance to fact and logic he had many allies who were neither so foolish in their folly nor so witless in their rascality as he, but whose justification and platform was the same incorrigible insistence upon a West that did not exist.

In 1878, just about the time when Adams was turned off by Congress for the last time, Major Powell was just coming to grips with the forces of Gilpin, in and out of Congress. But before we examine the proposals he made and the struggle that grew out of them, there is a year of uncertainty to look at, a year during which Powell and his survey could easily have lost the struggle to survive.

III

BLUEPRINT FOR A DRYLAND DEMOCRACY

1. 1877: The Problem of Survival

AT THE BEGINNING of 1877 the Geographical and Geological Survey of the Rocky Mountain Region, J. W. Powell in Charge, was the least of the official surveys operating in the West. It had not been recognized and accorded an appropriation until King and Hayden were well established and Lieutenant Wheeler had made his first field trip. Its annual appropriation had ranged from $10,000 to $45,000, less than any of the others had enjoyed. Its published results looked meager beside King's solid series, now about half completed, and the grab-bag releases, amounting to a general scientific magazine, by which Hayden had gained credit not only for his own work but for some done independently. The area triangulated by Powell's topographers was small by contrast with the sweeping coverage of Wheeler's reconnoissance.[1] In January, 1877, the Powell Survey could produce as evidence of its worth only Powell's own reports on *The Exploration of the Colorado River of the West* and *The Geology of the Eastern Portion of the Uinta Mountains,* the latter with an atlas, plus three brief progress reports and some magazine articles and photographs produced for private profit. It was not enough to impress a Congress interested in practical results useful to mining corporations, land speculators, and settlers[2] — particularly since Powell's chosen region showed neither mineral nor agricultural potentialities. The reports then in preparation, Gilbert's *Henry Mountains,* Dutton's *High Plateaus,* and two volumes of *Contributions to North American Ethnology,* had the impractical sound of pure science, and though Powell had projected for himself a study of the history, resources, and uses of the Public Domain, that study was hardly begun. Outside the Uinta atlas and a map and diagram accompanying the *Exploration,* the Survey had published no maps.

Moreover, the Congress that convened in January that year had its eye on the inauguration of a new President, Rutherford B. Hayes, in March. At least until the politicians had tried out the new ground, this Congress would be reform-minded. It had two full Grant terms, a chain-reaction of scandals, and the splitting of the Republican Party for warnings. It had investigated the Western surveys without clear result in 1874,[3] haling Wheeler, Hayden, and Powell before its committees and airing all the private jealousies and public rivalries of the War and Interior Departments. The rivals were certain to come under scrutiny again. If Congress did not itself raise the question of consolidation and reform, Hayden or Wheeler would, for both were ambitious and had powerful friends, and Hayden in particular was beginning to have his withers galled by competition.[4]

During the hearings back in 1874, Powell had alienated Wheeler by advocating consolidation of all the surveys under control of the Department of the Interior, but his temporary alliance with Hayden on that issue broke down the moment Hayden began to view him as a dangerous rival for appropriations, publicity, or the directorship of the combined surveys. King was not a true party to the rivalry: he had completed his field work along the 40th parallel and was still in business only to finish and publish his series of reports. Though an employee of the War Department, he was personally friendly to Powell and to Powell's ideas. But from either Wheeler or Hayden, Powell could expect only the knife.

It was in the interest of simple survival that he spent much of 1877 mending his fences, trying to insure the continuation of his own survey, balk the ambitions of Hayden and Wheeler, and at the same time bring some system into the chaos of the geological and geographical surveys. This last, since he had no power to reorganize and could work only by influencing members of Congress, was only a hope, but it was not a dim one. He had a powerful organizing mind. It hurt him, quite apart from his own survival, to see dissension, duplication, and waste in an area where there was important work to be done. When Hayden's field parties clashed with Wheeler's in the Colorado mountains and precipitated a disgraceful squabble about priorities, all the surveys suffered. Such influence as Powell had, and such experience and information and persuasiveness as he could bring to bear, he would use in the direction of unification. Whoever ran them, and under whatever jurisdiction, the surveys had to be raised out of their year-by-year, hand-to-mouth, unco-ordinated and competitive state, and brought into some sort of permanent system.

The wider and less personal interest in the future of government science led him to expand a simple struggle for survival into something much larger. Events and the development of his own ideas pushed him that way, and so did his contempt for Hayden, his passion for order, his knowledge and experience of the West and his swiftly clarifying vision of what the West must do to grow into a strong part of the American commonwealth. What perhaps began as mere opportunistic tactics shortly became grand strategy.

The general engagement to which he finally forced the reform party and the Western Congressmen adamant against change or planning resulted eventually in a stalemate, or at best in the most limited sort of victory, but the way in which he fought it showed Major Powell already cunning and effective in behind-the-scenes political maneuver, and with a very clear idea of his objectives. As Henry Nash Smith has remarked,[5] his activities during 1878 and 1879 indicated a voluntary acceptance of public responsibility rare in public life at any time. In the Gilded Age it was close to unprecedented.

He was David against Goliath, Beowulf against Grendel's dam. He challenged odds and he met the enemy on his own ground. Behind him was none of the automatic support that many of his contemporaries, including some of his opposition, could count on. He was not wealthy and well placed like O. C. Marsh, socially prominent and much-befriended like Clarence King. He had not Hayden's well-developed lobby and no long-term friends in high places, and he could count on the backing of no university. From the only university with which he had had important contacts — and that a one-horse college in the West — he had departed abruptly in 1873, looked upon as one grown too big for his breeches.[6] What he had to fight with was what he had always had: his clarity of understanding and his personal vigor, plus the general support of disinterested scientific men. He could also depend upon a few interested ones, especially the personal enemies of F. V. Hayden. His campaign of 1877 and 1878 he ran as he had run the Colorado, by a combination of foresight, planning, and calculated risk.

First things first. Feeling the cold breath on his neck when Congress convened in January, 1877, Powell wrote a good many letters, including notes to King, Julius Bien, John Strong Newberry of Columbia, and F. W. Putnam of Harvard,[7] begging help in getting his appropriation for the continuation of the Powell Survey the next year. The tone of these notes is perturbed, almost desperate. The day after he dictated them to his secretary, James Pilling, he hurried into the hands of Eugene Hale of the House Appropriations Committee a summary of the work and publications of the Powell Survey, and he also sent Hale as a gift a set of Jack Hillers' Grand Canyon photographs and some proof sheets from Gilbert's coming monograph on the Henry Mountains. At the same time, for reasons not exactly opaque, he requested a personal interview.

Whatever the effect of his conversations with Hale, his letters brought results. Newberry, formerly one of Hayden's collaborators but now his bitter enemy, wrote as Powell requested to Representatives Garfield and Hewitt, champions of the liberal wing in the House, and he not only praised the scientific work of Powell and Gilbert but he went out of his way to denounce Hayden as a power-mad lobbyist no longer worthy the name of scientist.[8] Putnam and others of the scientific fraternity gave Powell, in less vehement terms, the letters of character he needed.

Their help was enough, just enough. The weight of presumably disinterested Science applied to interested Politics got the Powell Survey continued life, but on minimum terms. Congress dropped the appropriation for 1877–78 from $45,000 to $30,000, a reduction that hurt at a time when Powell was hoping to strengthen himself for the eventual showdown with the other surveys. As a matter of fact, he had already incautiously committed himself to things that would cost money. Dutton, Gilbert, and Thompson were all, in addition to topographical and geological work, gathering data on water and irrigable lands in Utah for the use of the General Land Office and Powell's projected report on the Public Domain. The Dutton and Gilbert monographs, as well as the two volumes of *Contributions to North American Ethnology,* were all partly completed, and their publication, an expensive matter if one were to compete with Hayden's lavish reports full of illustrations and plates,[9] was essential as a lever under Congress. A map of Utah containing the hydrographic data his parties had gathered languished for lack of funds to print it. And now early in 1877 came a golden opportunity to acquire some easy credit and win the approval of most scientific men if he could only find the money to take advantage of it.

As a consequence of the gold strikes in the Black Hills in 1874, Congress had authorized still a fifth Western survey, under the direction of W. P. Jenney and Henry Newton. The resulting report had been practically finished but never published, and there was now no apparent intention on the part of Congress to appropriate funds for it. The strong suspicion on Science Street was that Hayden's jealousy of intrusion upon a territory he considered his own had led him to block the printing of the report. Newton, as it happened, was a student and protégé of John Strong Newberry. And Newberry was convinced that Hayden blocked the report because he feared the exposure of his own geological incompetence.

Newberry had been a stout ally in the matter of the appropriation. On March 17, 1877, again at Powell's request, he wrote Secretary of the Interior Carl Schurz asking that the Black Hills report be authorized as a publication of the Powell Survey. On that same day he put in a requisition for a chunk of Powell's budget to finance a fossil-hunting trip to Colorado,[10] but money at that time was more than Powell could grant, even when the *quid pro quo* within the austere walls of Science had been satisfactory. To gratify Newberry then would have ruined him. Fortunately, Newberry was good-natured, and could wait.

Meantime, Powell was moving much faster than Schurz. The Secretary had hardly had time to receive Newberry's letter before the Major had calculated his risks and plunged. He arranged to pay half of Newton's expenses for a trip back to the Black Hills to clean up doubtful points, and without authority to do so he guaranteed publication of the report. If deficiency appropriations could be had later, Newton would also be compensated for his time. Even while scientific gentlemen under the nudging of Powell or Newberry were bombarding Schurz with letters urging publication of the Newton-Jenney monograph, the arrangements had all been made. It was the end of May before Schurz got around to approving the deal, which by that time he could have repudiated only at the expense of a squabble with the Major.[11]

Immediately there were additional drains on the Powell Survey purse, first an engraving bill for the Newton book for $1840, and next a proposal that Professor R. P. Whitfield, who was to analyze the Black Hills fossils, be permitted to publish a preliminary pamphlet establishing his priority in the matter of new species. New species were the breath of life to paleontologists. Othniel C. Marsh and Edward Cope, the two great rivals in vertebrate paleontology, controlled their own avenues of publication and were sometimes in print with preliminary descriptions within a few weeks of the time the bones came out of the ground. Whitfield's request had to be granted, though it strained the already overstrained budget. With the engraver Powell arranged time payments; the office correspondence for that year is loaded with importunities for money from tradesmen and instrument makers and lithographers and engravers, and equally loaded with Pilling's inspired replies stalling them off.

Henry Newton died of typhoid in the Black Hills before the money for his book had even been transferred to the Powell Survey account. By that time the Major was after Schurz for funds for other purposes: $600 of General Land Office funds to print the map of Utah, $4000 for office furniture and rent, hitherto not supplied by law for his bureau. That whole summer saw him trying to get his entire program through with only two thirds as much money as he had hoped for.

And he did not get through the summer without running afoul of Hayden, who had eyes and ears working for him throughout official Washington[12] and who could not have helped comprehending to the full the meaning of Powell's adoption of the Newton report. The two had words in Schurz's office on May 19, and the words on Hayden's part were mainly about duplication, undercutting, and waste. The argument brought, three days later, a careful letter from Powell to Schurz, a long, scrupulous, and almost weary letter. Powell gave Hayden credit for great contributions (more than he actually believed he had made) and suggested a division of labor within the two Interior Department surveys.[13] Let Hayden have the whole field of natural history, for which he had built up an elaborate organization, and leave to Powell the whole field of ethnography, in which he was already collaborating with the Smithsonian. The yeast of this letter worked in the fermenting pot until November, 1877, when the Department approved it in principle and Hayden concurred, with the difference that he wanted all the geology and geography as well as the natural history, leaving Powell only his Indians.[14]

Thus the season of 1877, a lean year moving toward an uncertain future, and with a hectic pressure perceptible in its field work and its office work and its rushing of publications to catch up with the wordier surveys and impress skeptical lawmakers. Despite his amputated appropriation, Powell managed to finish the season much stronger than he had started it. The field parties in Utah had made great headway both in topography and hydrography. Volunteer and part-time ethnologists in every part of the West and South were busy on a hundred Indian languages in preparation for the general study of the Indian tongues that Powell planned. Gilbert's *Henry Mountains* was out, a solid and original contribution certain to reflect great credit on the Survey in scientific if not in political circles. Whitfield's preliminary bulletin on the Black Hills fossils was out. Volumes I and III of *Contributions to North American Ethnology, The Tribes of the Extreme Northwest* and *The Tribes of California*, were out, tying the Powell Survey more closely than ever into the Smithsonian, with which its relations had always been close. Working closely with Professor Henry, Powell had well under way for the use of his workers among the tribes a *Manual of North American Ethnography* to replace the outgrown ones of Schoolcraft and Gallatin.[15] And he had much additional data for his study of the Public Domain.

More important than these, and including them all, was the broad plan for future action that was coming into focus, growing in clarity, precision, and urgency. Early in November, 1877, Powell requested that the War Department transfer Captain Dutton from the Department of the Platte for detached winter duty in Washington. Dutton came as a mounted officer, thereby getting a little extra pay for the expenses of his horse. But he did not come to take care of any horse, or even to hasten the preparation of the *High Plateaus* monograph. He came to help the boss in putting over the "general plan,"[16] which from this time on began swiftly to evolve out of the realm of abstract thinking and into the realm of practical — and explosive — politics.

2. *1878: The General Plan*

POWELL'S LETTER to Schurz on May 22, 1877, had made it clear that he was prepared, if necessary, to step completely out of topography, geology, and natural history and devote himself to ethnology, to which both his inclinations and his opportunities had led him. The 670 vocabularies already in his possession would keep him occupied for a long time on the classification of the Indian languages, and his relations with Joseph Henry and Spencer Baird were cordial and uncomplicated by the political jealousies that riddled the surveys. Actually he had been far less free since acquiring governmental support than he had been while running his personal shoestring scientific expeditions in Colorado and on the river. Now, with a little urging, he might have retired into the scientific quiet of the Smithsonian.

But he didn't. Abandonment of ambitions for his own Western survey liberated him from personal motives to a very large extent, and that liberation had the effect of making him both more aggressive and more successful in promoting his version of the ideal government survey. From the moment when he began to care less about continuation on the old terms of the Powell Survey, he began to care more about efficient organization and the public good which federal science ought to serve.

In his letter books of 1878 there are no desperate pleas for help and no hurried summonses of influential friends to Washington, though the omission may reflect only a growing caution about what sorts of things were preserved in his official files. He did ask Thomas Donaldson to come to Washington to help him get an item on the Deficiency Appropriations Bill, but that was carry-over business from 1877, an additional $5000 needed to cover the public land classification and hydrographic map of Utah done by Powell's survey for the General Land Office.[1] And he did ask Professor Putnam of Harvard to return some loaned collections so that he could impress Congressmen with them.[2] The bulk of his time and thought, however, went not into getting an 1878 appropriation, which he seems to have taken for granted, but into the expanding problem of the organization of government science.

On February 22 he wrote nearly identical letters to Professors J. D. Plunkett, N. S. Shaler, J. B. Killibrew, and Elias Loomis,[3] who at the Nashville meeting of the American Association for the Advancement of Science had been appointed a committee to see if Weather Bureau reports might be made useful for other scientific purposes. Powell told these gentlemen that there was a Congressional committee now considering what permanent disposition to make of the Weather Bureau, one of the Smithsonian's scientific fledglings which had outgrown the nest. The committee's discussions would probably provoke an examination of all the scientific bureaus, including the Western surveys. Powell asked the AAAS committee to meet with him in Washington to talk over what pressures men of learning ought to apply in the possible reorganization.[4]

Major Powell had an acute political sense, and he was well informed. On March 8, Representative Atkins of Tennessee introduced a resolution asking a report from the Secretary of the Interior on the possibility of consolidating all the Western surveys. He thus reopened the debate that had never quite subsided since 1874. Schurz replied to the resolution by forwarding letters from both Powell and Hayden saying what they had all three agreed on in November, 1877 — that Powell would take ethnology and Hayden the rest. The War Department made its customary claim that the Topographical Engineers were the proper people to survey the West and make the maps. Those were the expected opening moves. But in the very beginning of the maneuvering, most probably after consultation with Schurz and perhaps with others, Powell made up his mind to go after something a hundred times more sweeping than a mere division of labor or a mere systematizing of Western surveys. The surveys were not the only thing in the West that was being mishandled, wasted, and misapplied. The very laws and the philosophy behind the laws were inadequate.

While Powell had been fighting for survival in 1877, Congress had passed the Desert Land Act, which its advocates described as providing a workable plan for settlement of the arid lands but which one historian has described as designed "to encourage monopolization while throwing dust in the public's eyes."[5] Right now it had before it a bill that would be passed in two months as the Timber and Stone Act, and this would further complicate a land policy already snarled with red tape, riddled with loopholes, and rotten with dishonest practices. Insofar as they were scientific operations, government surveys were not concerned with policy. And yet their findings compelled settlement of policy questions; the examination of any natural resource, minerals, arable land, grazing land, timber, stone, water, led directly to the political question of how these resources should be controlled, reserved, or distributed, whether they should be held by the government or given or sold to the people, protected or exploited. The vision of William Gilpin held no such problems, for in Gilpin Land the beneficent working of social and economic law was like the grand slow inevitable rolling of the earth. But the practical observation of Powell revealed a hundred unpleasant possibilities of conflict, spoliation, monopoly, and waste.

A plan had been growing in his mind for years. Undoubtedly it had become more immediate with the election of Hayes and the entrance into the Cabinet of Schurz, an avowed reformer. There is no evidence of intimacy between Powell and Schurz, but there is every evidence of essential agreement. Perhaps the fortunate meeting of their minds explains why Powell, with his report on the Public Domain only partly finished and with no appropriation for its printing even if it had been done, rushed the fragments together into printer's copy without even waiting for proofreading by Dutton, Gilbert, Thompson, and Willis Drummond, who had contributed chapters. On April 1 he presented it to Schurz as a *Report on the Lands of the Arid Region of the United States, with a More Detailed Account of the Lands of Utah.*

Fragment or not, this was heavy artillery. By submitting his hurried and partial report Major Powell committed himself; he took issue with every delusion of the Gilpin state of mind. Embodied in the scant two hundred pages of his manuscript — actually in the first two chapters of it — was a complete revolution in the system of land surveys, land policy, land tenure, and farming methods in the West, and a denial of almost every cherished fantasy and myth associated with the Westward migration and the American dream of the Garden of the World. Powell was not only challenging political forces who used popular myths for a screen, he was challenging the myths themselves, and they were as rooted as the beliefs of religion.[6] He was using bear language in a bull market, "deficiency terminology" in the midst of a chronic national optimism well recovered from the panic of 1873. Though he opened with his heavy batteries hurriedly, as the opportunity offered, he did it deliberately and on nobody's initiative but his own.

3. *The Public Domain*

AS A FACT, the public domain dates from October 30, 1779, when Congress requested the states to relinquish in favor of the federal government all claims to the unsettled country between the Appalachians and the Mississippi. As a problem, it dates from the Act of Congress of May 18, 1796, which authorized the appointment of a surveyor-general and the survey of the Northwest Territory. As the responsibilty of a special branch of government, it was created with the General Land Office in April, 1812, eight and a half years after Jefferson's Louisiana Purchase had superimposed mystery upon wilderness, and added unmeasured millions of acres, unrealized opportunities, and unpredictable headaches to the national inheritance.

One of the principal reasons for the federal government's desire to take over the public domain intact was to efface interstate boundary quarrels stemming from royal charters and grants. Its principal aim in establishing a plan of rectangular surveys of the public lands into ranges, townships, and sections was to avoid the irregular, difficult, badly marked, and often confused plot lines of the disorganized surveys of colonial times. The same system was continued in newly acquired Louisiana. Across the public lands, from 1812 onwards, the General Land Office imposed a grid of surveys upon which the small freeholds of the ideal agrarian democracy could be laid out like checkers on a board.

In any wilderness region surveys could be run as soon as it appeared that settlement was on the way[1] — a skirmish line of squatters was as sure a sign of the need for surveys as swallows are of spring. Surveys were let out to local surveyors under the general supervision of the General Land Office, and if the original scientific intentions rapidly were lost, and if Land Office meridians sometimes had less than the desirable reference to true meridians,[2] and if compass and chain erred, and though some men grew rich on the graft incidental to the partitioning of the land, nevertheless the Land Office Surveys made out to do their practical job. They divided the land so that titles could be issued to pioneer farmers, speculators, and the states and corporations given grants for wagon roads, canals, railroads, colleges, and other internal improvements. They proceeded without having to mind the debates between advocates of free land and those who believed the government should sell off the public lands for profit and a balanced budget. They were utilitarian only; policy was none of their business.

When J. A. Williamson took over as Commissioner in 1876, he could summarize the conditions under which he took office[3] and show that the Land Office Surveys had reached westward clear across Missouri, Arkansas, Kansas, across all but the upper Niobrara district of Nebraska, across the Red River Valley in Dakota Territory. Eastern Colorado, like the mountainous western slope, was unsurveyed. Wyoming had been touched only in its southeastern corner and along the line of the Union Pacific. Idaho had survey stakes only in three scattered districts around Bear Lake, Boise, and Lewiston. Montana was virgin unmarked plains except in its west-central section. In other words, the whole public domain from the Appalachians almost to the Rockies was laid out in townships and a great part of it disposed of by sale and grant and homestead. West of the Nebraska-Colorado line the surveys had touched the better-watered areas where settlement had first clotted. Like settlement, and as an inevitable corollary, the grid surveys were now beginning to fill in the areas between the Missouri and the Sierra-Cascade Mountains. And like the settlers who ventured out into the arid belt, the General Land Office was beginning to find that what worked well to eastward worked increasingly badly beyond the 100th meridian.

A firmly fixed pattern of settlement, of which the rectangular surveys and the traditional quarter-section of land were only outward manifestations, though in some ways determining ones, began to meet on the Great Plains conditions that could not be stretched or lopped to fit Procrustes' bed. A mode of life that despite varying soils and a transition from woods to prairies had been essentially uniform from the east coast through Kentucky and Ohio and on to the Missouri or slightly beyond, met in the West increasingly varied topography, climate, altitudes, crops, opportunities, problems. The Middle West, geographically and socially and economically, was simple; the West was complex. Instead of the gentle roll of the great valley there were high plains, great mountain ranges, alkali valleys, dead lake bottoms, alluvial benchlands. Instead of trees or oak openings there were grasslands, badlands, timbered mountains, rain forests and rain-shadow deserts, climates that ran the scale from Vermont to the Sahara. And more important than all the variety which was hostile to a too-rigid traditional pattern was one overmastering unity, the unity of drouth. With local and minor exceptions, the lands beyond the 100th meridian received less than twenty inches of annual rainfall, and twenty inches was the minimum for unaided agriculture. That one simple fact was to be, and is still to be, more fecund of social and economic and institutional change in the West than all the acts of all the Presidents and Congresses from the Louisiana Purchase to the present.[4]

One of the most difficult operations for imperfect mortals is the making of distinctions, of stopping opinion and belief part way, of accepting qualified ideas. It is a capacity demanded by and presumably encouraged by the democratic process, and perhaps over a long period of time the history of America demonstrates its comforting presence among us as a people. But the individual who can modify or correct beliefs molded by personal interest or the influences of his rearing is rare, and was rare in the eighteen-seventies.

It is easy to be wise in retrospect, uncommonly difficult in the event.

The Great American Desert, for example.

The notion of a Great American Desert east of the Rockies is almost as old as the public domain.[5] Lewis and Clark, whose report was not published until 1814, did not use the term, though they mentioned dry streams and the lack of timber along the upper Missouri. But Zebulon Pike, in his report published in 1810, had told of finding a desert between the Missouri and the Rockies, some of it suitable for grazing but some of it bare dunes. He saw a real value in this desert, in that it would be a bar to settlement and would prevent the reckless extension and perhaps disintegration of the Union. John Bradbury and Henry M. Brackenridge, going up the Missouri in 1811, and Thomas Nuttall in 1819, contributed to the vaguely growing public notion of the lands beyond the Missouri, and they used terms such as "pathless desert" which had ambiguous connotations.

In part the notion of the Great American Desert is a matter of mere words, a semantic difficulty. The poetic and romantic meaning of "desert" was one thing, the popular meaning another. According to the one, any unpeopled wilderness, especially open grasslands but even dense woods, could be called a desert. According to the other, a desert must be a waste of naked sand and rock. Confusion between the two terms partly explains both the growth of the belief in the Great American Desert's existence, and its denial. But specific reports had much to do with it too. Dr. Edwin James, the official chronicler of Major Stephen H. Long's 1820 expedition to the Rocky Mountains, attested to the presence of a "dreary plain, wholly unfit for cultivation, and of course uninhabitable by a people depending upon agriculture for their subsistence," and hoped that it might "forever remain the unmolested haunt of the native hunter, the bison, and the jackall." His map, which showed the "Great Desert" between the 98th meridian and the Arkansas, was widely influential, and his observations were borrowed by popular magazines and popular historians. By the mid-thirties the Great American Desert was firmly established on the maps and in the American mind, and it continued to be acknowledged for more than a generation. Thomas Farnham in 1843 divided the pre-montane West into three zones, the last one, from the

100th meridian to the Rockies, "usually called the Great American Desert." Josiah Gregg's *Commerce of the Prairies* made a desert of all the plains between the Red River and the sources of the Missouri. Captain Gunnison, traversing the plains on his survey for the Pacific Railroad in 1853, arrived at the same conclusion. The report of the first Kansas State Geological Survey in 1866 held out no hope of an immediate settlement of the plains, and John Hanson Beadle in *The Undeveloped West* saw only wasteland for eight hundred miles west of the 100th meridian, and from British Columbia to Mexico.

Many of those reports are the soberest truth. But what came out of them is an indication of how an objective report, by the misinterpretation of a single word, can produce popular error. There was certainly a "desert" between the Missouri and the mountains, but it was not the endless waste of drifting sand that the word brought before the eyes of many readers.

The exaggeration of the Great American Desert is one expression of the unmodulated mind. The reverse expression comes from the tribe of Gilpin. Beginning in the late fifties and early sixties, when gold strikes had bred settlements at the foot of the Colorado Rockies, and venturesome farmers were led by the presence of a lucrative local market to try the soil and steer some mountain water onto a few acres, the conviction began to grow that the Great American Desert was poppycock. How could a desert support buffalo by the million, and Indians of fifty tribes? Local patriots loved anyone who, crossing the plains in the green of spring, scoffed at the calamity howlers. Travelers caught in one of the torrential cyclonic storms of the plains could look up and comment dryly, or wetly, on the aridity.

And circumstances combined with wishfulness to erode the notion that had been fixed for thirty or forty years. The seventies were a time of heavy rainfall; they were also the time of the panic of 1873 brought on by Jay Cooke's collapse, and the perception that it was easy to pinch a farmer but hard to starve him may have encouraged the movement to the homestead country. Drouth and grasshoppers hurt the first years of the decade, but by 1878 a series of wet years and heavy crops had precipitated a rush. Between 1870 and 1880 the population of the wheat states and territories — Nebraska, Kansas, Dakota, and Minnesota — grew from less than a million to more than two and a half million. Final entries under the Homestead Act exceeded one and a half million in 1874, two million in 1875, and two and a half million in 1878.[6]

Farmers put their foot in the door of the West and waited. When nothing happened, they poked their heads in. When nothing still happened, they went all the way through. By 1878 they were jubilantly confident that the grain belt was safe. The Great American Desert was laughed away, washed away in the flow of Gilpin oratory, advertised away in the broadsides of land companies and the railroad proselytizers. The enduring faith of William Gilpin that the desert was a myth was shared not only by travelers and publicists but by thousands of dryland farmers who could point to flourishing crops and steadily increasing rainfall. What had seemed to Pike a permanent barrier against settlement became a garden, a Canaan.[7]

Major Powell had watched that Canaan open. He had led his first expedition westward from Omaha by horse and mule team in 1867, through the dwindling buffalo herds. Cattle then were already moving north from Texas to the railroad towns. From Abilene, Kansas, the first cowtown, Texas cattle started east by rail in September of that year. In the next five years a million and a half longhorns reached Abilene from Texas over the Chisholm Trail,[8] and by the same time the drives had reached far to the north and west. Jack Sumner, the Howlands, and Bill Dunn, moving leisurely from the winter camp on the White to their rendezvous with Powell at Green River in the spring of 1869, had found a herd of thousands wintering in Brown's Hole.[9] Two years later Powell's second river expedition had found other thousands, with two Texan and ten Mexican herders, making use of the public range in that sheltered and temperate valley.

The plains north of the Union Pacific tracks were then still Indian country, full of hostiles and potential hostiles, the last stronghold of the horse Indians and their sole resource, the buffalo. But the gold strikes in the Black Hills, the series of punitive campaigns after the Custer fight, the pinching of Sioux and Blackfoot and Crow and Arapaho and Snake into tight reservations, opened the northern plains that had been pioneered for cattle by Nelson Story's drive along the Bozeman Trail in 1866. The big cattle rush in Wyoming and Montana was reserved for the eighties, but by 1878, according

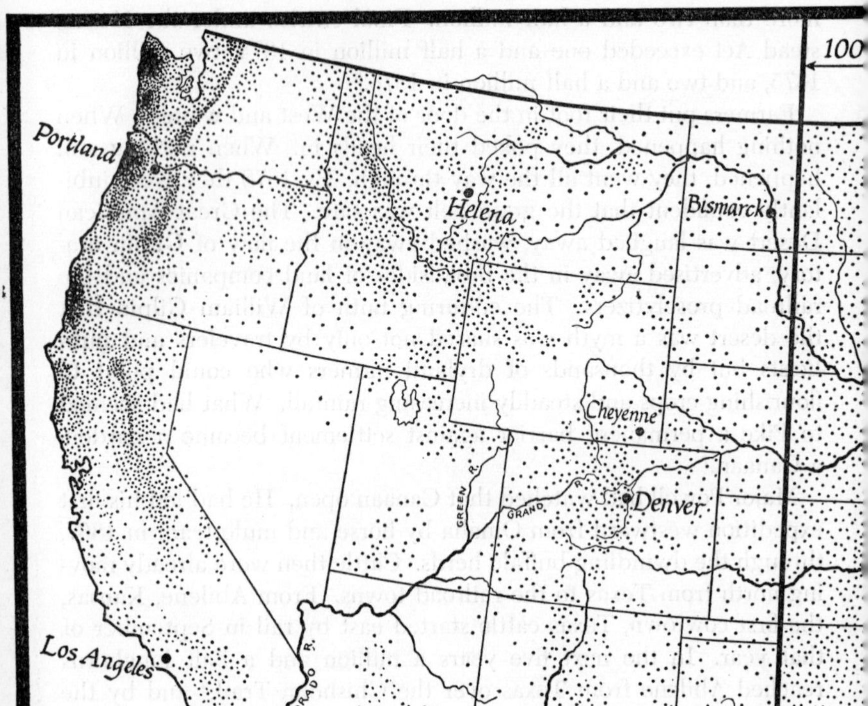
100
Portland
Helena
Bismarck
Cheyenne
Denver
Los Angeles
GREEN R.
GRAND R.
COLORADO R.
100th Meridian
Average Annual Rainfall
in inches
Below 8
8 — 16
16 — 28
28 — 40
40 — 60
60 — 80
80 — 100
Over 100

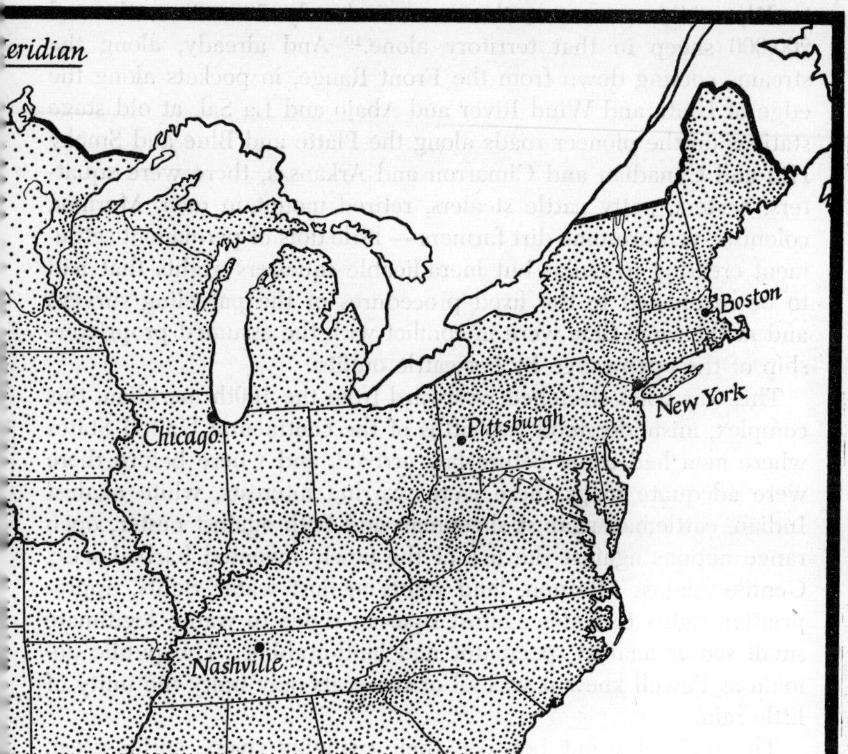
eridian
Boston
New York
Pittsburgh
Chicago
Nashville
New Orleans
Key West

to Wyoming's governor, there were already 300,000 cattle and 200,000 sheep in that territory alone.[10] And already, along the streams coming down from the Front Range, in pockets along the edge of Uinta and Wind River and Abajo and La Sal, at old stage stations on the pioneer roads along the Platte and Blue and Smoky Hill and Canadian and Cimarron and Arkansas, there were squatters, nesters, petty cattle stealers, retired mountain men, Mormon colonists, venturesome dirt farmers — little dots of permanent settlement creating irregular but ineradicable squatters' rights that had to be reconciled to the fixed procedures of the parceling surveys and at the same time were in conflict with the assumed proprietorship of the open range by big cattle outfits.

This was what stretched westward from the 100th meridian, this complex, misunderstood two fifths of the continental United States where men had come before law arrived, and where before there were adequate maps there were warring interests, white against Indian, cattleman against sheepman and both against nester, open range notions against the use of the newly invented barbed wire, Gentile against Mormon, land rights against water rights, appropriation rights to water against riparian rights to water, legitimate small settler against speculator and land-grabber. The public domain as Powell knew it was all of these, its only unity the unity of little rain.

The plains lay out between their swinging rivers, spring-green and summer-brown, treeless except for the belts of cottonwood along water, deserted except for coyotes, an occasional shanty, the ungathered bones of the buffalo, domed over by a great bowl sky that filled and overflowed with dramatic weathers, with cloudburst and cyclone and blizzard and heat wave, but that occasionally glowed with a bell-like purity of light and at whose western edge the sun set in clear distances of lavender and saffron. Beyond the plains went the wrinkled spine of the continent, range after range, bare granite, black spruce, gold aspen on the autumn slopes, timbered valleys where the warriors of Antero and Douglas and Ouray still found elk and bear, and where even while Powell organized his support for a political fight in Washington those same Ute warriors were falling upon Nathan Meeker and all the men of his agency for the sin of Calvinist inflexibility. Beyond those mountains and plateaus westward from the final scarp of the Wasatch above the Mormon New Jerusalem, the veritable and incontrovertible desert stretched across salt flat and dead lake bottom and barren range after barren range to the Sierra where the West ended and California began. On the eastern edge of the Sierra the Sutro Tunnel had just begun draining the hampering water from the Comstock Lode.[11] From there on, other interests than those of cattleman and Mormon and nester were entrenched. There the public domain, to all intents and purposes, ceased. Much California real estate was obscured by Spanish and Mexican land grants, by early squatting before any surveys, by mining claims, by such legislation as the Swamp Land Act which endowed the state with 2,000,000 acres of public land. But in the 1400-mile strip between the Sierra and the ragged front of settlement in Nebraska, Kansas, Dakota, and Colorado the public domain was a fact, a problem, a challenge, and a threat. Left to the folklore of farmers and the greed of land-grabbers, it could come to spoliation, waste, frustration, anger. Quilted by their land-grant strips, the railroads that reached through it, including the Northern Pacific that Henry Villard had just raised from the wreck of Jay Cooke's collapse, might tap a rich empire or they might tap bitterness and rebellion. The inevitable beneficence of the railroad was part of the garden-myth that American and immigrant settlers took west with them. Henry George, who would prick that bubble, was in 1878 just about to send to press a book called *Progress and Poverty* that would become a bible for Grangers and Populists and Single-Taxers and breed something close to revolution among the very men whom the myth designated as the happy beneficiaries of railroads and free land. George would offer a public of millions of readers an analysis of economic facts, and no one would seriously shake his diagnosis of what was happening to the American West. But in the *Report on the Lands of the Arid Region* Powell offered an analysis quite as revolutionary and original, and a solution more practicable than the Single-tax. He offered a blueprint for laws and human institutions that would, if adopted, remake society and thought in the area they affected, and in doing so might alter even the seemingly inevitable movement of Henry George's economics.

The justifications for reform were extensive, for every condition of land and climate, and every successive land law except the

Timber Culture Act of 1873 worked against the city mechanic, immigrant, ambitious farm boy, or struggling three-time-pioneer who according to the myth would create the happy American yeomanry in the Western garden land. By the time the Homestead Act was passed in 1862, settlement was already at the edge of the subhumid belt. By the time the Timber Culture Act of 1873, the Desert Land Act of 1877, and the Timber and Stone Act of 1878 were piled upon the existing jumble of Pre-emption Act, public sales, railroad grants, Indian and soldiers' scrip, and Homestead Act, there seemed to be many avenues to opportunity for the yeoman, and yet every one tempted him into an enterprise with a sixty-six per cent chance of failure. Despite incandescent enthusiasm for the Homestead Act at home and abroad, the forty years before 1900 saw no more than 400,000 families — about 2,000,000 people — homestead *and retain* government lands. Yet in that time the population of the United States grew by 45,000,000.[12] The function of the open West as safety valve was greatly exaggerated if in that period 43,000,000 potential home-seekers either could not take advantage of free land or failed to hold their claims.

Suppose a pioneer tried. Suppose he did (most couldn't) get together enough money to bring his family out to Dakota or Nebraska or Kansas or Colorado. Suppose he did (most couldn't) get a loan big enough to let him build the dwelling demanded by law, buy a team and a sodbuster plow and possibly a disk harrow and a seeder and perhaps a binder — whatever elements of the multiplying array of farm machinery he had to have. Suppose he managed to buy seed, and lay in supplies or establish credit for supplies during the first unproductive year. Suppose he and his family endured the sun and glare on their treeless prairie, and were not demolished by the cyclones that swept across the plains like great scythes. Suppose they found fuel in a fuelless country, possibly digging for it, as Gilpin suggested, but more likely burning cow chips, and lasted into fall, and banked their shack to the window sills with dirt against the winter's cold, and sat out the blizzards and the loneliness of their tundra-like home. Suppose they resisted cabin fever, and their family affection withstood the hard fare and the isolation, and suppose they emerged into spring again. It would be like emerging from a cave. Spring would enchant them with crocus and primrose and prairies green as meadows. It might also break their hearts and spirits if it browned into summer drouth. The possibilities of trouble, which increased in geometrical ratio beyond the 100th meridian, had a tendency to materialize in clusters. The brassy sky of drouth might open to let across the fields winds like the breath of a blowtorch, or clouds of grasshoppers, or crawling armies of chinch bugs. Pests always seemed to thrive best in drouth years. And if drouth and insect plagues did not appear there was always a chance of cyclones, cloudbursts, hail.

It took a man to break and hold a homestead of 160 acres even in the subhumid zone. It took a superman to do it on the arid plains.[13] It could hardly, in fact, be done, though some heroes tried it. Most of the city mechanics whom Destiny had called to earn prosperous homes by the labor of their hands were driven back to the cities sooner or later. Even the ambitious farm boys who knew wheat farming from the clods up and were inured to the hardest kind of labor, the boys like Hamlin Garland, did not do much better. Quite as often as not it was the immigrants who stuck it out and eventually made it. Having gambled their savings and their entire lives for the chance, they were not often driven out by anything short of annihilation.

Those who were defeated, and up to 1900 two thirds of those who tried it were, were by the normal course of events in peonage to the banks. A mortgage was more common on a western farm than a good team. The Homestead Act and other laws made no provision for government loans and did not insist, as they might have, that abandoned claims be returned to the public domain for the benefit of other homesteaders. The land of the failures went to the banks, and thus onto the market, and often into the accumulating domains of speculators or large ranch companies. In the end, the Homestead Act stimulated the monopolizing of land that its advocates had intended to prevent.

Later acts, though their passage indicated a dawning and confused awareness of the inadequacies of the existing system, helped the small farmer very little. The Timber Culture Act, which permitted a man to file on an extra quarter-section if he planted and sustained a certain acreage of trees, did allow some farmers in the subhumid zone to acquire the additional land that all western farms had to have before they became economic units. A quarter-section in the arid belt, or in the subhumid belt during a dry year, would hardly graze four steers. Timber culture, being necessarily confined to the easterly fringe of the arid lands, did not ordinarily conflict with the land accumulation of big cattle outfits, and it did create some belts and groves of trees in country where every tree is beyond price, and it did help some Kansas and Nebraska farmers achieve independence by doubling their acreage. But succeeding acts, the Desert Land Act and the Timber and Stone Act, could hardly have been better devised to help speculators and land-grabbers if they had been written for that specific purpose. Even if the provisions of the laws had been honorably observed, which they were not, the net effect would have been to concentrate western grazing and timber land in the hands of large companies. The irrigation demanded before title could be obtained under the Desert Land Act was usually impossible for the single farmer. And those lands "unfit for settlement" which were open under the Timber and Stone Act were, like the desert land, transferable before final proof of title, unless fraud was provable. Fraud was never provable, but it was estimated that ninety-five per cent of final title proofs were fraudulent, nevertheless.[14] For a fee, settlers filed, and then sold to some corporation and moved on.

In actual practice almost the only real benefit that the landless and moneyless man, the mechanic or immigrant or farm boy, could derive from the public land laws was the chance for a little graft. There were plenty of men, big and little, who observed Simon Suggs' motto that it is good to be shifty in a new country. The more enterprising of these provided examples and opportunities for the smaller fry. Instead of breaking back and heart trying to work a hopeless quarter-section, a yeoman might do better to build a little birdhouse say twelve by sixteen inches, and carry it around to strategic places suggested to him by entrepreneurs, and later swear, for a fee, that he had seen a house twelve by sixteen on such and such a claim. He might mount a little shack on a wagon and do the same; for many purposes mobility in a shack was worth more than durability. Or he could drive around from claim to claim with a barrel and a bucket and pour a little water on a parcel of desert land and later accommodate the boss of some cattle company by swearing that he had brought water to that claim. Under a series of names he could file one claim after another and after six months commute each one — that is, buy it outright at $1.25 per acre — and turn it over to the speculator in whose interest and with whose money the whole transaction had been made.

There were several ways in which the land laws benefited the little man, but the acquisition of land was seldom one. The alien sailors who were hired to do a little service for the California Redwood Company discovered one of the best. In batches of twenty-five they were marched from boardinghouse to courthouse, where they filed first citizenship papers. From the courthouse they passed to the land office, where each filed on a timber claim. From the land office they went to a lawyer's, where they "executed an acknowledgement of a blank deed." From there they proceeded to the office of the company which now owned twenty-five new timber claims, accepted fifty dollars each for their labors, and marched back to the boardinghouse.[15]

Those sailors had a fast look at the American Way as it was developed under some of the public land laws in the West. If they were either very smart or very considerate of themselves they would probably not be tempted by that other American Way represented by the yeoman farmer who from Jefferson to Theodore Roosevelt was held to be the backbone of the Republic. The yeoman and his version of the American Way were having a hard time as settlement approached the arid zone, and under the existing system of improvised, loosely phrased, loophole-riddled, corruptly administered, and universally abused law he would continue to. The German butcher boy Henry Miller, who at his peak would own or control a million acres in California, Oregon, and Nevada, and would dominate a hundred miles of both banks of the San Joaquin, was only one of many whose practices gave weight to the words of Henry George.[16] The public domain was going, and going in useless and unworkable parcels to impossibly handicapped small farmers, or in wholesale lots to great landholders and great corporations. But even yet it was not too late to do something.

Almost alone among his contemporaries, Powell recognized the opportunity that lay there to be seized, but already pulling away, already beginning to vanish. Almost alone among his contemporaries he looked at the Arid Region and saw neither desert nor garden. What he saw was the single compelling unity that the region possessed: except in local islanded areas its rainfall was less than twenty inches a year, and twenty inches he took, with slight modifications for the peculiarly concentrated rainfall of the Dakotas, to be the minimum needed to support agriculture without irrigation. In no other part of the United States did that aridity pertain, though in what he at first called the subarid zone between about the 97th and 100th meridians there were sure to be dry years.

He saw also the variety, caused by altitude, latitude, topography, climate, soil, that characterized the West in contrast to the essential unity of the Middle West and East. A state like Iowa, nearly one hundred per cent arable, was one thing; a state like Utah, where the arable land was probably less than three per cent of the total area, was another. Land in Utah lay at altitudes varying from three thousand to over thirteen thousand feet. Much of it was too high for crops, much of it too stony, almost all of it too dry. For Utah, and for the whole arid region of which it provided the type, it was essential to differentiate the uses to which land could be put. For several years he had had his crews designating lands they surveyed as mineral, coal, timber, pasturage, or irrigable lands, and he knew that each of these would require different laws and perhaps different kinds of survey.[17]

Mineral lands, already well segregated by prospectors and by the formation of mining districts, were fairly easily set aside, and coal lands were so extensive, especially through the Plateau Province, that it would be impractical to separate them except as they lay in accessible regions. Powell was not much interested in mineral and coal lands anyway: he would have agreed with Brigham Young, who damned miners to hell across lots and forbade his people to dig for precious metals. So far as the federal surveys went, minerals were the special province of Clarence King and his associates Arnold and James Hague, Samuel Emmons, and G. F. Becker. The timber lands, lying almost wholly at high altitudes and in difficult terrain, were almost certain to be developed by special timber interests; he thought then they could be of little usefulness to settlers. But farmlands were another matter. Powell was a son of the midwestern farming frontier. He had run a farm almost by himself before he was into his teens. His interest in the public domain was primarily an interest in the land as it might be settled by small farmers. Hence his report gave irrigable and pasturage lands primary attention.

The two differed little except in the availability of water, for most western soils were exuberantly fertile if water could be applied. But topography controlled what lands could be irrigated, and the amount of water that could be brought was limited. Powell had watched the pioneering of irrigation among the Mormons, and had followed the difficulties that attended the establishment of waterworks for the raw settlement of Kanab. He knew the man-hours needed to harness a creek and engineer miles of ditch to water the fields of a town. The irrigation which was "as easy as fencing, which it supersedes," he knew nothing of — that was an illusion of Gilpin's. But he knew the sweat, the labor, the anxiety, the danger of flash floods that could wash out a dam and bury fields in unprofitable gravel, the wasteful breaks in ditch that could leave a village dry. For two field seasons he had had Thompson, Dutton, and Gilbert checking the water supply and the irrigable lands of Utah and testing the maximum acreage that under varying conditions could be irrigated by a second-foot or an acre-foot of water. All three men, Gilbert and Dutton especially, were first-class observers. In all of Utah, the type area, they had located only 2262 square miles of land even potentially irrigable. That was less than three per cent of the area of the territory. Nobody has corrected them notably since: in 1945 the cultivated area of the state, including dry farms, was 3.3 per cent.[18]

Where water was available an irrigated farm was the safest in the world, for it depended on no meteorological luck, and properly watered it had its fertilizer spread upon it naturally every year in the form of silt. One hundred and sixty acres in the arid region was utterly incapable of supporting a family without irrigation, but with irrigation it became more than one man could handle. Irrigation agriculture was intensive, it took time and care, and it produced extravagantly. Powell therefore recommended eighty acres as the homestead unit for irrigated farms. But for pasture farms he proposed units of 2560 acres, four full sections, sixteen times the normal homestead.[19] That was calculated to shock the orthodox, and yet in making the suggestion he apologized to many of his Western friends who assured him that he had made the unit too small.

In multiplying the usual homestead by sixteen, he was taking into consideration the native grasses, nutritious but scattered, many of them annuals that reproduced only from seed. In country where it took ten, twenty, fifty acres to graze one steer it was easy to overgraze and destroy the range. That was why a herd that would support a family needed at least four sections, and preferably more, to run on. Also, before this pasturage farmer who was possessed of what would have been a dukedom in a humid country could make a living off it, he needed other things as well. In his suggestions for these, Powell broke even more sharply with tradition.

Water, for instance. In general, American law was based on English Common Law. But the Common Law, accumulated out of the experience of a rainy country where water was no problem, affirmed only what are known as riparian rights to the water of streams. The man who owned the bank could make any use that he pleased of the water, but he had to return it to the stream when he was through with it. That worked for running grist mills, but it did not work at all for irrigation, which used the water up instead of taking advantage of its passage. In the West, before and since Powell's time, there have been heads broken with irrigation shovels because of someone's attempt to apply riparian law upstream, and take uncontrolled advantage of the water. In an irrigating country, appropriation becomes an essential criterion, and delicate refinements about more or less beneficial uses, and priority, and dipping rights, and a great many other complications still unheard of when Powell wrote. There was nothing wrong with riparian law for the West except that downstream bank-owners sooner or later found themselves with riparian rights to a dry creek bed.

Water is the true wealth in a dry land; without it, land is worthless or nearly so. And if you control the water, you control the land that depends on it. In that fact alone was the ominous threat of land and water monopolies.

To prevent this — or to stop it, for it was already beginning to happen — Powell made two proposals. One was that each pasturage farm should have within its 2560 acres twenty acres of irrigable land with a water right that was inseparable from the land. Those twenty acres would insure a garden patch and a plot of irrigated hay or alfalfa for wintering or fattening stock. But to arrange either pasturage farms or irrigation farms so that water and irrigable land were equitably divided meant making an entirely new kind of survey. The rectangular grid of the General Land Office could easily leave all the water for miles within a few quarter-sections, and the man who obtained title to those quarters could control thousands of surrounding acres. Instead of rectangular parcels, therefore, Powell proposed surveys based on the topography, letting farms be as irregular as they had to be to give everyone a water frontage and a patch of irrigable soil. By that system it would be possible not only to prevent monopoly of water and hence of land, but to carve the maximum number of freeholds out of any usable part of the public domain. Whether any region should be divided into 2560-acre pasturage farms or into 80-acre irrigation farms was a matter to be determined by survey or by the settlers. In either case, a homesteader would have a guaranteed water supply and an assurance that with normal diligence he could not be burned out.

Up to that point, Major Powell was proposing a revolution in the land laws and in the nature of the General Land Office surveys, both sufficiently sacrosanct in the popular mind, but both open to corruption and misuse, and both already under fire. He went further by recommending the abolition of the surveyors-general and the practice of farming out survey jobs to local contractors. To eliminate waste and graft, he wanted land parceling turned over to the Coast and Geodetic Survey, which with its precise determination of points and elevations was equipped to make a much more accurate job of it and which as a central scientific bureau was above being bought. That would have taken surveying out of politics and restored it to science.

But his logic led him further still. The Mormons of Kanab and the Sevier Valley towns had taught him more than irrigation. From them he had also got a notion of how salutary co-operation could be as a way of life, how much less wasteful than competition unlimited, how much more susceptible to planning and intelligence, how much less destructive of human and natural resources. The last step of his proposal to Land Commissioner Williamson, and through Williamson to Carl Schurz, and through Schurz to the Congress, embodied official encouragement of a social organization thoroughly revolutionary in 1878. It was so far beyond the social and economic thinking of the period that popularized the pork barrel as a national symbol and began the systematic gutting of the continent's resources and developed to its highest and most ruthless stage the competitive ruthlessness of American business, that it seems like the product of another land and another people.

It was clear that individual initiative and individual labor and individual capital were inadequate to develop the irrigation works needed on an arid-belt farm unless the farm were located high on the headwaters of a small stream. It was equally clear that the earliest development would be and had been on these high small streams, and that on the larger and lower reaches where cultivable land was much more extensive and the growing season longer the cost of dams and ditches was prohibitive. It was also clear that use of the water at high levels on marginal land with a constant danger of frost damage robbed the potentially more productive areas below. In those circumstances there were three possibilities: (1) Private capital could develop — and monopolize — the water of the streams, thus putting the small farmer in a status close to peonage. (2) The government could develop and distribute the water for the public good. (3) The people themselves, by co-operative effort such as that of the Mormons, could organize and develop in unison what was impossible for anyone singly.

Similarly, if range put under fence tended to become unevenly grazed, and often overgrazed, and if fences were death traps to cattle drifting with the winter storms, then the open range was preferable. But the open range was useless without water, and sources of water were often far apart. Under the present laws, a man or a corporation could gain title to the water, or seize the water by force or priority, and fall heir to thousands of surrounding acres. To combat that tendency, Powell proposed leaving to the people in co-operative unions the control of pasturage lands: in effect, he advocated the sort of community common range — the *ejidos* — that the Spanish villages in New Mexico had had since the beginning of the seventeenth century.

The gun he handed Congress was loaded, for included in it were two sample bills. One provided for the legal organization of any nine bona fide settlers of irrigable lands into irrigation districts capable of self-government. The tract involved should be continuous and should be split into farms not exceeding eighty acres. On demand the Surveyor-General of the United States would provide a cadastral survey on a pattern established by the farmers' association itself, conformable to the topography and the agreement among the individual settlers. After three years of demonstrated irrigation of the lands, the Land Office should issue titles to each person in the irrigation district, this title to include a water right. Only if the water were not used for five years could the water right be separated from the land. The second sample bill was similar in that it provided for co-operative organization of pasturage districts for the communal grazing of cattle and the communal use of limited water rights for a maximum of twenty acres per farm.

Both proposals were predicated on an abrupt halt to the characteristic design of settlement. Here would be no pioneer farmer hewing out a clearing and burning stumps to make a corn patch, no Illinois immigrant turning the prairie sod and planting his potato peels to make a first-year crop. The inflexible fact of aridity lay like a fence along the 100th meridian. From approximately that line on, more than individual initiative was needed to break the wilderness. Powell's way was a way tested by New England barn raisings and corn huskings and all the co-operative habits of country America, tested even more fully by the Mormon experience of thirty years and the New Mexican experience of ten generations. It was recommended by logic and demanded by the hard conditions of western climate and geography. In details it could probably bear revision; in general it was inescapable. If it had been adopted it might have changed the history of a great part of the West.

But it was revolutionary. It was as bold as Powell's plunge down the canyoned river, for it challenged not only the initiative, individualism, and competitiveness which were quite as marked as co-operation in the American character (de Tocqueville had commented on that dichotomy in the infancy of the Republic) but it challenged as well the folklore bred up through generations of frontier farmers in a country of plentiful rain. It challenged too the men who were already beginning to ride like robber barons and kings over the public domain, and the corporations who were already, with Scottish and English and American capital, beginning to acquire those water-bearing half- and quarter-sections upon whose possession depended the control of range to support a cattle empire. As a government scientist, Major Powell was not now defying ignorance. He was taking on vested interests and the vested prejudices by which they maintained themselves.[20]

Seven years after submitting the Arid Regions report, Powell spoke before the Anthropological Society in Washington, and in an entirely different connection gave fuller and more philosophic expression to his belief in man's social responsibility and the need for co-operation which dictated and underlay at every point his program for the West. He was enough of a believer in Lester Ward's dynamic sociology, or enough of an advocate of Lewis Morgan's systematic view of development among the tribes of men, to have made for himself a clear connection between Western land laws and the evolution of *homo sapiens Americanus.* There were ways in which mind and forethought could modify the social evolution of a people. Actually, it is a kind of testament:

> By the division of labor men have become interdependent, so that every man works for some other man. To the extent that culture has progressed beyond the plane occupied by the brute, man has ceased to work directly for himself and come to work directly for others and indirectly for himself. He struggles directly to benefit others, that he may indirectly but ultimately benefit himslf. This principle of political economy . . . must be fully appreciated before we can thoroughly understand the vast extent to which interdependence has been established. For the glasses which I wear, mines were worked in California, and railroads constructed across the continent to transport the products of those mines to the manufactories in the east. For the bits of steel on the bow, mines were worked in Michigan, smelting works were erected in Chicago. . . . Merchant houses and banking houses were rendered necessary. Many men were employed in producing and bringing that little instrument to me. As I sit in my library to read a book, I open the pages with a paper cutter, the ivory of which was obtained through the employment of a tribe of African elephant hunters. The paper on which my book is printed was made of the rags saved by the beggars of Italy. A watchman stands on guard in Hoosac Tunnel that I

may some time ride through it in safety. If all the men who have worked for me, directly and indirectly for the past ten years, and who are now scattered through the four quarters of the earth, were marshaled on the plain outside of the city, organized and equipped for war, I could march to the proudest capital of the world and the armies of Europe could not withstand me. I am the master of all the world. But during all my life I have worked for other men, and thus I am every man's servant; so are we all — servants to many masters and master of many servants. It is thus that men are gradually becoming organized into one vast body-politic, every one striving to serve his fellow man and all working for the common welfare. Thus the enmity of man to man is appeased, and men live and labor for one another; individualism is transmuted into socialism, egoism into altruism, and man is lifted above the brute to an immeasurable height. . . .[21]

He did man more honor than he deserved. Not everyone was yet willing, at least in 1878, to work for the common welfare or even agree on what the common welfare was. Not everybody in the West, not everybody in Congress.

4. *Inside Politics*

PUBLICATION of the *Report on the Lands of the Arid Region* did not have to wait for Powell's appropriation. Two days after Schurz received it, on April 3, 1878, he passed it on to the House, where it was referred to the Committee on Appropriations and ordered printed.[1] While it was still in press, and before the campaign of reform had got past the jockeying stage in committee, the situation was given a new turn by the death of Joseph Henry.[2]

From the time of his nearly profitless trip to Washington in the winter of 1867 Powell had been able to count on Henry as a backer and friend. His scientific eminence and his position outside of politics made Henry at once peculiarly dependable and peculiarly unusable. His death, in terms of its effect on Powell, was similarly ambiguous, for though it deprived the Major of a man whose friendship and advice he had needed and valued, it created a power vacuum in government science. Henry's death opened possibilities that Henry's living sobriety and objectivity might have annulled.

When he died, Joseph Henry was President of the National Academy of Sciences, that congregation of the country's best scientific brains which had been chartered by Congress in 1863 with the function of advising the Congress on technical subjects when called upon. Its advice had not previously been asked in the survey squabbles, perhaps because as a body it might be too fair, and none of the contestants was quite prepared to risk a fair judgment.

But now into Henry's emptied shoes stepped Professor Othniel C. Marsh of Yale,[3] one of the greatest of American paleontologists, friend of Huxley and Darwin, contributor in real measure to the documentation of biological evolution, and nephew moreover of the philanthropic banker George Peabody. Marsh had single-handed run Columbus Delano out of his job as Secretary of the Interior in the 1875 scandal about the cheating of Red Cloud's Sioux. He was more than an illustrious scientist with a firsthand knowledge of the West; he was a man of power, shrewd in political manipulation, solidly backed. And he was a far more eager ally for Powell than Henry would have been. For years he had been engaged in a bitter and rather disgraceful running fight with Professor Edward D. Cope of Pennsylvania in the collection and identification of vertebrate fossils — and Cope was a Hayden man many of whose scientific papers had appeared in Hayden's reports and bulletins. More than that, Marsh personally disliked Hayden: he thought Hayden had tried to blackmail him into supporting the Hayden Survey in exchange for election to the National Academy in 1874. Anti-Hayden, pro-reform (as he had demonstrated in the Red Cloud episode), a close friend of Clarence King, Henry Adams, Abram Hewitt, and the group of liberal Republicans vocal through Godkin's *Nation* and social in the Century Club, Marsh was a powerful ally. And not only was he eminent, powerful, and incorruptible, but he was also, in his personal and scientific rivalries, peculiarly mean, intemperate, and vindictive. When he took over as acting president of the National Academy he brought the Academy for the first time to the place where it might be used in the service of private or public causes.

It is not clear who first suggested using the Academy to help arrange the consolidation of the Western surveys to eliminate duplication and waste. Abram Hewitt took the responsibility, or the credit;[4] Samuel Emmons credits the idea to Clarence King.[5] But from the way in which Powell loomed larger and larger behind the scenes as the situation developed, the way in which the reformers of the surveys began to incorporate more and more of his "general plan" for land policy, and the way in which the Academy came to sound more and more like his mouthpiece, it is not extravagantly unlikely that the idea of using the Academy may have been his. Henry Nash Smith, who has studied this episode most closely, sees Powell as the motive force.[6] In any case, whether Hewitt acted on his own initiative or whether someone else put the idea into his head, he was playing directly into Powell's hand when on June 20, 1878, he inserted a clause in the Sundry Civil Appropriations Bill referring the vexed question of the Western surveys to the National Academy for advice and suggestions.

In that same Sundry Civil Appropriations Bill, without serious debate or strain, Powell got his largest appropriation to date, $50,000. Hayden got his customary $75,000, but it was noteworthy that he remained stationary while Powell grew by two thirds. The size of the appropriation was a clear index to Powell's increased political importance.

For lack of documentary evidence, it is as hard to tell who selected the *Report on the Lands of the Arid Region* as the principal blueprint of reform as it is to tell who first suggested asking advice from the National Academy. But the importance of the report was obviously very clear to its author from the beginning, and he went to great trouble to obtain copies for strategic distribution. The first edition, printed exclusively for the use of Congress, would be out of his hands. Only nine days after the passage of the Sundry Civil Bill containing Hewitt's resolution, Powell asked Schurz for an extra $4000 for a second edition, though he could hardly have hoped a second edition would come out in time to do him much good. Actually the second edition was not authorized until March 3, 1879, when Congress approved two thousand copies for the House, one thousand for the Senate, and two thousand for the Department of the Interior. For use in 1878, Major Powell had to devise other expedients, and he was hampered excessively by the rule which said that Congressional publications could be dispensed only on the signed order of a member of Congress. He had his amanuensis, Joseph Stanley-Brown, send form order slips to every Congressman; any one which came back signed entitled him to extract a copy of his book from the custodian of documents.[7] That way, he managed to obtain enough copies for his immediate needs. But in the meantime he did not neglect the National Academy.

Marsh, upon his return from Europe in August, 1878, appointed a committee to investigate the surveys. There was not a Hayden man on it, though John Strong Newberry, acutely anti-Hayden, was a member, Joseph D. Dana of Yale, a Marsh colleague, was another, and Simon Newcomb of the Naval Observatory, a close friend of Marsh, was a third. The others, William B. Rogers, William P. Trowbridge, and Alexander Agassiz of Harvard's Peabody Museum, were a reasonable cross-section of the country's important scientists without special bias or affiliation.

On September 24, 1878, Powell scraped together eight copies of the *Arid Region* and sent them to Marsh to be distributed to the Academy committee. He also asked to be allowed to talk to the committee when it met. While he waited for this opportunity he busied his staff in sending out copies of the report, however obtained from the watchdog of documents, to western newspapers.[8] In promoting his own survey he had not much bothered to woo the press, but the issues here were of another and higher order, and their importance to Westerners extreme.

Presumably he had his chance to talk to the committee. He also had other opportunities that made him virtually a *sub rosa* committee member. On October 3, 1878, when Marsh wrote Schurz tentatively outlining the group's thinking, Schurz passed his letter on to Powell for comment and suggestion,[9] though as head of one of the surveys concerned Powell might have been thought outside the deliberations. Certainly Hayden and Wheeler were given no such opportunity. It was a tight inside job. On November 6 the committee made its report to the Academy and the Academy accepted it in full, with Professor Cope casting the one dissenting vote. On November 26 Marsh forwarded the Academy's recommendations to Congress.

They called for much more than the consolidation of the four surveys. The Academy suggested the elimination of the surveyors-general and the practice of subletting the land-parceling surveys to local contractors. It wanted land parceling made the job of the Coast and Geodetic Survey, and that whole survey moved over from the jurisdiction of the Treasury to that of the Department of the Interior. It reduced Hayden and eliminated Wheeler by recommending the consolidation of the Hayden, Wheeler, and Powell Surveys under the Department of the Interior. (The King Survey had finished its job.) And it suggested appointment of a public lands commission to study and codify the public land laws, presumably in directions sketched in Powell's report and in his testimony before the Academy's committee. Except in their cautious withholding of specific cures for the land law ills, the Academy's report was identical with the program that Powell, Gilbert, and Dutton had been actively advocating from the Survey headquarters,[10] and almost wholly derivative from Powell's *Report on the Lands of the Arid Region.*

But the most revealing comment on the Academy's action, the wink that tipped the hand of the insider, came from Powell's confidential clerk James Pilling. At the time of the Academy report Pilling was in Boston searching among the libraries for titles to go into his comprehensive bibliography of the Indian languages. On December 5 he wrote his boss with his tongue in his cheek: "I see the Academy has made its report and it sounds wonderfully like something I have read — and perhaps written — before. What will become of we poor ethnologists?"[11]

5. *Half-Victory*

SO CONCENTRATED and vigorous a sponsorship as Powell's could not be kept secret, especially when advocates of the reform in Congress depended upon its creator for ammunition. As the implications of the Academy's recommendations began to percolate through the Congressional bone there was sure to be a violent reaction from Western members involved through sentiment, personal interests, or venality in the old fixed rectangular survey system, the 160-acre freehold, and the cobbled legal structure of Preemption Act, Homestead Act, Swamp Lands Act, Desert Land Act, Timber and Stone Act, and the other improvisations. No sooner had the report been referred to the House Committee on Public Lands than the lines were drawn. On December 19, 1878, Representative P. D. Wigginton of California, one of the few Western Congressmen favoring land-law reform, wrote to Powell saying that he, Abram Hewitt, and Thomas M. Patterson of Colorado had been named a subcommittee to study the subject. Both Patterson and Hewitt, Wigginton said, "are opposed to us." He wanted Powell to write up a full, thorough, and unanswerable report, since he was sure the two in opposition would submit something in writing and would be aided by Hayden and perhaps others.[1]

Wigginton's letter is a sign of how confused even a supporter could be at that stage. He was entirely wrong about Hewitt's opposition, for though Hewitt had at first leaned toward War Department direction of a consolidated survey, and had perhaps been astonished to see how many other issues had got attached to a simple problem of consolidation, he later made it clear that he had been convinced by the Academy's report, which he specifically attributed to Powell.[2] As for Hayden, his position was obscure. Though he might out of spite assist the enemies of consolidation and reform, he was personally an advocate of consolidation under the Department of the Interior, and he had a strong candidate for the directorship: himself. Shut out from the inner councils, misinformed by his Washington scouts,[3] Hayden had already been unhorsed, but neither he nor Congress knew it yet.

Perhaps because of the fear of losing its bill in the Public Lands Committee, which had been known to sit on reform measures before, the reform group suddenly changed its attack. Schurz wrote to Powell asking the precise wording of the legislation he proposed for embodying the Academy's suggestions (by now even Schurz was coming to headquarters for his data) and on the 23rd Powell sent back drafts of four items: a bill specifying the duties and salary of the superintendent of the combined Coast and land-parceling surveys; specifications of duties and salary of the director of a consolidated United States Geological Survey; the authorization for a commission to study and codify the land laws; and a proposed system for handling the publications of both the Coast-Land Parcelling Survey and the Geological Survey. But he prepared only the first of these as a separate bill. The second was to be attached as a rider to the Executive, Legislative, and Judicial Appropriations Bill, the third and fourth as riders to the Sundry Civil Appropriations Bill.[4] That way, the Public Lands Committee would be by-passed, and the drafts would go instead to the Appropriations Committee, chaired by John D. C. Atkins of Tennessee, a strong supporter of the reforms. Of this committee too Abram Hewitt was a member — as it turned out, its most important member. To Hewitt, it appears, must be traced the last-minute parliamentary maneuvering, some of it distinctly dubious, by means of which such important legislation found its way onto the floor of the House hidden behind the skirts of an appropriation bill.

In introducing the first appropriation bill for discussion on February 10, Atkins remarked that he thought the survey and land clauses the most important items in it. Events swiftly proved him right. Western Congressmen of the tribe of Gilpin sniffed the bill and smelled heresy, for the major premise of the land clauses and the *Arid Region* report upon which they were based was that a point had been reached in Western settlement where neither natural resources, especially water, nor social institutions were any longer adequate. To the Gilpin mind, here were people trying to talk the Great American Desert back into existence just after it had finally been established as a garden. Inadequate rainfall, sir? Why I can show you statistics, figures taken on the spot in Dakota. . . .

This was the high tide of the late seventies when homesteaders were tearing up the buffalo grass of Kansas and Nebraska and Colorado. These were years of big rains and fat crops, the years when facts and myths clashed sharply along the 100th meridian.[5] A wishful public and political consciousness had already accepted the doctrine of a climate changing for the better as settlement turned the sod and planted crops and trees.[6] That doctrine would persist through every plains frontier, into the Dakotas and Montana, across the international line into the Peace River country and all across the prairie provinces where it was gospel as late as World War I. In 1878 that folk belief matched a whole people's hopeful optimism, which had had none of the calamities of the eighteen-eighties to correct it, though the 1871 drouth in Kansas had temporarily discouraged extension of the farm frontier. No wonder Western legislatures angrily protested the proposed reforms. The reforms were aimed at the wheat belt, a region with a one-crop economy, and wheat farmers knew better than any politicians what was best for the country. And behind the incomprehension of the average man there was a somewhat less innocent resistance from landowners who did not want the convenient existing laws changed. They were doing fine with the laws already on the books.

Upon the flames of regional disgust the copies of the *Arid Region* that Powell had sent to western newspapers fell like gasoline. Though Godkin's *Nation* reviewed him seriously and with respect, Powell got no support from the western press. But though the hookups between land speculators, local land offices and surveyors, and the politicians were important in his opposition, what we have called the Gilpin mind was quite as important. To the Gilpin mind facts are not essential, though they are sometimes useful. What is more essential is vision, and the vision of Western politicians representing commonwealths eager for population and pressing for statehood was full of settlers, full of trainloads of immigrant farmers, full of new tracks, new roads, new towns rising on the prairie. The novel of settlement which classically ended with the first train chuffing into a bare western town between lanes of cheering farmers would emerge a little later as the dramatization of an abiding faith. Politically and economically the West as a boom market depended on vision far more than on facts; the facts could be taken care of later. Now here came Powell and the reform group with insinuations that were bad for business. The colonial bumptiousness of the lands they called the Arid Region grew violent at intimations of deficiency. Gilpin had said that the Mississippi Valley between the Alleghanies and the Rockies could support a population of 180,000,000. There were Congressmen who would probably have raised him, at least for rhetorical purposes.[7]

They made the most of the fact that this reform movement was sponsored by "scientific lobbyists" and supported mainly by representatives of states outside the so-called Arid Region. They squawked like captured ducks at the way in which the reformers had tried to slip their measures through by tying them to appropriations bills. They put the finger of ultimate responsibility squarely on Powell, where it belonged. Representative Patterson of Colorado called the whole program the work of one man, "a charlatan in science and intermeddler in affairs of which he has no proper conception." [8] The Hayden-Cope group circulated privately a defamatory report on Powell, and spread rumors of dissension within the Academy. The tearful defenders of the little man with 160 acres and a plow misconstrued the intention of the proposal completely and either through misunderstanding or malice pictured it as the preamble to landlordism. Somewhat more rationally, they attacked it as a step toward paternalism in government, though how the attempt to protect the small freeholder from speculators, the forces of Nature, and the manifest failure of the current public land laws could be considered a vicious undermining of the free American spirit is not quite clear. Still, Patterson and his fellows thought they recognized an enemy when they saw one, and these "new-fledged collegiates" and "scientific lobbyists" had all the earmarks.

The winds blew through the halls of Congress and the myths were invoked and the shibboleths spoken and the gospels reasserted. Like some Civil War battles, the struggle went on to the point of exhaustion, and beyond exhaustion to stalemate and compromise. It was February 18, 1879, after nine days of bitter debate, when the House voted by 98 to 79 a gutted measure consolidating the surveys and appointing a public lands commission, but dropping out entirely any actual alteration in the land laws or the surveying system. This would have been acceptable as something between defeat and victory, but the Republican Senate turned it into an absolute defeat, and incidentally attested the continuing potency of Hayden's lobby in the upper house, by repudiating the whole thing and writing in an amendment discontinuing every survey but Hayden's.

Active and astute as he had shown himself, Powell was at that point powerless to avert the complete ruin of his plan. What was saved was saved by Hewitt, who hung on tenaciously through the conference committee meetings on the appropriation bill, and at the last minute managed to write into the Sundry Civil Bill the clauses consolidating the three Western surveys under the Department of the Interior and authorizing a commission to study the problems of the public lands. The clauses thus returned to the condition the House had left them in, and in that condition were passed by Congress.

At the point when the Sundry Civil Expenses Bill passed on March 3, 1879, silence should have settled upon the field. Immediate attempts to reform the land laws were blocked; Western Congressmen had no real interest in the survey and little to fear from an investigating commission, whose report could easily enough be covered over with dead leaves when it appeared. But silence could not fall until a director had been picked for the joined surveys. That directorship was intensely and persistently sought by Professor Hayden. Apparently, with Wheeler and the War Department out, he feared only Powell as a rival. But Powell had been sincere in his offer the previous May to pull out of geology and devote himself to ethnology. By his own specific request to Atkins, there was in the same Sundry Civil Expenses Bill that created the United States Geological Survey [9] an almost-unnoticed item:

> For completing and preparing for publication the contributions to North American ethnology, under the Smithsonian Institution, twenty thousand dollars: *Provided,* that all of the archives, records, and material relating to the Indians of North America, collected by the geographical and geological survey of the Rocky Mountains, shall be turned over to the Institution, that the work may be completed and prepared for publication under its direction. . . .

That changed the Powell Survey into the Bureau of Ethnology [10] and made it again an adjunct of the Smithsonian, out of the political wind. Pilling's question, "What will become of we poor ethnologists?" was answered while everyone was looking in another direction. There was no need for Major Powell to spoil his look of impeccable, though somewhat political, rectitude by becoming a candidate for the directorship of the united surveys. Nevertheless, his refusal to enter the competition did not mean that he intended to keep hands off. He threw his weight solidly behind Clarence King for the job; he took pains, from motives that were a peculiar mixture of personal dislike and concern for science and public probity, to denounce Hayden to Representative Garfield, to

Atkins, and to President Hayes. He smoked out King's friends — Marsh, William Brewer, Hewitt, and others — to intercede with Hayes in King's behalf. He or his office clerks kept nudging scientific correspondents to work on their Senators to confirm if King were appointed.[11]

King was nominated on March 20 and confirmed by the Senate, without incident, in April, 1879. The scientific battlers wiped their blades. King wrote Powell a letter of deep gratitude for his support. "I am sure you will never regret your decision [presumably the decision to eliminate himself as a candidate] and for my part it will be one of my greatest pleasures to forward your scientific work and to advance your personal interest." [12]

"The best and brightest man of his generation" was thus established at the head of the bureau whose potential for the future so stirred Henry Adams.[13] Lieutenant Wheeler was out, scheduled to go on disgruntledly attacking civilian surveys and chewing the bitter weed of the Powell-Hewitt coup for a good many years.[14] Hayden was down. To retain anything at all of what he had had he was forced to accept a position as a geologist under King, and that position he would fill in taciturn obscurity until failing health drove him to retirement shortly before his death in 1887. And Powell was snug in his Bureau of Ethnology, securely wedged between friends at the Smithsonian and friends in the United States Geological Survey. Consolidation itself could not have turned out better. In the struggle for public land law reform, the Gilpins had won, but they knew they had been in a fight. At the very least, system and organization in government science had benefited, and that could lead to other gains, as could the Public Lands Commission to which Powell, Thomas Donaldson, and Alexander Britton had been appointed to assist Clarence King and Commissioner Williamson of the General Land Office. There was no doubt at all that the report finally brought in by that group of men would echo the thesis and at least some of the proposals of the *Arid Region* report and the report of the National Academy.

It did, a year later, and it was acknowledged and ignored by the Public Lands Committee of Congress as Powell expected it would be.[15] But it was on the record, and like a spore that lies around for years awaiting the chance to germinate, it might come to something in the future. It couldn't help doing so. The fat report compiled by Thomas Donaldson from the committee's investigations is a complex and not always statistically correct volume, but it was the first systematic study of the public domain and it has been indispensable to scholars and planners ever since. In a cumbersome and inadequate way it represents the completion of Powell's plan for a comprehensive study of the public domain and its needs and laws and history. Like so many of his projects, he had had to delegate it instead of finishing it himself.

But in the meantime it must have been some satisfaction to provide ideas for the nation's great men, and play politics for stakes vital to two fifths of the United States, and have the ear of Presidents. A self-taught Illinois schoolteacher could have done worse.

He stood, as a matter of fact, near the top of the scientific society in which he had chosen to conduct his life. Professor Hilgard of the Naval Observatory was already pushing his nomination to the National Academy.[16] He was an active member of the Philosophical Society of Washington which included practically every notable scientist in the capital. He had been once, briefly, a kind of national hero, and he had established a solid reputation as a geologist and ethnologist. On November 16, 1878, busy as usual in a dozen directions, energetically persuading Congressmen, directing research, pursuing his own studies, providing opinion for the National Academy, drawing up sample bills, trying to convert Western editors to his land policies, and circumventing Hayden's lobby, he had taken another step calculated to enhance and insure all his other activities and at the same time consolidate his gains. On that evening he invited over to his home on "M" Street a group of friends and colleagues that included Henry Adams, Dutton, Captain Garrick Mallery, Fred Endlich, James Kidder, and some others, and before they broke up they had organized the Cosmos Club — ever since that night the closest thing to a social headquarters for Washington's intellectual elite — and elected Powell its temporary president.[17]

Despite his innocent and non-political station as head of a bureau of the Smithsonian, he was already a man with power in his hands. Only a little more growth and two more years of extending his acquaintance and his influence would make him in fact the most powerfully situated scientist in America.

IV

THE REVENUE OF NEW DISCOVERY

1. The Best and Brightest Man of His Generation

BY 1879 CLARENCE KING had shown every sign of living up to the extravagant expectations of his multitude of friends. The qualities that had instantly captivated Henry Adams when the two met in a shack in Estes Park in the summer of 1871, that combination of "physical energy, social standing, mental scope and training, wit, geniality, and science, that seemed superlatively American and irresistibly strong,"[1] had brought him very young to great prominence. His *Mountaineering in the Sierra Nevada* gave him a place with Bret Harte and Joaquin Miller as a founder of a California school of literature. His exposé of the 1872 Diamond Swindle was a spectacular stroke of imagination and integrity. His *Systematic Geology,* the culminating volume in the reports of the King Survey which he had conceived and promoted when he was barely twenty-five, gave him entrée into any scientific society. He had expensive tastes, glittering friends. Schurz and others in high places were his intimates; with Henry and Clover Adams and the John Hays he was one of the tight little group that called itself the Five of Hearts and made the most fascinating conversation that any American salon ever heard. King's conversation was proverbial, almost fabulous. He must have been one of the nimblest and most challenging talkers of his time, and in the Pacific Union Club of San Francisco or the Century Club in New York he drew hearers as light draws moths.[2]

"He knew more than Adams did of art and poetry; he knew

America, especially west of the hundredth meridian, better than anyone; he knew the professor by heart, and he knew the Congressman better than he did the professor. He knew even women; even the American woman; even the New York woman, which is saying much. Incidentally he knew more practical geology than was good for him. . . . He had in him something of the Greek — a touch of Alcibiades or Alexander. One Clarence King only existed in the world." [3]

So much for the man. As for the job, the consolidated survey now inherited by this paragon was thought by Abram Hewitt the solidest accomplishment of his twelve years in Congress — and Hewitt was considered by Adams the "most useful public man in Washington." [4]

The possibilities were stimulating, the director fantastically able. Yet at the very beginning King ran into ambiguities in the organic law, which was a last-minute compromise written in as an amendment to an appropriation bill and so loosely phrased that no one could be sure either of the director's duties or the scope of the survey's activities. The law discontinued the existing surveys and made an appropriation of $100,000 for the new one, directing that all its collections go to the National Museum. It further said that the director, at a salary of $6000, should "have the direction of the Geological Survey, and the classification of the public lands, and examination of the geological structure, mineral resources, and products of the national domain. And that the Director and members of the Geological Survey shall have no personal or private interests in the lands or mineral wealth of the region under survey, and shall execute no surveys or examinations for private parties or corporations." [5] And that was all.

Very early in his administration King consulted with the Appropriations Committee and with Schurz in an attempt to discover what the law meant by the term "national domain." [6] Upon their definition depended the whole scope of the survey, for if "national domain" meant "public lands," (as Schurz shortly and rather absurdly ruled that it did) then no real survey of mineral resources was possible. All working mines were on private or corporate land, as were many undeveloped mineral veins. Only if "national domain" could be interpreted as meaning the whole area of national sovereignty could these be examined.

Also, what sort of classification of the public lands did Congress have in mind? Did it want a careful scientific examination based upon accurate — and slow and expensive — topographical and hydrographic and geological surveys, or did it want merely a quick rule-of-thumb classification for the use of the General Land Office? And if it wanted this latter, how about the fact that up to now the General Land Office had always made that rough classification for itself?

The uncomfortable fact was that the organic law of the Geological Survey contained unrelated leftovers from Powell's campaign for a reform of public land policies, and the leftovers now embarrassed King. Powell was himself unable to unsnarl the practical difficulties. The Public Lands Commission of which he was the dominant member finished its deliberations in the spring of 1880, and it had to conclude that no bureau, either the Geological Survey or the General Land Office, could accurately classify the public lands in advance of sale without temporarily halting the spread of settlement. It was a dilemma Powell would face later in connection with his irrigation surveys: planning for a completely empty public domain would have been simple enough, but planning for a public domain already planlessly, wastefully, and competitively filling up was another matter. King, assuming that Congress had not contemplated the closing of the public domain while he classified its lands, and seeing that his appropriation was nowhere near large enough for that sort of classification anyway, simply accepted that aspect of his stated duties, and then ignored it in practice.[7]

Restriction of his geological work to the public lands was more hampering, for a national survey whose field of work was steadily shrinking as settlement spread, and whose preparation of maps and tracing of geological strata and mineral veins were constantly being stopped at uncrossable boundary lines, would be completely frustrated. Mineral surveys would be most impeded, and minerals were precisely the thing King was most interested in. Though he might give up the classification of the public lands, he could not give up on this other issue. Immediately he stimulated the introduction of a resolution authorizing the extension of survey activities to the states as well as the "national domain" as interpreted by Schurz.[8] He pushed that resolution hard, but it ran into opposition and died in committee. During the recess he maneuvered for its consideration, and when Congress re-convened he pushed it again with Chairman H. G. Davis of the Appropriations Committee. To forestall local jealousies and fears, he sent telegrams in February, 1880, to the directors of all the extant state geological surveys, assuring them that he had no intention of infringing their rights and territories and promising his fullest co-operation with their work.[9]

His assurances were not enough, and King's personal charm was not enough. Throughout his brief administration the Geological Survey was restricted to the public lands. Even if King had been in the best of health and had remained completely absorbed in his job it is doubtful that he could have pushed the resolution through. And actually he was neither healthy nor absorbed. During the summer of 1880 there were two ominous symptoms of what was in store for the best and brightest man of his generation. One was a bout of illness, prophetic of the breakdown that some years later would put him into the Bloomingdale asylum. The other was an increasing tendency to give only the minimum of time to the affairs of the Geological Survey, and in his off weeks to go whoring after Mexican gold mines. In a few months they would lure him completely out of the government service.

King's friends all believed, and wrote it voluminously into the record, that he left the Geological Survey to devote himself to personal scientific studies. They could have seen by his production and by his actions that he didn't. His scientific work after 1880 is negligible, even trivial, and his days and nights after he retired from the survey were obviously not spent over scientific books. He quit the Geological Survey because he frankly wanted to be rich. The six thousand dollars he received as salary was a contemptible fraction of his money needs. He had relatives to support and his own tastes were extravagant. He maintained a valet, he belonged to expensive clubs, he collected art objects, his bachelor habits ran strongly to expensive suppers and champagne. By 1880 his personal indulgences were a more compelling motive than his love for abstract science.

He took leave from the Geological Survey in September, 1880, to go west and recover from his illness. When he felt himself well again, in Arizona, he wrote for further leave and used it for a trip by muleback into Sonora to examine a mine — a thing his government position prevented him from doing in the States. He did more than inspect it: he liked its looks so well that he exerted his charm on owners and public officials in Hermosillo and convinced them that he was just the man, as actually he was, to import modern methods and turn the property into a big money-maker. Returning to New York in February, 1881, after more than five months' absence from his office, he paid little attention to the office. In his pocket he had authorization to promote and develop and modernize the Prietas mine, and during the next few weeks when he might have been fighting the Survey's battles in Congress he was out on other business half the time. Much of the time while his clerk McChesney sent shotgun telegrams to a half dozen people trying to locate the boss, King was in a close huddle with Alexander Agassiz, already rich on Lake Superior copper, and his brother-in-law Henry Lee Higginson, whom Boston would remember as the founder of the Boston Symphony and the donor of Soldiers' Field and the Harvard Union.

Both Agassiz and Higginson were as open to a good investment as they were to a sound benefaction, and they were no more immune than other men to King's persuasiveness. The Grand Central Mining Company had already been formed with the three as partners when King sent his resignation to President Garfield on March 11, 1881. On March 17 Mrs. Henry Adams wrote her father, "King went away for good on Monday, to our extreme regret, having got out of office, named and seen confirmed his successor, Powell of Illinois, in whom he has great confidence. He did it so noiselessly that Professor Hayden, who would have done his best to upset it, knew nothing of it till it was done." [10]

One may be permitted a small doubt about how much persuasion King had to use on Garfield to get Powell named in his place. Garfield, just inaugurated, had been a Powell supporter since 1868, had carried through Congress the bill granting Powell's party the right to draw supplies from army posts, had backed him in the investigations of 1874 and supported his consolidation and land-reform scheme in 1879. He had even got a favor in return, when Powell loaned him his young secretary, Joseph Stanley-Brown, in

1878. When Powell's name came before the new President in 1881, Stanley-Brown was Garfield's confidential secretary, and in a little while would be his son-in-law. Through Stanley-Brown, through years of personal friendship, through Garfield's position as a regent of the Smithsonian, Powell was closer to Garfield than to any President under whom he served in more than thirty years. Actually he was a good deal closer than King was. And Garfield himself told the National Academy shortly after the change that he consulted only one man about a successor to King. The man was not King, but Spencer Baird, Secretary of the Smithsonian, who recommended Powell. The discrepancy between the two stories would be frivolous if it were not a symptomatic revelation of how King's friends, and perhaps King himself, exaggerated his influence and effect.

Overpraised or not, Clarence King in the spring of 1881 left science and began a period of fabulous money-making, fabulous eating and drinking, fabulous coursing of Europe's artistic capitals, fabulous and quixotic benefactions, fabulous and nearly criminal carelessness in the conduct of his firm's London office. "The chances were great," Henry Adams had felt in the early days of their friendship, "that he could, whenever he chose to quit the Government service, take the pick of the gold and silver, copper or coal, and build up his fortune as he pleased. . . . With ordinary luck he would die at eighty the richest and most many-sided genius of his day." [11]

He looked to be well on the road. And he left to Powell his infant bureau, hamstrung on the problem of land classification and imprisoned within the public lands, a bureau with a small staff and a hundred-thousand-dollar budget and with the unknowns of half the continent for its targets.

Powell already had in hand another bureau that might have been considered sufficient occupation. Though its 1881 budget was only $25,000, it took for its province the whole Science of Man as it was revealed among the North American Indians. Four years before, Henry Adams had urged such an organized study upon Lewis Morgan as an indispensable foundation for the modern study of history,[12] and Morgan's preface to his monumental *Ancient Society* in 1877 had echoed Adams' conviction that American ethnology was destined to make over the fashionable theories of history.

Powell, Morgan, and Adams would all be involved in that making over, Adams not the least. A passenger visiting the engine room of American society, curiously watching the thrust and stroke of pistons and drivers, Adams saw more, and saw it more acutely, than any of his contemporaries. He was one of the few non-scientists who understood the importance and the implications of the developing scientific bureaus in Washington. As a historian who read "tubs of geology" because geology was after all only history carried a little farther back than Mr. Jefferson, he could appraise the effect on thought of the revolutionary discoveries in American geology and the study of the rich tribal cultures of America. That sort of study he might have selected for Morgan, the most eminent anthropologist in the country, or for his friends Agassiz or King, superbly equipped and with the wealth and social standing that made them better companions at dinner.

But who in fact undertook it was a one-armed little man with a bristly beard, a homemade education, and an intense concentration of purpose. When he assumed the joint directorship of the two bureaus he had created, Powell had in his control a good part of the Science of Man and the Science of the Earth, and he conceived both in the broadest possible terms. In most things he was quite as clearsighted as Adams; in some he saw even clearer. Both anthropology and geology were, as he put it, "nascent." Both stood in need of what he was best equipped to give them — system — and system not imposed arbitrarily from without but system developed during years of hard work in the field and the office. Not only could he see more of the possibilities of his government bureaus than King could but he wanted both these jobs, his life was in them. He was incorrigibly sane, and he was also as shrewd as any opposition he was likely to encounter. He understood the Congressman, it turned out, better than King, better perhaps than Adams, who understood that "criminal class" to its foundations. And he had no ambition to get rich. If he had any single ambition it was the remarkable one of being of service to science, and through science to mankind.

In his dozen years in Washington he had grown incomparably more skillful and confident in promotion, direction, administration. By now he knew an amateur from a professional, and though he might still practice a little amiable nepotism he never put anyone but a man of the highest competence in a responsible position. He chose his men for ability and training, and his hands were on the levers of some of the most important, though not necessarily the noisiest, machinery in the engine room. Also, somewhere along the line the youthful vanity and self-importance had worn off. A scientific public hero had grown into a scientific public servant.

He was supremely and cheerfully confident. In the National Academy, the Philosophical Society, the Association for the Advancement of Science, the Cosmos Club, he moved at the core of the group which was itself the core of American science. In his two bureaus he could enlist the collaboration of the greatest, he was in correspondence with scientists the world over, and he controlled several series of enviably lavish government publications. Finally, he was blissfully, almost alarmingly free of Congressional controls. The Bureau of Ethnology was responsible only to the Smithsonian. The Geological Survey, having been created in an appropriation bill, drew a lump-sum budget without specific and detailed expenditures. Powell could spend his appropriation as seemed best to him, subject only to Treasury audit.

Thus at the beginning of the eighteen-eighties the three men whose careers inevitably suggest comparisons and contrasts to a student of history had each made his characteristic move. By 1880 Henry Adams had published his novel *Democracy,* though its authorship would not be commonly known until Henry Holt, the publisher, revealed it in 1918. That novel, good humored as it was, sprang from Adams' disillusion and disgust with the country that his family had helped start on a more promising path. The cynicism and the outrageous exaggeration and paradox would grow on Adams, but they were already clear in his first anonymous novel. By 1880 Henry Adams was already on the verge of retreat from the spectacle of his country. As for Clarence King, he was already turning away from the public service at the time when he might have done most in it, and shoving off into the current of exploitation and promotion that swept along so many of his contemporaries. He was not, like Adams, hopeless and cynical. On the contrary he was a man of an extraordinary and ebullient optimism. But his hope was a hope of private wealth and personal indulgence, sadly in key with the self-interest that drove the politicians and the tycoons.

And while Adams was dipping his pen in acid to record the bazaar along Pennsylvania Avenue, and Clarence King was hopping on his mule to track down a Mexican gold mine, John Wesley Powell was sitting down in a shabby hand-me-down office to organize the sciences of the earth and the Science of Man.

A decade later he would have more sweeping powers, for a brief time and in certain matters, than any man in the nation, not excepting the President. But even in 1881 there was perhaps not a scientist in the world who enjoyed as much real power or as many opportunities.

2. *Adding the Stone Age to History*

WHEN IN THE EIGHTEEN-NINETIES Powell attempted to summarize what he had learned in sixty years of intense receptivity to knowledge, he divided the grand Science of Man into five smaller "sciences." The fifth of these he called "Sophiology"[1]—a term that like many of his coinages has not caught on. Under it he grouped all the speculations that men have made in the attempt to understand or explain phenomena, everything from the most primitive animism to experimental science. And of the thousand methods the tribes of men had discovered, only science was verifiable; the rest was mythology; to modern science all human history funneled down. From thaumaturgy to research was not merely a progress, but a triumph. The method at least was final. Through it, phenomena could be indefinitely studied and the results verified, whether the phenomena concerned the natural world or the very superstitions and metaphysical systems and magics that science had replaced.

Primitive cosmologies and mythologies, Powell said, persisted in more advanced stages of society in the same way that vestigial organs persisted in the body. Evolution worked upon institutions as it worked upon the physical organism, but it worked irregularly and slowly. "More people believe in mascots than believe in telephones, and those who believe in mascots believe that telephones are magical." The mythological and magical beliefs of recorded history, plus their folklore survivals, could be directly compared with the similar mythologies of the American Indian tribes, as Lewis Morgan had compared tribal kinship patterns with kinship patterns the world over, and the comparative study could shed, for the first time, real light on the development of civilization.

For Powell, though he adopted Morgan's savage-barbarous-civilized stages of society and accepted without revision Morgan's theory of the kinship basis for savage institutions,[2] social evolution was not quite the even stairway that Morgan and some European anthropologists would have it. The diversity of culture among the American Indians made rigid systematization difficult. But there was a human progress, nevertheless, a series of bench marks that Morgan had defined. The lowest level, savagery, built its institutions on a system of kinship traced through the female line. Children belonged to the clan of the mother; husbands were mere visitors in the wife's clan. Property was of the clan, not of the individual; on the individual's death any strictly personal property was normally buried with its owner or destroyed. Marriage within the clan was taboo; religion was ordinarily a zootheistic adjunct of the clan system, each clan having its tutelary animal deity. Roughly, this was the pattern of Indian tribal society as Morgan had unearthed it in his study of the League of the Iroquois and of many other tribes. The tribes were not "nations," and they were not made up of "families," and the notion of owning land individually was as repugnant to most of them as the notion of owning the air. Inheritance in white patterns was impossible, our treaties with the Indian "nations" absurd: few tribes numbered more than a few hundred souls, though confederacies sometimes brought together a few thousand.

Morgan's discovery of some of the true bases of savage society was rich in consequences, one of which was the decision of the United States in the seventies to stop treating with tribal chiefs as if they were kings of petty nations, and to quit drawing up treaties that neither side was capable of abiding by. Other consequences were of the kind Henry Adams envisaged, the kind that would force the reconsideration of historical beliefs. It is no accident that Marx and Engels found in Morgan's work scientific support for the materialistic view of history, and that to some Marxist believers even today Morgan stands very little below Marx as a philosopher of ineluctable social change.[3]

His work led directly toward the notion of an evolved and perfect state, for above the savagery of the Indian tribes he saw a middle stage of culture which he called barbarism, and which was best exemplified by the patriarchal herdsman society of the Old Testament. In this stage, agriculture had been developed, animals domesticated, property diverted from communal to personal use. Morgan drew the dividing line between savagery and barbarism at the development of pottery, Tyler at the development of tillage. Powell, regularizing Morgan's system, made it at the line where kinship in the female line gave way to kinship through the male, when the clan was replaced by the gens.[4] The difference is small, for one cultural change was the logical consequence of the others. In barbarism, thaumaturgy and its shamans or priests still colored every phase of life, but as in savagery, civil and religious authority were separate. By the "civilized" stage of society, feudal or monarchical institutions made their appearance: serfdom, guilds, caste, sometimes slavery. Civil and religious authority tended to coalesce, shaman and chief fused, and all the institutions of private property emerged full blown.

It is easy to see why Morgan's theories appealed to Marx and Engels. They made private property an ephemeral incident in human history, they challenged the notion that any institution was either sacred or permanent, most of all they assumed a world-wide, verifiable, and inevitable progress from stage to stage of human society. Neither Morgan's theories nor Powell's slight modifications of them are unusual in their time. Not only Marx and Engels but Herbert Spencer and Lester Ward and a host of lesser thinkers were moving on roughly parallel tracks. But it is interesting to note where Powell, at least, diverges from the inevitabilities of Marx, for though he accepts at every point the evolutionary view of history, he does not sound like a materialist all the way.

Beyond the monarchical stage of civilization Powell saw "Republickism" — another of his mildly hideous coinages — in which the chief sanctions of power were not magic, not kinship, not raw force, not property, but ethics and conscience. At that level representative government and social and political equality replaced divine right and caste. Society was organized in nations, on a territorial basis, rather than by caste or gens or clan. *Civitas* replaced *Societas.* Somewhere in that shining future when Republickism would be attained by all the world, there would be a responsible delegation of powers to elected or appointed representatives. That is, Powell's utopian last stage of social evolution looked very like a vacuum-cleaned Illinois. To republican institutions, to Science, to responsibility and the social conscience, all the world must ultimately come.

Henry Adams would have smiled, but there have been worse dreams. Clarence King in a characteristic joke spoke of the development of society from savagery through barbarism to vulgarity, but cynicism was easier to a King or a Henry Adams than to a man bred on the midwestern frontier. Confronted with the dilemma of evolutionary thought, Powell chose the hopeful horn. In 1882, in a lecture on Darwin, he showed himself not merely undismayed but serenely confident: "Had philosophers discovered that the generation of living beings were degenerating they would have discovered despair. Had they discovered that life moves by steps of generations in endless circles — that what has been is, and what is shall be, and there is no progress, the gift of science to man would have been worthless. . . . The revelation of science is this: Every generation in life is a step in progress to a higher and fuller life; science has discovered hope."[5]

Man was no mere organism at the mercy of forces, as naturalist novelists had already begun to hint. Powell could cite Huxley in corroboration of his belief that man was in fact no longer subject to biotic evolution, but had acquired through intelligence the power to hold his own physical characteristics and to mold his environment to his desires. Evolutionary science as Powell interpreted it denied any and all theories of human degeneration from a perfect state. It repudiated alike the myth of the Garden and the Fall, the iron rigidity of Calvinism, the sentimental nostalgia for an olden and perfect time with which Arcadian poets and idealist philosophers had endowed the idea, and even the modernized version that Henry Adams, also reinterpreting history, would eventually issue as his historical application of the second law of thermodynamics.

For Powell the road led up toward Perfection, not down from it. Even his conception of the origin of language, which postulated many simultaneous or parallel discoveries of the arts of speech in many parts of the world, and their gradual concentration toward fewer and simpler and better languages, was opposed to the view which thought of diversity as a curse visited upon the sinful at Babel, or as the disintegration of some parent Indo-European or other complex and perfect tongue.[6] The world worked toward unity, toward co-operation, toward "Republickism," toward ethics and conscience and representative government, toward greater and greater cultural amalgamation, toward the final triumph of science. Gabriel has spoken of Powell as "the high priest of science" in the eighties.[7] Major Powell would not have liked the label, for it linked science and thaumaturgy. Thaumaturgy and its priesthoods were vestigial; science was climactic.

The will to discover all the possible means by which human aspiration and belief and custom had been institutionalized, and the conviction that every variant could be placed somewhere on an evolutionary stairway, gave direction and system to Major Powell's work in ethnology. Looking abroad from the vantage point of American industrial civilization he could include in his view the whole instructive spread of the American tribal cultures clear down to the level of a half housed, half clothed, half human, scatophagic tribe like the Seris of Lower California. The savage and the barbarous were there in many phases; their study could indeed, as Henry Adams had said to Lewis Morgan, profoundly alter the traditional views of human history.

When he eased into the directorship of the Bureau of Ethnology in the spring of 1879, Powell was in the best position in the world to direct a battery of scientific intelligences upon the origins and evolution of language, the forms and styles of Amerind art, the glacially slow growth of social and political and religious institutions within tribal cultures. Through study of these savage cultures he might throw light on the history of human culture at large. He could also help determine the pre-Columbian equilibrium of the continent and the impact of white upon red, mercantile and industrial upon neolithic.

The opportunity was not only unparalleled in that it gave him the chance to centralize in one bureau all the scattered, undirected, overlapping, and often amateur work being done on the Indians, but it was fleeting. For some things, 1879 was already too late.

One of the most obvious facts of history to the white Americans who by discovery, exploration, trade, bullets, rum, treaties, and the Word of God took over the continent from its aboriginal inhabitants was that the aboriginal inhabitants were doomed to extinction, and soon. The Kansas editor who prayed for the day when Lo and all his tribe should be obliterated felt that though the day was unwarrantably delayed, yet he could rest in hope. As early as 1823 James Fenimore Cooper, following Thomas Campbell, following Chateaubriand, had stamped the portrait of the vanishing Noble Savage indelibly on our literature, and elegiac Indian oratory of the Chief Logan kind was a staple of the salons even before the Revolution. Like a racing whippet after a mechanical rabbit, literary sentiment would pursue frontier ferocity across the westering nation. The same people who collaborated in the Indian's wrongs could — quite honestly and even simultaneously — denounce the juggernaut that was destroying him.

Quite honestly. For however sympathetically or even sentimentally a white American viewed the Indian, the industrial culture was certain to eat away at the tribal cultures like lye. One's attitude might vary, but the fact went on regardless. What destroyed the Indian was not primarily political greed, land hunger, or military power, not the white man's germs or the white man's rum. What destroyed him was the manufactured products of a culture, iron and steel, guns, needles, woolen cloth, things that once possessed could not be done without.[8] And the destruction visited upon the Indian was not precisely or always what the public thought it would be. It was not the literal extermination of the race. Though systems of counting differ, there are by some systems at least half as many Indians within the continental United States now as there probably were when Columbus touched the Indies, and this in spite of the obliteration of dozens of whole tribes by war, disease, and cultural disintegration.[9]

It was not the continuity of the Indian race that failed; what failed was the continuity of the diverse tribal cultures. These exist now only in scattered, degenerated reservation fragments or among such notably resistant peoples as the Pueblo and Navajo of the final, persistent Indian Country. And here what has protected them is aridity, the difficulties in the way of dense white settlement, the accident of relative isolation, as much as the stability of their own institutions. Even here a Hopi dancer with tortoise shells on his calves and turquoise on his neck and wrists and a kirtle of fine traditional weave around his loins may wear down his back as an amulet a nickel-plated Ingersoll watch, or a Purple Heart medal won in a white man's war. Even here, in Monument Valley where not one Navajo in ten speaks any English, squaws may herd their sheep through the shadscale and rabbitbrush in brown and white saddle shoes and Hollywood sunglasses, or gather under a juniper for gossip and bubblegum. The lye still corrodes even the resistant cultures. Some of the Pueblo villages are all but dissolved; some others are held together as much by white sentiment and assistance as by their own cohesiveness.

By the time Major Powell began to study Indians, urged on by Professor Henry's ambition to gather under the Smithsonian as much as he could of ethnological research, the cultures of the eastern Indians were either extinct or so altered, debased, interpenetrated and diluted and mixed one with another and with white civilization that much of the ethnologist's work was all but archaeological. The eastern tribes from the Abenaki of Maine to the transplanted remnants of Creeks and Choctaws in Indian Territory beyond the Mississippi were already difficult to study. For some tribes not even vocabularies had been preserved, few records of the legendry and lore, only random collections of artifacts. The Far West was in 1879 still the home of tribes with some of their traditional culture left, yet so interesting a tribe as the Mandans had been practically wiped out by smallpox before more than a handful of students reached them. The bellicose Arikaras were almost gone, their relatives the Pawnees were going. And the disruption and the consequent speedup of cultural exchange that began with the first white traders had not only moved many tribes from their ancestral homes, but sometimes had moved them clear out of one culture and into another. The Mohicans and Iroquois of Pennsylvania and New York were not quite as extinct as James Fenimore Cooper had implied: the chances were that their remnants were off beyond the Missouri acting as scouts and mercenaries for white cavalry. The Sioux, from woods Indians in Minnesota and Iowa, had become horse Indians of the Dakotas, and the horse revolution which was strictly a white contribution to Indian polity had transformed tribes from Texas to the North Saskatchewan.

All of this — what had been before white intrusion and what remained after four centuries of war and exchange — was a subject to excite a scholarly mind, especially a mind galvanized by evolutionary science and tempted by the nineteenth-century exercise of synthesizing and codifying human knowledge. The leaven that worked in Herbert Spencer, Lester Ward, Lewis Morgan, worked just as powerfully in Powell. Pre-eminently he was a synthesizer, and the steps that preceded synthesis in any science were organization, classification, system. It was inevitable that when he got the chance to expand beyond the part-time ethnological studies of the Powell Survey he would try to systematize the study of the American Indian, long neglected, cluttered with the guesses of amateurs and the mythology and wishful thinking of Welshmen, Mormons, and popular romancers, conducted out of ignorance into fabrication, clouded with blood and old feuds, burdened with the missionary zeal that wanted to put all Indians into overalls with hoes in their hands, complicated by governmental bad faith and misunderstanding and by Indian hatred and instability — and almost too late. It was inevitable too that his interest in Indians should be cultural, that he should be concerned with them not for their cranial index but for the structure and institutions of their ethnic groups.

This was one of the two great works of his life. From the winter of 1868–69 in the White River Valley until his death in 1902 he worked, not with utter single-mindedness but with an unremitting purpose, to bring order out of the chaos and to substitute knowledge for the hatred, fear, sentimentality, hearsay, rumor, and legendry by which we knew the tribes of America. There is no especial drama in such a slaying of the dragons of error and confusion, but the achievement of his bureau was enormous, and Powell was the heart and brain of his bureau. After his death his successor, William Henry Holmes, put into his official eulogy something more than conventional applause:

> The Bureau of Ethnology is peculiarly his, the lines of research initiated by him being in the main those that must be followed as long as the Bureau lasts — in fact as long as the human race remains a subject of study. . . . It was a fortunate circumstance that his energies were directed to a field little encumbered by the forms, methods, and determinations of earlier students, since it enabled him to conduct his investigations on new lines, and thus to raise the science to a higher plane.
>
> The series of volumes published by the Bureau, which are more completely Powell's own than the world can ever know, are a splendid monument to his memory, and will stand, not only for himself but for the nation, among the most important contributions to human history ever made by an individual, an institution, or a state.[10]

He gave away his ethnological ideas to his assistants as liberally as he had given geological ideas to Gilbert and Dutton; still, he did not give everything away. After 1876 he was not really a practicing geologist except through his collaborators, but he was an ethnologist all his life. The last field work he did was in the shell heaps near his summer home at Haven, Maine, and when, after years in the scientific and political wars had crippled him for further battling, he turned toward philosophy and the attempted synthesis of knowledge, it was the Science of Man upon which he focused, and ethnology from which he drew both his major ideas and their illustration.

By that time he and his bureau had remade the science of cultural anthropology as thoroughly as the Powell Survey earlier had remade — or made — the science of physiography.

Disregarding the accounts of travelers, which sometimes, as in the case of the *Travels in North America* of Maximilian of Neuwied, were of great ethnological importance, there was only a handful of major landmarks in the study of the Indians before 1879. It is a demonstration of our long neglect that none of these came until the second quarter of the nineteenth century. Albert Gallatin's *Synopsis of the Indian Tribes . . . of North America,* with which American ethnology properly begins, was not published until 1836, though preliminary studies had appeared earlier. *The Indian Tribes of North America,* by Thomas McKenney and James Hall, was published in three volumes between 1836 and 1844, George

Catlin's two-volume *Illustrations of the Manners and Customs and Conditions of the North American Indians* in 1844. Henry R. Schoolcraft's government-subsidized *Historical and Statistical Information Respecting the History, Conditions, and Prospects of the Indian Tribes of the United States* appeared as six serial volumes between 1851 and 1857. Morgan's *League of the Iroquois* came in 1851, his *Ancient Society* not until 1877.

The pictorial recorders were hardly more alert. Though dozens of people, beginning with Jacques Lemoyne de Morgues in 1564 in Florida, had sketched Indians and characteristic Indian ceremonies and customs, there was no concerted or official effort in that direction until John Calhoun, then Secretary of the Interior, collaborated with Governor Cass of Michigan Territory and Thomas McKenney, Indian Commissioner, in sponsoring an Indian Gallery in 1824. The gallery was begun at five dollars per painting by James Otto Lewis, and was continued by others — Charles Bird King, A. Ford, S. M. Charles, G. Cooke — some of them nameless or mere initials. McKenny and Hall's *The Indian Tribes of North America* assured itself a permanent usefulness by reproducing one hundred twenty portraits in color copied from the Indian Gallery by Henry Inman. Inman's copies are still preserved in Harvard's Peabody Museum, but almost the entire Gallery of originals, which found its way to the Smithsonian under Joseph Henry's sheltering wing in 1858, was destroyed in the Smithsonian fire seven years later.

By that time there were two other galleries of Indian paintings: that of George Catlin, painted in the years following 1831 and widely exhibited from 1837 on, and that of John Mix Stanley, probably superior as art and at least as valuable for its preservation of vanishing cultural details. The fate of the Stanley paintings was more lamentable than that of the Indian Gallery. They came into the national collection on loan in 1852, but their sponsors were unable to induce Congress to appropriate money to buy the more than two hundred paintings made among forty-three tribes. As another Congress would later do with the Civil War photographs of Matthew Brady, this one ignored a collection that on its very face was of inestimable national value. Before the end, Professor Henry was paying Stanley an annual pittance to keep the collection together. Eventually it too, except for a few canvases hung in another wing, went up in the 1865 Smithsonian fire. Not even copies or reproductions were saved, so that what might have been an influential record has had little effect on students or critics. Of the three early collections of Indian paintings, only Catlin's survives.[11]

The value to the student of all these paintings and drawings is great. The worth of the early ethnological summaries is variable. Gallatin is of first importance because his classification of the tribes by language provided the key to almost all later research, Morgan because he first understood tribal society. Catlin's Gallery, composed of equal parts art exhibit, waxworks, museum diorama, and Wild West Show, is debatable as art but unquestionably valuable as scientific illustration, for Catlin throughout his painting showed as commendable a desire for authenticity as if he feared he would have to establish it in court. There is hardly a painting without its affadavit. McKenney and Hall, with their ten dozen portraits in color, are an invaluable source for the fleeting details of broken tribal cultures — the styles of face and body painting, the costumes, the headdresses and modes of hairdress, the ornaments. As for Schoolcraft, though his six volumes comprise a virtual encyclopedia of the Indian and are thus important, they are wretchedly organized, somewhat pompous, and weakened by jealousy of rival authorities, notably Catlin. All these books contributed to the summary of the state of knowledge near mid-century, but only Gallatin and Morgan are seminal. When Powell began, he began with hardly any real tools of research except Gallatin's basic classification, and even that was in need of modernization and revision. When Gallatin divided the American Indians into twenty-eight linguistic families, he admitted that his division was preliminary only: the vocabularies collected by Lewis and Clark had been lost and not replaced, and "with the exception of Salish, and of a few words of the Shoshonee and of the Chinook, we have as yet no knowledge of the Indian languages west of the Stony Mountains. . . ."[12]

Powell was better off. He himself knew something of three Shoshonean dialects — Ute, Paiute, and Hopi — and he had nearly seven hundred vocabularies that he and Professor Henry had taken over or borrowed from many sources. He could at least go ahead revising Gallatin. Yet there were almost unbelievable lacks, and where there was not lack there was chaos. So fundamental a matter as nomenclature, for instance:

When white men met a tribe of Indians for the first time, they generally called it either by the name it used for itself, by some nickname freakishly applied, or by a translation or mistranslation from the oral or sign-language name. But when they heard about a tribe from its neighbors they often used the name the neighbors used. Thus the French working westward along the canoe track from the St. Lawrence heard the Chippewas refer to their western enemies as *Nadowe-is-iw* — meaning "snake," and by metaphor, "enemy." The French corrupted this to Nadowessioux and then to Sioux. But these same Indians were universally referred to in sign language by a throat-cutting gesture, and in places and at times white men called them *Coup Gorge* or Cut-Throat. They called themselves the Dakota. But within the Dakota nation there were Yanktons, Sissetons, Oglalas, Santees, Tetons, several sub-tribes speaking three distinct dialects. And all around them — scattered, in fact, from the lower Mississippi to the North Saskatchewan and from the Carolinas to the Yellowstone country — were tribes who whatever their culture or physical conformation spoke some variant of that same Siouan tongue: Biloxis, Quapaws, Osages, Poncas, Kansas, Omahas, Iowas, Otoes, Missouris, Crows, Minnetarees, Mandans, Assiniboins, Tutelos. Clearly the language relationship was the only clue to classification among these widely scattered people of at least three distinct cultures. But what did you call them for scientific purposes, so that ethnological terminology would have the precision of the language of botany, say, and stock and tribe and clan be as definitely labeled as order, genus, species, and variety in biological works? It was Powell's premise that human taxonomy should be as precise as zoological or botanical. But Indian sounds did not always translate readily into English orthography; all the tribes had several names, with a fantastic range of spellings (even Gallatin, on his ethnographic map of 1836, spelled the Pend d'Oreilles "Ponderays"). Many had been named and renamed at different times by different people speaking different tongues. Sometimes sub-tribes and mere clans or family groups had been mistaken for separate tribes.

The fact was that no one had ever sat down seriously to clarify the muddle of the tribal names. No one knew for sure how many tribes there were or had been or what they should truly be called. No one had even established a principle of naming, and said whether priority, accepted usage, euphony, or something else should dictate nomenclature. So before the tribes could be reclassified on Gallatin's pattern with the addition of all the new knowledge available, someone had to do this pre-chore of what Powell called a "synonymy." That meant reading all through the enormous literature that in four hundred years had accumulated about the Indian — and there was no comprehensive bibliography.

Start from near scratch, then, with first steps: a bibliography, a synonymy, a considered nomenclature, and a more accurate classification of the tribes by linguistic affinity. Before starting to write the science of American ethnology, create its alphabet.

For the bibliography there was a man at hand — James Constantine Pilling, trained as a court reporter but diverted to geology and ethnology by his devotion to Major Powell. Dependable, tedious, stuffy, he set Clarence King's teeth on edge. He reminded King of George Hearst, who in Tucson was bitten on the privates by a scorpion, which fell dead. Yet Pilling in his way was sincerely loved, and he proved himself indispensable a hundred times. He was made to order for bibliographical research — had in fact already begun it under the Powell Survey. That work so casually begun occupied him for years. He labored over it until he had a vast tome, of which 100 sets of proofsheets were printed in 1885 for the use of collaborators and correspondents. When additions came in, stimulated by the preliminary sheets, Pilling patiently went on adding, digging out, hunting down. In the course of his work, which he carried on for many years in addition to his duties as Chief Clerk of the Geological Survey, he accumulated for the Bureau an ethnological library the equal of any in the world; he toured American libraries, and when he went to England to receive an inheritance he scoured Europe's libraries and bookshops. The bibliography grew as Pilling's sight weakened. It far outgrew any possible single set of covers and was issued piecemeal in fat Bulletins: *A Bibliography of the Siouan Languages, A Bibliography of the Iroquoian Languages, A Bibliography of the Muskhogean*

Languages, Notes On Eliot's Indian Bible. . . . One by one he plowed on through the great linguistic stocks, Algonkian, Athapascan, Chinookan, Salishan, Wakashan. The aim was utter definitiveness, completion. When Pilling died in 1895 after twenty years as Major Powell's amanuensis he had cleared away the brush for future scholars, collected a major anthropological library, and was well into two new bibliographical bulletins on the Shahaptian languages and the languages of Mexico.

Fuss-budget, meechy foster uncle, a filing-system man with painstakingness where his imagination might have been and devotion in the place of his ambition, he rendered an enormous service. As soon as a man with more imagination than he gave him a course to run on, he did a more than respectable life work. "Do you want to do Powell a favor? Poison Pilling," Clarence King wrote to his engineer Becker.[13] But if Becker had acted on his chief's advice there would have been a cornerstone unlaid, a pre-chore undone.

A pre-chore, at least, as it was first conceived. It was characteristic of Powell's labors that a preliminary job designed to prepare the way for future important research should itself become a major area of research, should consume twenty years of diligent labor and remain unfinished at the end. Considering the state he found his favorite sciences in, his ambition to organize and then master them was promethean. Almost every project he began ended the same way — his master atlas of the United States, his survey of reclamation sites in the West, his inclusive study of the public domain, his synthesis of the Science of Man. The only thing clearer than the failure of his grandiose schemes of study is the compelling weight of their partial accomplishment.

Whether or not his plans were scheduled for completion, it is a beautiful thing to watch so capable an administrator set up and activate a bureau. Everything needed doing at once, everything depended on everything else before it could be begun, yet what needed doing got done. The pamphlet that Powell had printed in 1877 for the use of his field workers was revised in 1880 as "An Introduction to the Study of the Indian Languages," and in quick succession it was followed by other manuals on the study of mortuary customs, sign language, medical practices, tribal governments, and mythology. "It is the purpose of the Bureau of Ethnology to organize anthropologic research in America," Powell wrote in his first annual report. The manuals were the beginning, useful to the bureau's full-time students but even more useful to the missionaries, army officers, local savants, enthusiasts, and pot-hunters whom Powell now enlisted as collaborators. By providing a center, an organization, and a system of study he channeled enthusiasms that had formerly frittered themselves away, and steered them until their results could prove valuable. Sometimes a local amateur was put on a salary briefly for a special job, once in a while one proved so able that he was brought in as a full employee. And even while the alphabet and syllabary of the science were being prepared, specialized studies were continued or begun, and their product published in the *Annual Reports.*

Among the things that Major Powell had learned in a decade or more was the lesson Hayden had taught — that both collaborators and Congressmen were impressed by publications. He had learned also how to delegate sections of his extensive plans. By now he was an exceptional judge of men and talents, and he retained his faculty of stirring his colleagues to extraordinary enthusiasm. It would be an empty effort for anyone but the historian of science to trace strand by strand the lines of research that Powell and his bureau put out during the eighties and nineties. For that sort of historian the study would be indispensable. The laborious, continued, careful, planned effort that Pilling put into the bibliographies was put in by others on different subjects. Colonel Garrick Mallery, for example, detailed like Captain Dutton for special duty with Powell, devoted ten years and more to the study of Indian sign language and Indian picture writing — the pre-speech and pre-alphabet of a continent. He related the sign language to the sign language of the deaf, the picture writing to all the known forms of calligraphy as well as to tattooing and body painting the world over. Mallery was a Yale man, with a temperament and a career very like Dutton's. Humorous, somewhat ribald, quaintly and curiously learned, he could turn a scholarly lecture on tattooing into a hilarious smoker talk or attack a whole unmapped region of anthropological research with Pilling's thoroughness. His monograph on picture writing, called a preliminary report, ran to 807 pages, with 1295 figures and 54 full-page plates, one of the most exhaustive and one of the most lavishly illustrated of all the Bureau's publications.[14]

As soon as Pilling had attained some degree of completeness in his preliminary bibliography, and Henry Henshaw and his assistants had made some headway against the intricate problems of the synonymy, Powell assigned himself the classification of the tribes. This too, issued in the delayed *7th Annual Report 1885–86*, (not published until 1891), was called a preliminary study. Powell never got back to it, but he never had much cause to. Like Mallery on sign language and picture writing, Yarrow on mortuary customs, Cyrus Thomas on the mounds, Royce on Indian land cessions, and Pilling on bibliography, it is a cornerstone.

The Honorable William Gilpin in celebrating the unifying effects of the North American continent had seen in the Indians "from Darien to the Esquimaux and from Florida to Vancouver's Island a perfect identity in hair, complexion, features, religion, stature, and language." Evidently he had not believed travelers on the subject of pale, blue-eyed, and even red-haired Mandans. Evidently he had not read or believed Gallatin, who found so much linguistic variety that he could trace no relationship whatever among twenty-eight different linguistic families made up of hundreds of distinct languages and dialects. Now Powell, in revising Gallatin, found not twenty-eight but fifty-eight distinct stocks, made up of over five hundred languages as different from one another as the languages of Europe. Most of the new ones came from the linguistically diverse West. Some of these stocks represented single small tribes, some many tribes much scattered. Powell, like Gallatin, accompanied his report with an ethnographic map to indicate the homelands of each. From Henshaw's synonymy studies he extracted names which, on the usual scientific principle of priority of use, seemed most logical for every stock and tribe. To distinguish stock name from tribe name he added a suffix, *-an* to the names of the stocks. Behind that standardized nomenclature he threw the Bureau of Ethnology's already great prestige and the persuasion of its own publications. It remains, as do the tribal classification and the ethnographic map, altered only in details. Powell was not himself a distinguished field ethnologist, as some of his men were, but in the 142 pages of a preliminary report he fixed the language of a science, mapped its divisions, and completed its basic classifications.[15]

As the years enriched his Bureau's findings, he gradually evolved another and more abstruse classification — the five-fold or "pentalogic" categories into which he divided all human activity. His pentalogy became something close to an obsession during his last years, yet it was for a long time an effective framework for research. What he called "Aesthetology" covered all arts, games, pleasures. "Technology" included all crafts and industries. "Sociology" took care of the institutions of society, of trade, of property, of the family or clan or gens. "Philology" grouped all linguistic studies, from Pilling's bibliographies to the collection of vocabularies in the field or the analysis of primitive grammar. And "Sophiology" dealt with every manifestation of savage or barbarous religion, philosophy, and education, including the medicine which was in almost every case pure magic. Living or dead tribes, ethnology or archaeology, fitted equally well into the framework. Because of the structure of the research plans, the publications of the Bureau during its first twenty years comprise a remarkably cohesive whole.[16]

What modern anthropology has changed in Powell's system is not so much the organization as the names by which its parts are called. The prestige of the Bureau could standardize Powell's choice of tribal and stock names, but it could not quite, in spite of the half-embarrassed loyalty of his assistants, enforce acceptance of his high-handed and bizarre substitutions for the customary terms of science and philosophy. "Sophiology" is extinct: but if a student were curious enough he could dip into Powell's speculations on language and find there in his "sematology" the spore of modern semantics.

In the Bureau of American Ethnology now are thousands of Indian photographs illustrating — and preserving for study — types and customs and implements that might otherwise have gone to oblivion. Between four and five hundred of them are the work of Jack Hillers, the amiable, faithful, and bottle-loving Hillers who had been one of Powell's helpers since they ran into each other in Salt Lake City in the spring of 1871. He learned his photography in Powell's service, and he repaid the lesson by years of effective work both for the Bureau of Ethnology and for the United States Geological Survey. He was the first photographer of the Grand Canyon, and he recorded the failing cultures of many tribes. The best pictures he ever took were accumulated among the Uinkarets and the Shivwits, those timid and skulking savages who in 1870, when Powell first met them, had seen scarcely any white men except Jacob Hamblin, an occasional Mormon herder, and the three men from Powell's own party whom they killed. Hillers had a knack for portraiture; there are few better Indian portraits than his, and no better collections.[17] They are part of the riches that the Bureau assembled.

And the synonymy, begun right at the beginning and continued with changing personnel through a long time, the study that was properly preliminary to most others — what became of it? Like all the other basic studies, it could not be kept basic; it outgrew its preliminary purposes. Otis Mason, Garrick Mallery, Henry Henshaw, all took a crack at it. Powell based his nomenclature on it, but having served that purpose it went on. By the time Powell's "Linguistic Families of North America" was published, the synonymy had developed into a project for a dictionary of the Indian tribes north of Mexico. To complete that work, the ethnologists of the Bureau divided up the various linguistic stocks and began filling and sorting cards. In 1893 Henshaw was forced to resign because of ill health, and the dictionary's partially completed sections fell into the hands of Frederick Webb Hodge, who like Henshaw enlisted the part-time help of almost everyone in the office. In 1902 Major Powell died with the dictionary still uncompleted. But its fragments were of such obvious usefulness that Secretary Langley of the Smithsonian urged Hodge to finish it.

It took four more years. The preliminary synonymy upon which much else was to be based in 1879 was finally issued in 1907, five years after Powell's death, as the *Handbook of American Indians.* It is what Schoolcraft's six volumes pretended to be — what they could not in the eighteen-fifties have been made. In the *Handbook's* two fat volumes are summarized most of the contributions that Powell and all his force made to ethnology, as well as what was known before. For the study of the tribes north of Mexico it is as essential as a dictionary is for the study of a language. It is another demonstration of the system and the order, admittedly improvable but still astonishingly sound and astonishingly definitive, that Powell and his helpers imposed upon a science they found almost unformed.

In any final analysis, it is not Powell's personal contributions to ethnological research which most distinguish him. He did not hold himself to the careful and meticulous investigation that he inspired in his assistants, and he could not be bound down to the study of a particular tribe or a special problem. Every tribe, every culture trait, every problem, seems from the start of his work to have interested him not for itself but for its illumination of grand and often airy speculations. His assistants gathered facts; Powell attempted to use them like building blocks in his synthetic cultural history of mankind. As one of his successors said, his thinking characteristically involved at the very least the universe, and generally the cosmos.[18] When in his later years, in constant pain from his amputated arm and hazed by the bullies of an angry Congress, he let his ethnological studies lead him directly into the most abstruse and even cranky philosophical speculations, he was merely moving further along paths he had already surveyed.

But long before he arrived at that point, before he had much more than begun with ethnology, there was a good deal else to be surveyed, further scientific work to be organized and given system. There was, specifically, the United States Geological Survey which Clarence King, hot for Mexican gold and the sybaritic pleasures of wealth, dumped in his lap on March 12, 1881.

3. *The United States Geological Survey*

HENRY ADAMS said of Clarence King that he had induced Congress to adopt its first modern act of legislation, the establishment of a civil — not military — government survey. And when Adams went west to spend a summer in Estes Park and the Uintas he felt that he was spying on the land of the future, and that the future was in the hands of the men of King's Survey, who "held under their hammers a thousand miles of mineral country with all its riddles to solve, and its stores of possible wealth to mark." [1]

The emphasis upon wealth is characteristic, but not damaging. Adams, if not King, was quite as interested in the riddles. But to think in purely mineral terms of this "first modern act of legislation," or of the West, was to succumb to the same limitation of vision that afflicted King. In his initial survey of the 40th parallel it was probably legitimate, even necessary; in the conduct of the United States Geological Survey it was not.

King had made the Geological Survey into a scientific advisory bureau for the use of the mining industry. His principal achievement as director was to compile, in collaboration with the 10th Census, a statistical survey of mineral resources and production in the country, a report which he completed after his resignation. This, as *Mineral Resources,* was thereafter an annual publication. But King had evaded the job of classifying the public lands and had submitted to the frustration of working only on the public domain. His organization had been purely regional, with branch offices in Denver, Salt Lake City, San Diego, and Colorado City. His staff had been the small nucleus left to him from his own and Powell's discontinued operations plus a few men from the Hayden and Wheeler surveys. His budget had been a modest $106,000 the first year, $156,000 the second.

Now came one whose conception of the future lying under his hammer was far more than mineral, who conceived geology to be no less than the science of the earth, and to include not only the economic mining geology of King but all earth history, earth sculpture, the laws of orographic change, the dawn and development of life, the discovery and mapping of the nation's resources of land, water, soil, timber, minerals, coal, oil. Powell was a government scientist in a way King never was. He believed more fervently that government should undertake research for human good. He understood scientific knowledge to be not only abstract but practical. Its immediate end was policy implemented by legislation, and its ultimate end was the improvement of man's lot and of man himself.

Since he had created the Geological Survey practically single-handed, he had a very definite idea of what it ought to be doing, but during King's directorship he had had no official connection with the Survey and had acted only as a consultant and as a substitute when King was out of the office. The last few months of his first fiscal year as director (from March through June, 1881), and all of his second year, he spent tidying up the jobs that King had left. During that time he undertook only one thing on his own, a thing so characteristic that it could almost have been predicted like the working of a natural law. He acted upon a roily situation as glycerin acts upon certain cloudy liquids: he precipitated, settled, clarified. The first roily situation he encountered as director involved the conventions of geological mapping.

Those conventions in 1881 were as little uniform as the nomenclature of American ethnology. Symbols, conventional colors for the hundreds of kinds and ages of rock, even the names of the great periods of earth history, differed from country to country and from scientist to scientist. European practices, diverse themselves, did not match American, equally diverse. Powell might have waited until the International Geological Congress met in Bologna in the summer of 1881, since it planned to take action on precisely that problem. He might have, but that was precisely what he did not choose to do. Perhaps he feared the influence upon the Congress of Lieutenant George Wheeler, lately deposed and disgruntled. Wheeler was a delegate to the Bologna meeting and he fancied himself as a cartographical authority and historian,[2] a judgment in which Powell did not concur. Perhaps Powell disliked the thought of a European system enforced upon American science. Perhaps he saw a chance to count *coup* and enhance the prestige of the young Geological Survey. Perhaps he was simply moved by his impatient urge to systematize sciences whose very alphabets were uncertain. Whatever his reasons were, he pushed through in a few months a strenuous study of geological map conventions, and in his first annual report (the second of the bureau) he published a system of symbols, nomenclature, and map colors that with some revisions has remained the American standard and has forced considerable modifications upon European conventions.[3] Rushing to squeeze through ahead of Wheeler and the Congress, he trod on some toes — he would have said justifiably. He was no Spencerian convinced that Progress and the evolution of institutions come inevitably by a system of laissez faire. In his conception of social evolution, intelligence took hold of its environment.

He could throw his weight where it counted, and damn the toes. Any bullheaded man could do as much. But Powell could also play at sleight-of-hand as deftly as the best. The House Resolution expanding the Geological Survey's duties nationwide, for which King had unsuccessfully fought, had been frustrated for numerous reasons, but principally because some members of Congress feared federal encroachment on the states even in science, and because the Coast Survey jealously fought it. In the spring of 1882, having cleared up King's leftovers and reorganized the bureau in his mind, Powell asked a quarter of a million dollars for an expanded program, and he saw to it that a bill extending the Survey's activities into the states was introduced. That bill passed the House but was killed by scientific States'-rightists in the Senate, and Powell was exactly where King had been. So he asked his old friend the Appropriations Committee for permission to add a short phrase to the Geological Survey section in the Sundry Civil Bill. The phrase added to the Geological Survey section the words "and to continue the preparation of a geological map of the United States."[4]

That did it. He was past the watchdogs before they saw him move. For to prepare a geological map of the United States he had first to prepare a topographical map: there was no adequate one in existence. And to make a topographical map of the United States he had to go outside the public lands to which King had been confined. A small leak in the legislative dikes can let a lot of authority through. By so simple a trick Powell emancipated the Geological Survey and made it into a bureau with national jurisdiction.

The regional offices that King had established were discontinued, and the Survey reorganized according to the work of the various divisions — geology, topography, paleontology, chemical and physical studies. Hayden was still a taciturn hangover on the payroll, permitted to work at his home in Philadelphia. But the Hayden group was further shouldered aside when Powell induced Marsh, still president of the National Academy, to become head of the paleontology division and allowed him to make his Yale museum virtually the paleontological headquarters of the Survey. Geologists and topographers trained in the Western surveys were at hand — Gilbert, Dutton, Hague, Becker, Emmons, Pumpelly, Peale, Holmes — all King, Powell, or Hayden men. Mapping was directed by Hayden's topographer Henry Gannett, assisted by Thompson and others of those who had learned surveying in the Plateau Province and the Great Basin. The disbursing officer, McChesney, had been taken over by King from Wheeler: before too long Powell moved his own clerk Pilling into the place. Charles Walcott, destined to succeed Powell as director in 1894, had been brought in from the New York State Survey, and Bailey Willis and other bright young men were steadily fed into the Survey by the universities. The day of the amateur was past.[5] So was the day of the twopenny appropriation. In the first year of his directorship Powell contented himself with the $156,000 that had been King's portion the year before, but the next year he jacked the appropriation up above a quarter of a million, and the next year to a third of a million. In 1884–85 he reached $489,000, and in 1885–86 he topped a half million dollars, fabulous for the time and for a mere bureau.

Even before he got the budget up to where he could feel comfortable about it, he had put himself in an almost impregnable position. The peculiarities of the organic law relieved him of the necessity of specifying individual salaries or expenditures in his budget requests; he got a lump sum. In 1882 he clinched his independence by obtaining from the Secretary of the Interior an authorization as Special Disbursing Agent for the Survey. That gave him a completely free hand in spending, and put all the great and growing powers of his bureau into his one personal fist. From the standpoint of his enemies, and he had them, the Geological Survey was a little empire run by a despot and kept under control by favors, jobs, and publications. Created by a rider on an appropriation bill, its jurisdiction extended nation-wide by a piece of trickery, its staff packed with personal friends and protégés of the director, its scope widened by the inclusion of the Bureau of Ethnology which now became almost an annex run by the same clerical staff, the Survey impressed some as a sign of government responsibility and farsightedness, and others as an unprincipled grab of power. Powell was a Success Story around the capital; he was also, and increasingly, a target.

Mr. Science. The High Priest. But he did not — and nobody

ever accused him of this — turn either his power or his inside knowledge of resources to personal gain. And if he consolidated his position as craftily as Grant besieging Vicksburg, he did so in the sure knowledge that power in Washington was characteristically unstable and fleeting, and that only a consolidated position could withstand the inevitable counterattacks.

He did not want to be dislodged. He wanted to last, for he had many things to do. Among them was another of those basic prechores that he was always running into, a job of summary and systematization impossible until the continental nation had been opened and reconnoitered, but indispensable the moment it was.

He wanted to map, carefully, with a consistent system of symbols and colors, and on a scale large enough to serve all normal foreseeable uses, the 3,000,000 square miles of the United States.

4. Maps for a Nation

You claim this to be a map of the United States?

Yes, sir; in one sense; a skeleton map.

Including a part of Mexico and a part of Canada, our neighboring countries?

Yes, sir.

Where did you get that map?

From a great variety of sources; it would be a long story to give you all of them. Several hundred original sources were consulted.

This represents the configuration and dimensions of the United States in every direction?

Yes, sir; imperfectly.

As well as its political divisions?

Yes, sir; but not with any great degree of accuracy.

Then we have no official map of the United States defining its frontiers in respect to foreign nations, except, perhaps, on the coast?

No, sir; no general map of the United States which gives its proper relation to other countries.

Likewise we have no official map showing the boundaries of the political divisions of the United States?

No, sir; not with any degree of accuracy.

Nor of the Territories and the District of Columbia?

No, sir; only so far as the topographic work of the Geological Survey has progressed.

We have no complete official map showing either the outline of our territory on land or sea, or showing the boundaries of the political divisions within the domain?

That is true.

(Major Powell before the Joint Committee of Congress, Dec. 19, 1885.)

Once the entire continent lay sunny and unknown with no names on its face, a vast Unity of ignorance. The fragmentation of Unity began with the first map and continued with every step of the European seizure, every increment to recorded knowledge. From the time when the Portuguese Diego Ribero incorporated on his 1539 map the discoveries of Magellan, and so anchored the uncertain continent of North America in approximately its proper place, the record was one of a gradual dispelling of the mists, a gradual clarification of the roil of speculation, superstition, guesswork, wishfulness, fear, and misunderstanding. What ignorance had been able to generalize, knowledge had to particularize, and that was a long process.[1] The America that shows in Abraham Ortelius' *Theatrum Orbis Terrarum*, the first modern world atlas, published in 1570, has an immensely wide top penetrated deep down by an Arctic sea. It has no Alaska, no Great Lakes. It is a vague outline struggling toward definition, the kind of continent that could still contain Northwest Passages and other wonders, and from whose edges men would sail up the James or the Potomac or the Hudson or the St. Lawrence hopefully looking for the Great South Sea. On those early maps California drifts in and out of the mists, now a nameless peninsula, as in Mercator's map of 1569, now an island. It did not get permanently tied down to the continent until DeLisle's map of North America in 1700.

And even after the outlines began to come into focus, the interior was guesswork and mystery and misunderstanding mixed with a few facts. One example taken from Powell's own part of the country will illustrate. Father Escalante and Don Bernardo de Miera, talking with the Indians in Utah Valley in 1776, heard of a great lake to the north and of a salt lake to the south of the Lago de los Timpanogos (Utah Lake) which partially filled their valley. On his map,[2] Miera correctly joined the northern lake (Great Salt Lake) to his Lago de los Timpanogos by a short strait (Jordan River). He was not too far wrong in the Rio de los Yamparicas which he brought into the northern lake from the northwest: that was either the Bear or the Weber, or a confused mixture of the two. Out of that northern and larger section of the Laguna de los Timpanogos, however, Miera drew a great and nameless westward flowing river, and that was a river of fable.

The southern, brackish lake that the Indians spoke of was Sevier Lake. Miera named it Laguna de Miera, gave it vague and indeterminate extensions into the westward *tierra incognita,* and endowed it too with some fabulous rivers: the Rio Salado, an affluent from the southeast, and the Rio de San Buenaventura, a much larger affluent from the northeast. This last was a confused mixture of the Sevier and the Green.

There were considerable elements of truth in Miera's and Escalante's geography, and in the map which Baron von Humboldt, drawing upon their exploration as upon the explorations of all the Spanish adventurers and priests in the West, published in 1808. All Humboldt did to Miera's geography was to switch the Yamparicas around so that it came into the Laguna de los Timpanogos from the west, and to leave Miera's name off Sevier Lake.

Humboldt's was a tremendously influential map; it was the only map. But the elements of fable in it would not be dispelled for a long time, for upon the base of this Miera-Humboldt map were imposed the additions of information — fact and myth — brought home by Lewis and Clark. Lewis and Clark had (after missing its mouth twice) discovered the Willamette, which they called the Multnomah, flowing north into the Columbia. They thought it must drain that vast unknown interior south of the Snake River as far down as the 37th parallel, and they drew it on their map as coming from far to the south and east.

Later map makers drew conclusions and made improvements. The two parts of the Laguna de los Timpanogos were compressed into one, the great nameless river that Miera and Humboldt had shown draining it to the west was attached to the trailing end of Lewis and Clark's Multnomah, and the maps, with their misconceptions, were inseparably joined. For years those mythical rivers flowed westward from the half-formulated mountains and half-defined lakes. Different cartographers gave them different names: the Buenaventura ran straight westward into San Francisco Bay on one map; on another the Timpanogos, on still another the Multnomah; they flowed sometimes from the Laguna de los Timpanogos, sometimes from the Lago Salado which had replaced the Laguna de Miera. Eventually the Buenaventura, squeezed out of the Great Basin, got itself mixed up with the Sacramento and acquired a new lease on life. The other rivers — Multnomah, Timpanogos, Mongos, Salado — disappeared before the eyes of the mountain men who came poking into the deserts looking for beaver, excitement, knowledge, wonder, whatever else.

Yet as late as 1828 there could be published in New York a *Mapa de Los Estados Unidos de Mejico . . . construido por los mejores autoridades*[3] which still clung to most of Miera's misconceptions and some of the embroiderings of later cartographers. The Rio Timpanogos still bravely drained the Great Basin into something like a fusion of Drake's Bay and San Francisco Bay. The Rio Buenaventura still came down from the region of the Wind River Mountains where the Green did actually rise, and it combined itself as in Miera with the Sevier, and emptied into the Lago Salado. Out of the Rio Salado, in defiance of the law which says that salt lakes have no outlets, went a continuing great river, the Buenaventura, to join the Pacific in the vicinity of Morro Bay. On that map the Colorado River headed near the headwaters of the Del Norte (Rio Grande) and ran almost straight southwest to the Gulf of California. The Gila joined it at right angles, precisely at its mouth.

In his instructions to Lewis and Clark, Jefferson had spoken disparagingly of the Spanish maps, but it was decades before American exploration provided something materially better. One of the final acts in that long drama of clarification was Powell's exploration of the Colorado and the country back from its canyons. He had played a part in disproving fable, added to the sum of knowledge. And in doing so he had, inevitably, contributed to complexity. His Plateau

Province had little of that grand simplicity and unity that Gilpin's and Sam Adams' had; his West, the more he learned about it, became less and less a single thing susceptible to Jeffersonian agrarianism, laissez faire institutions, Common Law practice, or the Land Office surveys. Whether it occurred to him or not, he was in the position of the evolutionist who according to Henry Adams had succeeded in bewildering himself by his own study of change in form and force. "The wisest of men," Adams said, "could but imitate the Church, and invoke a 'larger synthesis' to unify the anarchy again."

A larger synthesis. Specifically, a topographic map laid down on the scale of four miles to the inch for desert areas, two miles to the inch for most of the country, and one mile to the inch for special industrial districts. This map to be divided into quadrangles bounded by parallels and meridians, and printed on sheets seventeen by twenty inches. The smallest-scale map thus would cover a space of one degree of longitude by one degree of latitude, the middle-sized one thirty minutes by thirty minutes, the largest fifteen by fifteen. Most areas were surveyed by the method Powell had borrowed from the King Survey and had used from the very first. An initial point was determined by astronomical observations, a base line was measured from it, and from the two ends of the base line a triangulation network extended in all directions. Elevations were established by barometrical measurement (Gilbert devised a three-barometer method that gave additional accuracy) and by leveling, and were checked against the known elevations determined by the Coast and Geodetic Survey and the railroads. Elevations were expressed in contours, which were harder for the inexperienced to read but much more accurate than the hachures that Wheeler had preferred. The two-miles-to-the-inch scale was large enough to show not only every hill and valley of any size, but the most important cultural features — towns and villages, canals, railroads, roads. Those quadrangle maps could be, and have been, useful to every sort of citizen, whether a farmer wanting to establish the fall of an irrigation ditch or a city official authorizing a suburban development or a vacationer planning a trip into the back country. Upon them, too, could be overprinted in colors, at first by lithography but later by cheaper and more flexible engraving on copper, the surface geology or the hydrography or the land classification or the ethnography or whatever other scientific data were desired. Where the Land Office maps showed a hopeful homesteader nothing but the two-dimensional outline and location of his land, maps like these could tell him its altitudes (and consequently its desirability for irrigation or for various crops), its classification as desert, swamp, timber, arable, pasturage, or irrigable land, its water supply, whether spring or creek or pond, seasonal or permanent, its degree of settlement when the map was made, the development of its roads and improvements, and its more or less precise position with relation to the fixed meridians and parallels. Powell was not planning maps for the mining industry, as King might have, or for land disposal, as the General Land Office long had; he was planning maps for a nation.

Characteristically, he took on more than he could finish. He was a Thor, always getting caught in an attempt to drink the ocean dry or uproot the Midgard serpent. In the year after he took over from King he was confined to the public lands, but he immediately restored topography as a Survey activity, rehired his brother-in-law, Thompson, whom King had let go, and had a party mapping in the vicinity of Fort Wingate, New Mexico. The next year, with his enlarged appropriation and his authorization to map the whole country, he collated the usable work already done by his own and the other surveys, including the state surveys, and he divided the nation into seven districts and began work in six of them, with Henry Gannett in general charge of all topographical surveying. He threw a third and more of his appropriation toward topography, which he considered the prerequisite to accurate geological work. He hit the line like a fullback, and he made about a yard. After his first optimistic report (1882–83)[4] in which he had summarized the accomplishments of previous surveys and presented a map showing the areas adequately mapped already and those still needing surveys, his reports of progress were increasingly unsatisfactory to a Congress wanting to be shown miracles. In 1884 he could report 57,508 square miles surveyed and mapped during the year. The next season, after a considerable currying by committees, he stepped it up to 81,829 square miles, but when the Congressional pressure was relieved, the 1886–87 accomplishment dropped back to 55,684. In

1885 he had to admit to a Joint Committee that not a single sheet of the map was printed and that only thirteen were engraved.[5] The total area covered by atlas sheets engraved up to June 30, 1887, was approximately 250,000 square miles. By 1894, when Powell retired as director of the Geological Survey, he reported 619,572 square miles surveyed and mapped — approximately one fifth of the United States. Some quadrangles had been compiled from earlier surveys, some done by state surveys working under matching-funds agreements, most by the Geological Survey's own parties. And already some of them were having to be done over.

When Congress investigated government scientific bureaus in 1884–85 and called on Powell to justify his topographical expenditures, he said he could finish the work in twenty-four years at a cost of $18,000,000. Some members of Congress a little later were ready to bet him that he couldn't do it in a hundred years for a hundred million, and though they ignored what was palpably true — that the maps were worth anything they cost, and more — they were closer to right than he was. By December, 1952, with the costs approaching the $100,000,000 Powell's worst enemies had extravagantly predicted, 10,500 quadrangle maps on scales ranging from 1:24,000 to 1:250,000 had been published by the Geological Survey. The original estimate had guessed that 2600 quadrangles would complete the whole map, but the 10,500 completed by 1952 represented only about sixty per cent of the country.[6]

Even while he was energetically pushing his topographical work, Powell got trouble from both sides. Certain members of Congress, notably Representative Hilary Herbert of Alabama, attacked all the surveys as too detailed and expensive, and certain rivals, particularly the Coast and Geodetic Survey whose triangulation across the continent was much more painstaking than Powell's topographical triangulation, denounced Powell's as not detailed enough. Powell himself believed he was building, if not for the ages, then for a long time to come. He foresaw no uses, except possibly irrigation works, which would demand a special engineering survey, or the determination of the exact shape of the earth, which was the business of the Coast and Geodetic Survey, that his own maps would not serve. He admitted he was not absolutely accurate; he insisted that he was accurate enough.

Congressman Herbert's criticisms, read now, do not give him a high rating for prophecy, or even for intelligence. Powell and the Coast Survey were both right, Powell in his actionist policy of providing good maps as quickly as possible, the Coast Survey in insisting that the most accurate survey methods would eventually have to be applied. They are being applied now — but meantime the nation has had the use of Powell's maps for a multitude of purposes.

The Chief of the Map Information Office of the Geological Survey reported in 1952 that though more than half of the United States was topographically surveyed and mapped by that year, only about twenty-five per cent was mapped on the scale needed for contemporary planning.[7] Massachusetts, Rhode Island, and Puerto Rico were adequately mapped, no other states or territories were. And Kentucky, which was then beginning a five-year co-operative mapping project in conjunction with the Geological Survey (a pattern of collaboration between state and federal surveys that Powell inaugurated in 1883) was committed to a scale twice as large as Powell's largest. A scale of 1:62,500 such as Powell used in his collaborative survey of Massachusetts was larger than he thought necessary for any but the most special uses. Kentucky will be mapped at 1:24,000, or one inch to two thousand feet. Presumably, so will much of the rest of the United States, and before the atlas is completed at that scale, it may be overtaken again by newer needs and newer methods. The larger synthesis is like a temporary platform erected in the raising of a building. The building itself overtakes it, the unity is formed only to be swamped in multiplicity again, to become one more complication in the maze of complexity.

Today there are more than two dozen government bureaus engaged wholly or partially in the preparation and printing and use of maps. Their work is so intricate, complex, and overlapping that it takes a special agency to keep them straight with the public. Geological Survey, Coast and Geodetic Survey, Bureau of Land Management, Hydrographic Office, Corps of Engineers, Forest Service, Bureau of Reclamation, Office of Indian Affairs, International Boundary Commission, Lake Survey, Post Office Department, Bureau of Chemistry and Soils, Bureau of Public Roads, Soil Conservation Service, TVA, National Resources Committee, OSS, Navy, Air Force, the prodigious Army Map Service, have proliferated out of the handful of map producing and map using agencies since Powell's time. There is often close co-operation among them, and undoubtedly there is some duplication. But their continued existence makes one thing abundantly clear: that though the Geological Survey remains the chief mapping bureau of the federal government, Powell's hope of providing map sheets good enough to meet all foreseeable needs was a pipedream.

Yet the roughly 10,500 sheets completed in the first seventy years are the most important maps ever made in America, if we measure them by actual distribution and use. In the beginning Powell did not even have authority to print topographical maps, except in small quantities for the use of his own staff, for they could be justified only as preliminary to the geological map of the United States. By 1885 he was beginning to have so many calls for them that he had to press for sanction of their publication and sale. By 1952 more than twenty-three million of them had been distributed.

Nevertheless, the larger synthesis couldn't quite synthesize, foresight could not sufficiently foresee. Good as they were and are, the topographical quadrangles of the Geological Survey could not serve every need that arose.[8] Industrious as their production has been, they could not in seventy years cover much more than half of the nation's area. Carefully as Powell worked out his system of symbols and colors, later and greater experience would modify it. And accurate as was the Hoffman-King triangulation method, later methods, especially aerial photography, whose possibilities Powell overlooked, would revolutionize mapping.

The topographical atlas of the United States as Powell planned it is only now nearing completion, and when it is done it will be the accomplishment of the Army Map Service, not of the civilian agency Powell established. The detailed geological atlas which Powell planned as a second step is, in its perfected state, a project for the twenty-first century.[9] But the Geological Survey remains what Powell more than any other man made it: the authoritative source of cartographical information. Even the Army Map Service's topographical atlas is printed by the Survey's Map Information Office, and in most respects the mapping of the United States has been since the eighteen-eighties largely a civilian operation for the benefit of the whole nation. Though his individual maps have been in large part superseded, the institution which he created for making them, and the general plan of attack which he outlined, are as solid as when they were laid out. Solider, for in 1952 government investment in science has few enemies. In the eighteen-eighties it had plenty.

5. *Spies and Whisperers*

THE ORGANIZATION, reorganization, and disorganization of government science in the eighteen-eighties was similar in many ways to the organization, reorganization, and disorganization of government welfare in the nineteen-thirties. The motive power was not a depression and a social revolution, as in the nineteen-thirties, but a scientific revolution. The aim was not the correction of catastrophe, but the seizing of opportunity. The tone was not desperate, but hopeful. But the result was in each case a sudden multiplication of government bureaus, a pronounced shift of the national emphasis as reflected in budget bills, an intense and often wrathy debate about the propriety of governmental intrusion into the preserves of private enterprise, private scholarship, private charity. It was as inevitable as that apples fall off trees that Major Powell, being one of the truly effective creators of the system of government science, should acquire, inherit, or create antagonism.

His enemies matured along with his power, and like his power they were personal, scientific, and political, sometimes all in one and sometimes separately. He moved in a scientific world, so that his personal and scientific enemies merged. His political enemies were sometimes personal and sometimes merely anti-scientific, or anti-federal, but more often than either they were the representatives of vested interests or petrified beliefs which seemed to be threatened by Powell's policies. Their essential tone was set by the Western Senators and Congressmen who stomped his *Arid Region* proposals to death in 1879; their full hatred would not be generated for a decade, when it would drown whole days and weeks of congressional debates and committee hearings in adrenalin and bile.

Congressmen were his most dangerous enemies because they were, as law-makers, the immediate source from which he derived power. Personally and scientifically Powell could be attacked but hardly hurt; politically he could be destroyed. And it was mainly as eavesdroppers, whisperers, and spies for these politicians that Powell's personal and scientific enemies, always lurking behind the arras, could hope to be effective.

Ferdinand Vandeveer Hayden, like a bull elk defeated and driven from the herd by a younger rival, had all but retreated from Washington after King's appointment in April, 1879. His health grew steadily worse.[1] He was, moreover, in spite of his personal weaknesses and his dislike of Powell, not so murderously envious as some of his followers, so that after 1879 he caused Powell no trouble. The Geological Survey was very truly a consolidation, and contained men of all four of the earlier Western surveys among its personnel, but one man it could never placate was Professor E. D. Cope.[2] He took over Hayden's place as leader of the anti-Powell forces among scientists; he sedulously beat the bushes for disgruntled former employees who might talk spitefully against Powell or Marsh. He and his engineer Fred Endlich made every effort to suborn Gannett, Holmes, Peale, and other former Hayden men from loyalty to the Survey. Undoubtedly much of his detestation for Powell was a spilling over of his monomaniac hatred of Marsh, now enjoying a comfortable appropriation as Powell's paleontologist, but that did not lessen its malevolence. Cope was a character out of fiction, a distinguished scientist with an emotional life like that of the villain of a Jacobean tragedy. The very bones of Tertiary mammals, as he cleaned and arranged them in his Philadelphia home, cried out to him "Revenge!" Vanity and hatred stained Marsh's career, but they utterly corroded Cope's. He resisted Powell's efforts to bring him into the fold, and as he could, through his connection with the holdover work of the Hayden Survey, he did everything in his power to disrupt the bureau. His vote against the committee's report in the National Academy in 1878, a vote which he cast because he knew the report stemmed from Powell, had put him in a minority of one. He submitted an angry and ineffectual minority report to Congress in that squabble, and in later years he never changed his position by a hair.

Spite and ambition can be direct or devious. From the moment when Powell, at Hayden's request, undertook to see the unpublished Hayden reports through the press, Cope dragged his feet. His work on paleontology was to make up Volumes III and IV of the Hayden series. First he tried to build up each volume into two book-length parts and in that way stretch his contribution to four volumes. Throughout 1882 he kept gathering new bones and adding new sections to the manuscript and new plates to the illustrations. In May, 1883, a series of letters and telegrams from Powell and Pilling[3] failed to extract a finished manuscript from Cope, and the Public Printer stopped work on the book in disgust. In consultation, Powell and Hayden agreed that it was best to publish the work as it then stood, without further additions, and persuaded the printer to resume its preparation. But Cope balked. His book was not finished and he would permit no partial publication.

There the matter stood, with Cope holding the specimens, with part of Volume III set up and the plates engraved, and with an irritated Powell standing between an angry Public Printer and an angrier Professor Cope. Sometime during the months-long deadlock Cope showed his teeth. He sent back a batch of proof to Holmes, in direct charge of the Hayden publications, and in a postscript added, "Can't we scotch Powell?"[4]

Holmes had been a Hayden man but he was not interested in puddling old blood. He showed the letter to Powell, who could afford to ignore it. Cope was blocked in the National Academy and in the government bureaus, and could do no harm. But then in July, 1884, Congress passed the Sundry Civil Bill with a proviso: a Joint Commission should be appointed to investigate "the present organizations of the Signal Service, Geological Survey, Coast and Geodetic Survey, and the Hydrographic Office of the Navy Department, with the view to secure greater efficiency and economy of administration of the public service in said Bureaus."[5] That investigation was in part the work of Senators and Congressmen who, looking at Powell, had begun to ask themselves on what meat doth this our Caesar feed. In part it was a continuation of the 1874 and 1878 wrangles about the propriety of government in scientific research. Again, as in 1878, the National Academy was asked to submit a report, and again, as in 1878, Powell asked Marsh for permission to address the Academy's wise men. The value of his carefully nurtured connections, and his persuasiveness before committees, should again have paid off with a report entirely to his own liking.

In the event, it did not quite work out that way. The Academy's committee heard Major Powell, but he had barely begun to outline his notions of how the government should organize its scientific bureaus when he was stricken with a recurrence of the iritis he had been suffering from, and had to be led back to his darkened room. The Committee later submitted a report with which Powell did not entirely agree, and in December the Joint Commission opened its hearings.

If it thought that it could really report to Congress by the third Monday in December, 1884, as it had been instructed to, the first days of hearings disillusioned the Joint Commission. It was the end of February, 1886, before it was ready to submit the 1100 pages of testimony it had gathered. When that testimony appeared, Powell occupied more of the 1100 pages than anyone else.

There were a number of questions the three Senators and three Representatives on the Commission wanted to ask Major Powell. Eugene Hale wanted to know how that clause about "continuing the preparation of a geological map of the United States" had got into the Sundry Civil Bill in 1882. Why Senator, Powell said, everyone understood about that. It was thoroughly discussed in terms of its implications for the extension of the Survey before it was passed. But not everybody *had* understood; a good many Congressmen understood now, some of them angrily, but they hadn't all understood then. And Hale, a member of the Appropriations Committee that permitted the clause to be written in, quite evidently had not understood it. Also, how about that word "continue" — an obviously deceptive word? Oh, that, Major Powell said. The Survey was already making topographical and geological maps in the Territories and the Public Lands states. This clause gave it the authority to continue the same work in the rest of the country.

Hale did not press the questioning too far; he was friendly enough, and so, in the main, were Chairman Allison of Iowa and the rest of the Commission. They gave Powell every courtesy, as if they were indeed a fact-finding committee and Powell was indeed their chief scientific informant. He explained to them why the Land Office Surveys, made without reference to geodetic points, sometimes out of line with the true meridians and parallels, and without topography, were useless for anything but land parceling. They sniffed for illegitimacies around his arrangement with Massachusetts and New Jersey whereby the states paid part of the expenses of the survey and placed the conduct of the work in the hands of Major Powell. There was a technical illegitimacy, all right; Powell was as usual crowding the limits of his authority and assuming a function not specifically allowed him by law. Yet there was nothing venal about this arrangement; it was obviously mutually beneficial; it demonstrated a laudable co-operativeness between state and federal agencies; it cost the general government nothing; it produced a better map. They passed that question and went on.

They listened with attention while Powell read the statement he had prepared for the Academy on the organization of the scientific bureaus. The Academy in its report to the Commission had proposed a new cabinet Department of Science. Powell, fearing any mingling of military and civilian bureaus, proposed instead that all the "informational" bureaus — Geological Survey, Coast and Geodetic Survey, Signal Service, Fish Commission, Hydrographic Bureau, National Observatory, and National Museum — which was already there — be put under the directorship of the regents of the Smithsonian. That was where he himself had best liked to be; that was where the political winds blew least; that was, in fact, perhaps the best place that could have been suggested. But to put the bureaus there would take power from political or military hands and put it in hands that were scientific and perhaps even disinterested. Apparently no one seriously considered Powell's plan. As for the Academy's suggested Department of Science, that was opposed not only by Powell but by the Coast Survey, the Secretary of the Navy, and everyone else concerned.

Jealousies among bureaus cropped up: Though Powell went out of his way to credit the geodetic work of the Coast Survey, Coast Survey witnesses ungratefully doubted the worth of Powell's topography, and that too was an echo of the old debates of 1874 and 1878. The Academy-Powell plan of 1878 had recommended that the triangulation and topographical mapping of the continent be turned over to the Coast Survey, and perhaps by that concession Powell had for the time blunted the antagonism of General Patterson, the Superintendent. But now the Coast Survey was looking to the future. The survey of the coasts was nine tenths completed, and the principal work remaining concerned the belts of triangulation across the country by which the Coast Survey was meticulously working out the problem of the shape of the earth. These were a valuable preliminary to topographical mapping, as Powell admitted. The Coast Survey, fearing dissolution when the coasts were charted, would clearly welcome the authority to map the entire continent by its slow, careful, and expensive methods, and its witnesses therefore attacked Powell's maps as inaccurate. Powell replied, without heat, that when the width of a line on a map represented in itself a thousand feet or more, an error of a few feet was not vital, and could not even be shown. His triangulation, much faster and much cheaper, was accurate enough for mapping, though admittedly not for geodesy.

He was a sound, agile, and effective witness. Questions about the conduct of his own two bureaus he answered directly, frankly, and in great detail. He produced all his books and business forms, vouchers, receipts, regulations, and it was clear that his departments ran like fine watches and that in spite of his cunning status as special disbursement officer and his freedom from Congressional supervision in budget matters, he could account for every penny he spent. He went into his special arrangements with universities and with professors such as Marsh, and demonstrated that, as in his collaboration with the states, the scientific work of his bureaus gained by the relationship. He defended government science in all fields where the problems were too large for individuals or for private institutions, but he warned against the politically ambitious: "Whenever the scientific works of the General Government fall out of the control of scientific men, and into the hands of officers or functionaries whose interest is not in all research, but only in official position and dignity, such a political institution for the political advancement of science at once becomes severed from the great body of scientific men; it no longer takes a proper part in the great work to be done, and it speedily decays in influence and value."[6]

He justified his appointments, his co-operation with states and universities, his publications, his maps, his expenditures, and he did so with confidence and dash. His handling of the Commission was like a skilled muleskinner's handling of a twenty-mule team. He thanked it for the chance to answer its questions. Blandly assuming that the Commission was after facts and not anyone's scalp, he thanked it especially for the questions that he might have thought embarrassing. He pointed out that the changes made in the organization of government science in 1879 had had important results, and he asked for more: "If the work thus begun can be continued through the labors of this Commission, and all of the scientific operations of the Government placed under efficient and proper control, scientific research will be established in America upon such a basis that the best and greatest results will accrue therefrom. The harvest that comes from well-directed and thorough scientific research has no fleeting value, but abides through the years, as the greatest agency for the welfare of mankind."[7]

He could talk that way because he believed that way, and because the hearing gave him a chance to be a scientific missionary to Congress and the public. But there were those who thought the Joint Commission had been formed to smell out pollution rather than find facts, and who did their best to bring up old shoes and bits of clothing and other spoor to help the bloodhounds on the trail. In the midst of the hearings, in October, 1885, Fred Endlich, evidently on the suggestion of Cope, wrote letters to Holmes, Gannett, and A. C. Peale, all ex-Hayden men on Powell's staff. The one to Gannett was the model for the others:

> Dear Gannett —
> I presume you are aware of the fact that the Powell Survey is going to the wall. I have been called upon for certain information which I cannot just now get without calling on my friends. I want to know all about the deadheads on the survey, favoritism, misapplication of funds, waste of money, &c. If you are in the position to give me the information, I shall be very much obliged, and will remember it in the sweet by and by. Your name will not appear in any way, and I will ask you to keep this letter quiet. . . .[8]

Unfortunately for the industrious Endlich, all three correspondents turned his letters over to Powell, so that Endlich and Cope had to scrape up their gossip from less authoritative sources. But they scraped it up. Before long it began to be known that a 23,000 word document blasting Powell was circulating among members of Congress, and in the December 19 meeting Representative Hilary Herbert of Alabama, the one definitely unfriendly member of the Joint Commission, had new and ugly questions to ask.

Was it true that not a single sheet of the map Powell had been working on for three years had been printed? Yes, it was true; none had been printed, though thirteen sheets had been engraved.[9] Was it true that King, Wheeler, and the United States Geological Survey had all published voluminously on the Comstock Lode, and was it true that one of those books was not a scientific work at all but a history of the lode's discovery? And was it the province of a scientific bureau of government to publish the history of accidental discoveries, and was there anything in all that work on the Comstock that a private individual or corporation could not have done? Yes, and yes, and no, and yes. Under Herbert's grilling Powell had to admit that Elliott Lord's history of the Comstock, authorized by King, was a book he himself would not have undertaken. But he defended the extensive Comstock studies, he defended his own announced plan to send G. F. Becker to Spain to study quicksilver mines there, and he said that since it appeared outside his authority to send him with Geological Survey funds, he would ask the Smithsonian to send him. Well, how did he justify Dutton's being sent to Hawaii to study volcanoes? Did that have anything to do with a geological survey of the United States? No, sir, it did not. He had checked with the Secretary of the Treasury, found that he would not be authorized in sending Dutton with Geological Survey funds, and persuaded the Smithsonian to pay his expenses.

With the exception of the Lord book, which he could not defend, he parried Herbert's grilling, but the malice of Cope reached beyond Herbert, and threatened him scientifically as well as politically. Shortly after receiving the Cope charges, Herbert wrote to Alexander Agassiz, who as the son of the revered Louis and as one of the world's great marine biologists had the highest standing in scientific circles. Herbert asked for information favorable to the Coast Survey — Agassiz had worked closely with the Coast Survey and had published much of his work out of specimens collected on Coast Survey expeditions. But Herbert added that if the Geological Survey couldn't be confined it ought to be junked, and requested specific criticisms of Powell's topographical work, of the excessive Comstock coverage, anything else. Agassiz replied promptly and in a way to please Powell's enemies: [10] He disapproved of government science (but he went into detail about the valuable contributions of the Coast Survey in geodesy, topography, and zoology). He dutifully disapproved of the work of King and Powell on the Comstock, and thought private individuals had learned nothing from the reports. He thought that economic geology should be left to the mining companies, paleontology to the universities and private individuals. He saw no reason why scientists should ask more of the government than literary men or artists or any of the other learned professions. He thought the publications of the government bureaus wasteful and extravagant. And though he granted that it was impossible to make a geological map without a good topographical map as a base, he felt that the failure of the states to authorize topographical maps meant that they didn't want the general government to go to that expense for them.

And that, because it came from Agassiz, demanded an answer. Just why it came from Agassiz at all, why the man whom Henry Adams admired next to Clarence King should not only allow himself to be used by an anti-intellectual States' rights politician but should in the act criticize the work of his friend and business partner King, is not so clear. Perhaps Agassiz's close affiliation with the Coast Survey is enough explanation. Perhaps too he had already begun to cool off on Clarence King, perhaps he and Higginson had already begun to smell the rats in the London office which King ran but rarely entered, and perhaps the near-collapse of the company that Agassiz's and Higginson's personal investigation would bring on within a year was already becoming an unpleasant possibility.[11] Or perhaps, as Powell suggested, Agassiz as a very rich man did not understand the difficulties that individual scientists without wealth encountered in following their research, and perhaps his grandiose plan for making his own museum at Harvard a center of American research was threatened by the swift expansion of government science. In any case his was too influential a voice to be ignored. As his last act before the Joint Commission Powell wrote a long and careful letter answering Agassiz's general criticism.[12]

He had one central question to ask of Agassiz and those who

honestly held Agassiz's views: Was knowledge the private possession of an élite, or was it something broader? "Shall the work of scientific research and the progress of American civilization wait until the contagion of [Agassiz's] example shall inspire a hundred millionaires to engage in like good works? Before that time comes scientific research will be well endowed by the people of the United States in the exercise of their wisdom and in the confident belief that knowledge is for the welfare of all the people." And to the view that the government might monopolize scientific work there was only one answer. "The learning of one man does not subtract from the learning of another, as if there were a limited quantity to be divided into exclusive holdings; so discovery by one man does not inhibit discovery by another. . . . That which one man gains by discovery is a gain of other men. And these multiple gains become invested capital, the interest on which is all paid to every owner, and the revenue of new discovery is boundless. It may be wrong to take another man's purse, but it is always right to take another man's knowledge, and it is the highest virtue to promote another man's investigation. . . ."

That was the true crux of the hearings before the Joint Commission. At stake was Powell's concept of government science in areas where private initiative or private capital could not operate, the concept of publicly-supported science for the general welfare. Powell believed that such public science, far from robbing or suppressing private research, could by its centrality stimulate and encourage individuals, universities, or local governments, and on occasion could collaborate with them to their mutual benefit. Opposed to him was the notion of private property in science, the notion of Cope and Marsh and to a degree Agassiz, rich men all with a proprietary feeling for their specialities. The proprietary sense was so developed in Cope and Marsh that they snarled and fought over every bleached bone, every note in a learned journal. It was somewhat unfortunate that Powell was allied with Marsh, for he was certain sooner or later to have his flank exposed by Marsh's intemperate feuds. But for the time being, at least, and thanks mainly to the quality of Powell's testimony, government science and especially the Geological Survey came out of the Commission's hearings in 1886 very much strengthened. The Coast

Survey took a moderate thumping. The charges circulated by Cope and Endlich were not read into the record of the testimony, and the spies and whisperers slipped back behind the arras to await another chance. For a little while, at least, Major Powell would have the opportunity, relatively unhampered, to cultivate his "highest virtue."

V

THE OPPORTUNITY

1. Disaster on the Great Plains

TAKE THREE acts of God.

In the West the winter of 1886 clenched and loosened and clenched in blizzard and cold snap and January thaw, cold again, blizzard again. Sometimes after sundown the sky was the clear green of forty below, and sometimes wind reached down out of the north to whine across the flats. Snow moved before it, dry as sand, light as smoke, shifting in long ropy trails, and white coned against clumps of grass and the broken clods of fields, long cone and dark hollow formed in furrows and the ruts of wagon trails, and deeply, with edges like scimitars, around the corners of shacks and soddies. In some of the shacks, after five days, a week, two weeks, a month, of inhuman weather, homesteaders would be burning their benches and tables and weighing the chances of a desperate dash to town — lonely, half-crazed Swedes, Norwegians, Russians, Americans, pioneers of the sod-house frontier. Sometimes they owned a team, a cow, a few chickens; just as often they had nothing but a pair of hands, a willingness to borrow and lend, a tentative equity in 160 acres of Uncle Sam's free soil, a shelf full or partly full or almost empty of dried apples, prunes, sardines, crackers, coffee, flour, potatoes, with occasionally a hoarded can of Copenhagen *snus* or a bag of sunflower seeds. More than one of them slept with his spuds to keep them from freezing. More than one, come spring, was found under his dirty blankets with his bearded grin pointed at the ceiling, or halfway between house and cowshed where the blizzard had caught him.

Still farther west, out on the dry plains, the short-grass country, there were few shacks, but ranch houses crouched in the shelter of the river-belting cottonwoods along the valleys of the Powder, the Belle Fourche, the Cheyenne, the Niobrara, the Republican and Solomon and Smoky Hill. The ranchers were warm enough, their stocks of wood and shaly lignite sufficient even for such a winter as this. In some of them, men whose names adorned Burke's *Peerage* pigged-it between hunting trips with their Scottish or American managers.[1] But out on the ranges where a single company might own three or four hundred thousand acres, and control as much more by owning its water or fencing in with its own land large chunks of the public domain, the cattle drifted, and where the snow was deep found nothing to eat, and where the brown grass was blown bare found the wind. With ice-coated backs humped to the wind they were pushed off the flats and into the bottoms and the drifts, or they were forced like logs in a sluggish current along the lines of fences until they packed together in the corners, unwilling to turn again into the wind that had driven them there. Riders going out when winter finally released the land found them by the hundreds uncovered by the thaws, longhorns or Oregon cattle, sometimes even whiteface and Angus from British breeding stock. They lay like carefully packed fish, their bellies bloated huge, mouths open, vents blown and distended as if poles had been run through them, stiff legs jutting from the swollen bodies like the wooden legs of toys. Flies were busy on the eyeballs, and the spring-revived carrion beetles were so thick sometimes in a carcass that it seemed to move.

The winter of 1886, the end of the big bonanza of the cattle industry, the point upon which the "cattle bubble" broke in London and Dundee and Aberdeen. British companies, taking advantage of the disaster to correct their inflated "book count" of cattle, reported as much as 65 per cent loss of their herds. Even an honest report would have shown a 15 to 30 per cent loss, enough to break some companies and weaken all but the strongest, both British and American. The cattle interests which had gone a good way toward engrossing the Great Plains were not precisely stopped in their tracks, but they were slowed down, their power and their will to fight for their privileges temporarily weakened. And not only the cattle interests but the nesters, squatters, pre-emptors, homesteaders who like young Hamlin Garland had hopefully planted their straddlebug markers on quarter sections in the salubrious early years of the eighties, could take a warning. They began to comprehend how little stood between the Plains and the North Pole, and it began to be clear that neither their "improvements" nor their mortgages — the two things that all homesteaders had in common — could shelter them from the loneliness and the cold.[2]

The second act of God also began, on parts of the wheat frontier, in 1886. It too was a lesson in meteorology, but it did not come like a frantic, continued lashing from Heaven as the winter had. It was a slow starvation for water, and it lasted through 1887, 1888, 1889, into the eighteen-nineties. Homesteader hopes survived its first year; in fact, the speculative prices of land in eastern Dakota continued to spiral upward, and the rush to Indian Territory took place in the very heart of the dry years.[3] By the second year the marginal settlers had begun to suffer and fall away; by the third the casualties were considerable. By the fourth it was clear to everybody that this was a disaster, a continuing disaster. What began in 1886 was a full decade of drouth, the cyclic drying-out that Powell had warned of in 1878. But since the late sixties increasing rainfall, with only one short drouth, had persuaded the westward-moving nation that settlement, sod busting, and tree planting modified the climate, evaporated more water into the air and milked the clouds down again as rain, made something out of nothing. A year's drouth could not shake that belief, two would not seriously damage it, three or four would not by any means destroy it. Nevertheless the rumble of dissatisfaction and the clamor for help — government help — would begin early. Within a very few years it would become articulate in the Populist movement, and for a brief while radical agrarian politics and the economics of Henry George would bend the stubborn trend of American institutions. As stump-speaker and propagandist, busted-homesteader Hamlin Garland would help lead that last protest of the doomed Jeffersonian yeoman. But John Wesley Powell would have a better chance to do something practical about insuring the continued existence of the arid-belt farmer than any other man, and he would be angrily misunderstood and bitterly fought for his pains. Better than anyone else, he understood what was happening in the subhumid and arid lands, and he knew that not the railroads, for all their sins, nor the speculators and landlords, for all of theirs, nor the banks, for all of theirs, should be called the only villains. What was wrong was more basic: wet-weather institutions and practices were being imposed on a dry-weather country. But the settler did not generally understand that; what he wholly and completely comprehended was merely the result, the act of God, the human reality of drouth on the Plains.

There, a cabin had characteristically neither tree nor shrub nor grass.[4] Standard practice demanded that the yard be made "mudproof" and fireproof by throwing the soapy wash- and dishwater out religiously until the whitish earth glared like an alkali flat, which it was. As summer came on and the green of spring faded, Hamlin Garland says, "the sky began to scare us with its light."[5] From that sky like hot metal the sun blazed down on bare flats, bare yard, bare boards, tar-paper roof. Anything metal blistered the hands, the inside of any shack was a suffocating oven, outside there was no tree or shade for miles. There was no escape: east, west, north, south, July, August, September, the sun burned into the brain, the barrenness and loneliness and ugliness ate at man and woman alike but at woman most. Three hundred and sixty degrees of horizon ringed them, the sky fitted the earth like a bell jar. They smothered under it, watching the delusive south or east where thunderheads formed and heat lightning flared in the evenings. For a while they could watch the rain-directions with hope. After one ruined crop, or two, or three, their watchfulness was a kind of cursing from a circle of Hell. The prairie sloughs that in the good years had grown tules and sheltered mallards and teal were dried up, the ducks gone somewhere else. Windmills brought up sand. Only the chinch bugs multiplied. And down from the unseen mountains to the west the air currents that made their climate poured across the powder-dry plains and dust rose up ahead of them a hundred, two hundred, four hundred feet high. Grim-faced leathery women, seeing the cloud coming, slammed down windows and shut doors, and the family gathered inside with the thin, exciting smell of dust in their nostrils and wordlessly listened to the wind and watched the small gray drifts grow on window sills, below the doors.

What could be wonderfully beautiful in June, green and half flooded with runoff ponds grassy to their edges, blooming with primroses, withered into an utter desert, shriveled and dried up and blew away with the hopes of its settlers, with the nasturtiums by the doorway, the dried tendrils of sweetpea clinging to the store-cording against the wall.

Rain, Cyrus Thomas had said in 1868, follows the plow. By now Thomas was one of Powell's best archaeologists, an authority on the Ohio mounds and on the Maya codices. By 1888 he presumably regretted the opinion he had hazarded twenty years earlier on the strength of popular belief, local records, and the clear fact that since settlement the rainfall had increased and the streams had run larger. By 1888 he knew better. So, to their sorrow, did a good many others.

The third act of God was a sort of afterthought, as if to demonstrate that all human action is related, and that whatever men do to control their environment must be multiple and reciprocal, part of a related system, a link in what the philosophers call the infinite regressus of causes.

Twelve miles above the city of Johnstown, Pennsylvania, the Pennsylvania Canal Company in 1852 had dammed the South Fork of the Conemaugh River to form a storage reservoir sixty or seventy feet deep and seven hundred acres in extent. On May 31, 1889, after weeks of steady rain, the dam let the first leak through. Within seconds it was melting away like sugar; within minutes, in one convulsive act, it emptied fifty thousand acre-feet of water into the valley below. Twenty feet of brown water surged over Johnstown and obliterated it. It obliterated eight surrounding villages, it swept up houses, barns, sheds, horses, cattle, chickens, people, and washed them headlong down the valley. Hundreds of people drowned in the first wall of the flood. Hundreds of others, clinging to bits of wreckage or desperately swimming, were driven against the timbers of the Pennsylvania Railroad bridge, and there by ones and twos they began to pull themselves to safety. Then the bridge caught fire and burned them to death in the midst of the waters.

The significance of the Johnstown flood was not, though between two and three thousand people died, the horrible efficiency of God's ill will, as if Ararat had erupted and engulfed the Ark. What was significant was that at Johnstown, as in the Jim River Valley or out on the Wyoming range, men found themselves at the mercy of natural forces just when they thought they had them most under control. The Johnstown flood was a footnote to the lesson the western drouth had taught or was teaching. Water was the key to life, particularly in the West; water from heaven could fail, and continue to fail for years on end; water from the earth or from the rivers, therefore, was the only recourse; but water from the rivers meant dams, and dams might mean impounded waters hanging in constant threat above other Johnstowns.[6] The problems of water were all related; what happened on the upper Missouri might affect Louisiana; saving farmers in the Dakotas might aid or injure barge owners in St. Louis. Moreover, water was not only a necessity of life: in proportion as it *was* essential it was a matter of rights and properties, and for the equitable handling of those interests there were virtually no laws.

Nobody loved a good chaos better than John Wesley Powell. If he had known nothing whatever of conditions in the West, had had no experience whatever with irrigation and the arid lands, he would have been tempted to try his hand at ordering this one. But he did know, and he had the experience — no one so much of it. The decline of cattle-company power, the drouth, the clamor for help, came like an inevitable fulfillment of his prophetic report on the arid region. He had amplified, but not changed, his notions of what might be done. When Big Bill Stewart of Nevada was returned to the Senate in 1887 on a platform of free silver and irrigation, he fitted the plot like a St. John the Baptist, saying, "Prepare ye the way of the Lord."

Senator Stewart was one of many manifestations of change in the temper of Western Congressmen — or in the temper of the public which elected them. Not even a Congressman could by 1888 avoid the perception that the land laws as they were constituted worked not for the small settler but the land speculator and the large landlord, and that the "landlord system like that of Ireland" which they had prophesied if Powell's *Arid Region* proposals went into effect was rapidly coming into being under the beneficent protection of the

Homestead Act and the Desert Land Act. And few could avoid, by 1888, the uneasy guess that settlement had a little overreached itself in the subhumid eastern edge of the arid belt. It was there, where agriculture had been eminently possible in good years, and where the soil was probably better than anywhere in the entire United States, that the drouth hurt worst. The really arid country hadn't lured many homesteaders, and those who had established themselves had generally done so by some homemade irrigation system. But the subhumid belt had thought itself above irrigation; its public representatives had always blown fuses when it was hinted that their territories did not bask in God's smile. They were less inclined to blow fuses now, and more inclined to hunt out dependable sources of water to supplement the gentle rain from Heaven.

Early in the 50th Congress the new temper was strong enough and united enough to pass through both houses a drastic bill repealing the Desert Land Act, the Timber Culture Act, and the Pre-Emption Act — a repeal which if it had actually become law would have prepared a wholesale reconstruction of the land laws. It did not become law because it failed in conference committee. But another sprout from the same seed sprang up at once. On February 13, 1888, a Senate Resolution asked the Secretary of the Interior to report on whether or not he thought the Geological Survey should be asked to survey and segregate irrigable lands and reservoir and canal sites in the arid regions. That resolution, the work of Senator Stewart, Senator Teller of Colorado, and others of the "irrigation clique," was passed on immediately by Secretary Vilas to Major Powell and to the Acting Commissioner of the Land Office, S. M. Stockslager. Mr. Stockslager was "unable to see any urgent necessity" for such a survey. But Major Powell, confronted with an opportunity for which he had waited a full decade, rose to the Secretary's letter like a starving cat to a sardine.[7] The conclusions of his *Arid Region* had not been changed but only aggravated by ten years of settlement. The smaller streams were no longer a consideration, because by now they were mainly utilized; if action had been taken ten years ago much wasteful development could have been prevented. Now the only course was to concentrate on the larger streams, on reservoirs and storm-water basins, because "utilization of the large streams by owners of small tracts must wait until large numbers of the holders of small tracts can be induced to settle simultaneously . . . and be further induced to engage in the corporate or co-operative enterprise necessary to construct great headworks and canals." On those larger streams, in other words, his co-operative irrigation districts were still possible; a survey could still be made ahead of any extensive settlement, to avoid complication by squatters' rights and vested interests. And while it was true that the longer such a survey was held off the more knowledge could be brought to bear on it, the conflict with vested rights would grow more serious with every year's delay. The sooner the irrigable lands could be surveyed, therefore, the better. And there were additional reasons for a survey beyond the central and urgent one of irrigation. One was the effect on flood conditions in the lower courses of the great rivers. To take water out for irrigation above, on the headwaters, meant lessened floodcrests and reduced quantities of débris to jam the lower reaches. "For every acre reclaimed to agriculture in Montana another acre will be reclaimed in Louisiana." The urgency of the need was only increased by the difficulties: to relate the problems of water along great river systems raised tough problems of federal and state and individual rights, whole nightmares of inadequate and contradictory law. But the longer those problems remained unsolved, the less chance there was of solving them.[8]

From the very first moment when the opportunity opened, Major Powell thought of it as far more than an opportunity to bring water to the burned-out farmers of the subhumid belt or the future farmers of the arid regions. He thought of it as part of the "general plan" he had fought for in 1878, and that general plan was even wider now than it had been then. It had begun to incorporate whole river systems, the greatest on the continent. If he did not at first offer to organize the human control of the Missouri-Mississippi or the Colorado or the Rio Grande, such control was implicit in his thinking from the very first, the plan was there, and it was a complex and inclusive one whose parts fitted together and whose engineering was so vast that only the massive machinery of the nation could undertake it.

He had a plan ready, and he presented it before Senate Committees and in close huddles with Stewart and the irrigation clique. Within a month they had pushed through both houses a Joint Resolution calling upon the Secretary of the Interior to examine "that portion of the United States where agriculture is carried on by means of irrigation, as to the natural advantages for the storage of water for irrigation purposes with the practicability of constructing reservoirs, together with the capacity of streams, and the cost of construction and the capacity of reservoirs and such other facts as bear on the question." [9]

Anyone pondering that resolution might well have been appalled not merely at how much it asked for but by the uncertainties buried in its phrasing. Where was "that portion of the United States where agriculture is carried on by means of irrigation"? In the opinion of most competent people, including Powell, it was roughly the whole country west of the 100th meridian. But the worst hardship from the continuing drouth was in the strip between the 97th and 101st meridians, the subhumid belt where heretofore agriculture had not needed irrigation. The arid Far West was still largely public domain, a fact which raised the whole question of the survey's purpose. Was it to provide for each homestead in the still-open lands a guaranteed water right, and if so, how far should government benevolence extend? If the government surveyed and reserved reservoir sites and canal rights of way, was the government thereby compelled to the construction of dams and the distribution of water? And if government did not, who would? And would private corporations or co-operatives be bound by the government's surveys? Suppose they wanted to put a dam on a non-designated site? Did a mere joint resolution give anyone authority to compel them otherwise? Also, what might be the relationship of this irrigation survey with the General Land Office? And was it to be used merely for the information of legislators faced with the need of land-law revision, or was it a preliminary move toward government paternalism in what remained of the public domain?

To anyone easily appalled, the foreseeable future of legislation at once so sweeping and so ambiguous might have looked about as inviting as a snarl of barbed wire. Powell was not appalled in the least. Always one to take the utmost authority granted him by law, he now assumed the arid region to lie beyond the isohyetal line of twenty inches. This gave the Irrigation Survey authorized by the Joint Resolution two fifths of the United States to play in. He was quite aware of how the problem ramified, and knew that to do the things the Joint Resolution called for he would have to make a topographic survey, a hydrographic survey, and a preliminary engineering survey of millions of square miles. Yet he could still stand before committees and say he could finish the whole job in six or seven years if they gave him the appropriations. At first he thought it could be done for $5,500,000; later he raised his estimate to $7,000-000.[10] At only one point did caution enter. When Stewart and Teller, flushed with success, urged him to ask for a half million the first year, Powell demurred. There were not enough trained men available to make use of so large an appropriation.

And anyway Stewart and Teller and their helpers could not generate quite as much enthusiasm in Congress at large as they felt themselves. It took a considerable amount of finagling to get even a modest appropriation the first year, and that was gained by a method fairly familiar to Powell by this time. A rider was attached to the Sundry Civil Bill, over the protests of the Appropriations Committee, and by that means the Public Lands Committee was by-passed as Powell and Hewitt had by-passed it in 1879. When the Sundry Civil Bill came before the House, Representative George Symes of Colorado, sensitive to the anger of his constituents against land speculators, inserted an amendment that withdrew from settlement "all lands made susceptible of irrigation" by the reservoirs and canals which the survey would locate. The effect of this amendment was sweeping; it suspended all existing land laws for the irrigable lands. The worries that had led the conference committee to bury just that sort of repeal earlier in the session rose again. Great stretches of the best public land remaining would be reserved, settlers would be kept out, growth might be retarded, votes might be lost. All the forward-leaning disequilibrium of advance, progress, boom, growth, might be endangered. Symes himself began to waver, seeing what he had done. But there were so many members of Congress determined to end land grabbing that Symes was unable to withdraw his amendment though he wanted to. Finally Stewart and others in the Senate worked out a compromise. By another amendment the President was authorized to restore at his discretion, for settlement under the Homestead Act alone, any of the reserved lands.

The fears of free-land advocates were thus allayed, and the danger of speculation on the basis of the surveys apparently checked. On October 2, 1888 — a date that would be bitterly remembered — the Sundry Civil Bill went through with an appropriation of $100,000, and Powell had under his direction not only the Geological Survey and the Bureau of Ethnology and much co-operative work for the state surveys, but an Irrigation Survey more explosive in its social and political implications than all his other work combined.[11]

2. *Values Measured in Acre-Feet*

IN THE STORY of Powell's fight against the dragons of error, backwardness, and unchecked exploitation it is fairly inevitable that Senator Stewart should get cast as one of the chief dragons. But he was a dragon of a classical frontier American breed.[1] Everything that he ever was he owed to his dear mother; everything that he ever did he could justify. In the course of twenty-nine years in the United States Senate he did a good deal, some of it sound. He helped write the Fifteenth Amendment to the Constitution and he supported the Morrill Act that created the land-grant colleges, he promoted western irrigation and fought for the remonetization of silver. Some of his quarrels, such as that with Charles Sumner over reconstruction bills, made him look momentarily honorable. His capacity to claim credit for anything useful that Congress did during his term of office was large.

Robust, aggressive, contentious, narrow, self-made, impatient of "theorists," irritated by abstract principles, a Nevada lawyer, miner, Indian-killer; a fixer, a getter-done, an indefatigable manipulator around the whiskey and cigars, a dragon whose cave was the smoke-filled room, Big Bill Stewart was one to delight a caricaturist and depress a patriot. But he was also, in his way, a man of faith: he believed in Western "development," and he believed in the right of men — himself among them — to get rich by this "development."

He was a man of a hard, driving strength, a formidable partisan. The water that was life to his state, both for agriculture and for mining, had to come from the mountains, and to bring it from the mountains meant dams and ditches. Before he ever took up the law or entered politics, Stewart had built ditches and brought water to mining camps, and he thought he knew how it should be done. Now that sites for reservoirs were being picked off and water appropriated at the heads of the streams, some of Stewart's constituents down below were beginning to suffer, and the possibilities of settlement in the valleys, the hope of new voters and new votes and new powers, were threatened. It was primarily to promote water development in Nevada that Stewart had been returned to Washington. He was not one to hesitate before difficulties or to look past acts toward consequences. Ask for a half million the first year, he kept telling Powell. Get after it. Get it done.

Major Powell was quite as willing to hurry as Stewart was, but he had a better eye for the difficulties and he looked farther ahead. He said there were not enough trained men available, and he was right — not to do the thing he had in mind. He felt that he was now directed, or empowered (there was a subtle difference) to do something far more comprehensive than the hasty reservation of obvious sites that Stewart contemplated. That simple job he could have begun at once, working from maps in his office. But here before him was the opportunity of his life, the massive and complex problem of planning for the West whose parts meshed in an intricate system. And here was he with twenty years of experience and knowledge, every bit of which could be applied to the problem as an engine's power is applied to the axles. The action of Congress, stimulated by Stewart and Teller, had shifted him into gear, and he was not now going to be content with making a humming noise or moving pistons meaninglessly up and down. He was going to turn wheels.

The advent of the irrigation agitation was an advertisement of the value of his topographical maps; but the Geological Survey had completed only fragments of the atlas and no adequate sheets existed for millions of acres of the land included under the Irrigation Survey. The job was threefold, as Powell saw it. He had to complete the topographical mapping, make a survey of reservoir sites, catchment basins, stream flow, canal lines, and the lands to which water could most economically and efficiently be brought, and conduct an exploratory engineering survey to determine the practicability of headworks and canals. To some degree the three activities could go on simultaneously.

Six or seven years, six or seven million dollars, he had estimated. Much of the expense could be written off against the topographical work already under way: what the Irrigation Survey mapped the Geological Survey would not have to map later. The classification of the public lands, too, was a thing he had been concerned with since the mid-seventies, and he had had the old Powell Survey working on hydrography just as early. It was now as if the old Powell Survey had been re-formed within the framework of the Geological Survey, for in the beginning Dutton and Thompson were almost the only trained men he could lay hands on. He pulled Dutton off his studies of volcanoes and earthquakes and set him to training a corps of water engineers at Embudo, on the Rio Grande in New Mexico. And Thompson, within a few weeks of the passage of the Sundry Civil Bill which provided funds, had parties triangulating in Montana, Nevada, New Mexico, and Colorado. In the office, all the available maps came out, and draftsmen began inking among their contours the reservoir sites that could be located without further survey.

The field season of 1888 was largely preliminary, organizational. At the beginning of 1889, outlining his plan of the year's operations to the Secretary of the Interior, Powell asked for $350,000 for the Irrigation Survey.[2] As yet he had attempted no segregation of lands as irrigable and had designated no reservoir sites. Both operations waited upon the topographic and hydrographic work, and the segregation of lands was further delayed by the job of checking titles through the General Land Office records. But though he could not report great progress in the practical work, it is clear that he had been pondering the implications of the survey which had been put into his hands, and he was led to speculate on the questions of land policy involved.

How, he asked, should the irrigable lands be disposed of, once they were mapped and designated? The present multiple system of laws, far from helping settlers, might lead them into error and failure. Left to themselves, settlers naturally selected lands high up, where the streams were small and could be diverted by minimum labor; they would use on one square mile of marginal land the water that would irrigate four times as much better land farther down. They would select their land for personal gain or convenience rather than for the common interest. "Under these circumstances it would seem wise either to provide that the waters of the streams and reservoirs shall belong to the segregated lands, or to repeal the clause which provides that they can be settled only under the homestead laws. The effect of the last provision would be to make the ultimate choice of lands optional with the settler in each case, and the value of the official selection would be in giving to the settler the necessary information upon which his judgment could be formed." The survey, in other words, could be thought of as simply an informational matter, without in any way inhibiting the freedom of choice of the settler.

On the other hand, it might be something vastly different. "Again, it might be wise to temporarily suspend or possibly repeal the . . . pre-emption laws, desert land laws, and the timber-culture laws, in their application to the arid lands, and to let the homestead laws remain, to be improved from time to time as circumstances demand. With a degree of misgiving the Director begs permission to suggest as his own opinion that the best solution of the problem under the present circumstances is to withdraw all the lands of the arid region from 'sale, entry, settlement, or occupation' except those selected as irrigable lands, and to allow titles to irrigable lands to be acquired only through the operation of the homestead laws and the desert-land laws."

Now he was talking about something far more than a survey. He was talking about a policy, and a sweeping one. He was proposing to close, apparently forever, a great part of the remaining public domain, and to bring to a close, except within the irrigable lands, the agricultural expansion which had been part of the national expectation for almost a century. And even within those irrigable lands which would still be open he was implying a degree of strict federal control. Left to themselves, he said, settlers would choose their lands "for personal gain rather than for common interest." The thought that the government had any business imposing respect for the common interest upon the individual would have set the Western dragons to breathing fire. Up to now, the General Land Office could content itself with tidying up the confusion that laissez faire squatting created, or pushing its grid of surveys outward in advance of foreseeable settlement. Major Powell now proposed (though not yet publicly) the end of laissez faire, the beginning of government supervision to prevent not only land and water monopolies but the danger of individual failure among settlers. In 1878 he had advocated co-operative control of irrigation by the settlers within a natural district. Now he appeared to assume that only federal intervention could be effective. Government should now say to pioneers what lands they could settle, and enforce its directives by control of the water. Settlers should now be limited in their anarchic personal rights and brought up sharp against a thing that until now few had bothered to consider: the common interest. The justification was the abiding aridity of the West. Indian and Spaniard and Mormon had all been ultimately forced to community morality. Mutuality was a condition of survival. But community morality, especially if it was to be enforced by federal law, was a new and alarming notion in 1889, and especially in the West, and most especially among those Westerners devoted to the kind of "development" that Senator Stewart defended.

It would be a mistake to assume that Powell's notions could have found no popular support. They might have found a good deal in 1889, for "radicals" and "cranks," the Farmers' Alliance or the Populists, were beginning to mutter in terms close to Powell's in their political and economic significance. Those cranks and radicals who had a large part in bringing the initiative, referendum, recall, woman suffrage, and the Australian ballot into our political system were already turning for help to the only power which was apparently able to resist or control the railroads and the trusts. Precisely at this time, as Frederick Jackson Turner points out, "the defense of the pioneer democrat began to shift from free land to legislation, from the ideal of individualism to the ideal of social control through regulation by law." [3] But this influence, after a brief triumph in the elections of 1892,[4] would be considerably delayed in its effects, and for a long time the man who thought in these terms would remain a crank and a crackpot. Alexander Agassiz was not the only rugged individualist left in America, and science not the only activity with its shibboleths of personal initiative. The myths surrounding free land were among the most durable the nation ever developed. And the slow bending of institutions to fit the conditions of the arid West — a bending which included inevitably a growing amount of federal "welfare" legislation — has been so truly glacial in its slowness that it was still a symbolic campaign issue in 1952, and may be for many elections to come. Antithetical political philosophies can clash as appropriately on the battlefield of the Hungry Horse dam as on any other.

Fortunately for Major Powell, no one heard him proposing revolution except Secretary of the Interior Vilas, who was largely in sympathy with his views. And though Congress did not give Powell the $350,000 he asked for, it did give him a quarter of a million in March, 1889, and that appropriation allowed him to expand and to push the work that had been begun the fall before. There was a kind of red-letter day when he designated his first reservoir site on April 6;[5] and a kind of appropriateness in the fact that the first one designated was a symbol of the old and passing West. It was Bear Lake, the old trapper rendezvous in the Utah-Wyoming-Idaho corner. Quite as symbolically apt, in its way, as the choice itself, was the fact that the surveyors had hardly lugged their plane tables into the lake basin before speculators were posting notices and filing claims. The common interest was not yet a thoroughly understood doctrine, except among those actively trying to protect it.

Ignore works already installed or planned by private enterprise, Powell wrote Dutton.[6] Conceive unified plans for whole irrigation districts, without regard to the limited and perhaps interfering works already there. Plan maximum irrigation at minimum expense for the maximum number of people. "It is to be borne in mind," Powell wrote, "that this survey is not primarily designed for the benefit of private parties who may contemplate the construction of works, though if they should incidentally derive benefit therefrom it would be a matter of congratulation." One of the principal purposes to which Powell called his assistant's attention was "to guide the development of agriculture in the greatest practical area" and to prevent the hardship resulting from ill-considered settlement and the failure of homesteaders on family-sized farms.

To serve the common interest as he thought it should, the survey had to be accurate, and that meant it moved more slowly than the impatient wanted it to. And though the designation of reservoir sites did move along at some speed after the first selection of Bear Lake, it seemed that half the sites designated brought trouble. He had hardly named Clear Lake, California, before local residents began writing their Senator, that same George Hearst who had demoralized the scorpion in Tucson. They feared for their vested rights, they worried that inchoate titles could not now be perfected. Protests of these kinds would become commoner as the survey proceeded. Powell soothed them with assurances [7] that reservation would not interfere with either perfected or inchoate titles, but would merely prevent further filings. The reservation was only temporary anyway, and its only purpose was "to secure the site of the Lake as it now exists as a natural reservoir and to prevent it being destroyed for the purpose; and further to prevent the flooded lands around the lake and its arms and tributaries from being filed upon in order to sell relinquishments and rights to the public hereafter when the Lake is needed as a natural reservoir." His assurances may not have satisfied Hearst's constituents, some of whom may have had in mind just such profitable relinquishments. Still, the trouble over Clear Lake was trifling by comparison with what erupted on the Rio Grande.

Properly speaking, it was not Powell who first proposed to dam the Rio Grande, but Major Anson Mills; when Mills came to the War Department with his proposals, the War Department referred him to Powell, who empowered him to study the problems and possibilities of a site just above El Paso.[8] That was even before the passage of the Sundry Civil Bill that in October, 1888, gave funds to the Irrigation Survey; as soon as the funds were available, Powell made Mills a supervising engineer under E. S. Nettleton. It was apparently the intention of all concerned to push for government construction of the dam. But in the midst of the preliminary studies, Mills was detached to investigate a water row at Fort Selden, in New Mexico. There the War Department had granted a canal company a charter to build a ditch across the reservation, but the Mexican farmers, seeing that the new ditch would cut across their own and put them under the control of the new company, threatened to rise in arms. Mills, Senator Reagan of Texas, and other investigators satisfied themselves that the whole scheme was an unprincipled grab, and they so testified at a hearing in Washington on February, 1889. The War Department revoked the canal company's charter, and thereby earned for all the federal irrigation forces the ferocious enmity of men who had been hurt in the pocketbook. W. H. H. Llewellyn, the representative of the canal company, went back west after leaving a note like a challenge to a duel at Mills' hotel:

"Dear Major:

I have wired Messrs. Davis and Morehead to have their people keep out, that if there is no new ditch at Las Cruces there will be no new dam at El Paso."

That posed the fight in its most naked terms: local interests against the public interest, and it not only marked the beginning of a dreary and celebrated dispute, but set a pattern for others just as dreary and just as celebrated. The irrigation forces went ahead with their plans. Mexico laid claim by prior right to the waters of the river. Negotiations finally resulted in an acceptable compromise which was written into a bill introduced into both houses of Congress, appropriating funds for the construction of the El Paso dam and granting Mexico half the water in exchange for the relinquishment of its claims.

It could easily have been the first and most important step of the United States government into large-scale reclamation and multipurpose control of the great western rivers. But Llewellyn's threat had not been an idle one. Before the bill could pass Congress, entrepreneurs led by Dr. Nathan Boyd obtained a charter from the willing legislature of the Territory of New Mexico, giving them the right to build a dam at Elephant Butte, one hundred twenty-five miles upstream. So now the dispute was brought past the stage of conflicting claims, and was brought to the stage of conflicting authorizations by law. There, all complete, was the whole tangled mess of rights and claims and jurisdictions. Instead of quarreling with the government of Mexico about the Rio Grande waters, the United States government had sensibly compromised. But it had no such chance with its own rebellious territory, for New

Mexico said it owned the river within its boundaries and would dam it where it pleased. There was no court decision which ruled otherwise. Before the local entrepreneurs could be prevented from hogging the waters of the river and invalidating the federal government's pledged agreement with Mexico, the case would go three times to the Supreme Court. And when the Reclamation Bureau finally did dam the Rio Grande, many years later, it would choose the Elephant Butte site. There never has been a dam at El Paso.

This controversy that arose in the very first months of the Irrigation Survey would take years in the settling, and even then would not provide a clear precedent upon which future disputes could be decided. Like the federal land laws, the water laws would be a patchwork of improvisations, compromises, state law and federal law, interstate agreements and agreements between states and the federal government, riparian rights, appropriation rights, preferential uses, the Wyoming doctrine of tying water rights to land titles, the notion of canal companies not as owners but as common carriers like railroads — a tedium and a headache and a complicated and special branch of the law throughout the West. The "California doctrine," which holds that in surrendering certain political rights on the admission of a state the United States Government does not surrender ownership of the flowing streams, has yet to be weighed in the Supreme Court against the "Colorado doctrine" that the state on admission acquires all rights within its territory not specifically withheld by the constitution.[9]

No answers, only increasingly pressing questions. Before ever the Rio Grande trouble had burst, Powell had been asked by Congress to comment on how the upstream and downstream rights on the Platte and Arkansas should be adjusted between the citizens of Colorado, Kansas, and Arkansas. Having no law to base an opinion on, he had contented himself with pointing out how the available waters could be most economically distributed and used. The legal question he had to refer to the courts.

It was easy enough for his engineers to work out the best general plan for any district or watershed, but it would be very much harder to apply the plan, with existing water rights on almost every stream, many of them wasteful. and with the state-ownership doctrines of many states permitting water companies to defy federal direction or control. As reservoir sites were reserved, the federal control of the situation would grow. And yet too great haste could lead to carelessness, error, the necessity of later duplication of the surveys. Powell was constantly forced to compromise between his view of the inclusiveness of the job and his sense of how urgent it was that something be done fast.

He had been in the irrigation business nine months, had selected about one hundred fifty reservoir sites and approximately thirty million acres of irrigable land, and had the General Land Office full of his clerks checking records of title so that the selected lands could be withdrawn from settlement, when on July 5 he was invited by Senator Stewart to make a western tour with the Irrigation Committee of the Senate.[10] Presumably he went not only to refresh his information but to do what he could as a missionary, to explain to Westerners the broad needs of their region and the ways in which the survey hoped to serve them. Political considerations were not missing, for in that summer of 1889 five of the western territories most affected by irrigation needs were holding constitutional conventions and their admission as states was assured within a year or two.

On the last of July, when Stewart and Reagan both preached irrigation and free silver to the South Dakota convention, Powell had not yet joined the group in person, though his ideas were multitudinously present in Senator Stewart's speech, and without sufficient quotation marks.[11] By August 5 Powell had joined the committee. They addressed the North Dakota convention in Bismarck on that day, and Powell gave the delegates some home thoughts on water. Eastern Dakota, he said, nearly always had enough rain, central Dakota sometimes did, and western Dakota practically never did. Both the eastern belt, with adequate rainfall, and the western, which had to depend completely on irrigation, were safe. The danger lay in the middle, where if farmers did nothing to utilize the streams and artesian wells and storm-water reservoirs they could make up their minds to cyclic disasters of the kind they were experiencing now. He meant that central Dakota was what the British in India called a "famine belt," though he had the political sense not to use that phrase at that place and time. When rain failed in a region that had made no preparations against drouth, failure was complete.

It therefore behooved the delegates to write the new state's constitution with a view to conserving water and preventing the monopolization of the life that ran in the streams. On the critical question of state and federal rights he said nothing definite: he only advised the delegates to learn something from California or Colorado, either one, so that North Dakota's own water laws would be clear. And he told them again, as he had been telling the hopeful for fifteen years, that the climate was not changing. Nothing that man could do would change the climate materially. They would have cyclic drouths, and they had better prepare for them.[12]

It was not a spread-eagle speech, but it probably represented in its earnestness and the honesty of its convictions the highest pitch of eloquence Powell was capable of. His heart was still in the irrigation struggle, and the battle could still be won.

While he was telling North Dakota what was good for it and urging it to make maximum use of its streams, the *North American Review* published a Powell article [13] (the source of Senator Stewart's learning) pointing up the lessons of the Johnstown flood. It said what only an ethnologist might have been expected to know: that agriculture developed first in arid lands, that irrigation agriculture was historically the first agriculture worthy of the name, that on the Indus and the Tigris-Euphrates and the Nile, as well as in the American Southwest, stable civilizations had built themselves on the necessity of controlling streams for irrigation. The only truly agricultural American Indians were desert Indians living in areas where agriculture might have been thought impossible. There was the full hope and expectation, therefore, that the American West would become one of the great agricultural regions of the world, but the hope was predicated on wise use of water and control of the rivers. The Johnstown flood, which had told many Americans that it was fatally dangerous to dam rivers, told Powell something quite different: that it was essential to know in advance all the conditions and specifications of the engineering job. The lesson was one in intelligent surveying and planning. The Johnstown flood was actually the most eloquent justification of the long-range and careful preliminary work that his survey was then engaged in.

The Major did not let his whole plan out of the bag in a single speech or a single article, but distributed it. At Helena, where he spoke to the Montana convention four days after the Bismarck speech, he showed another and more political side of it.[14] He spoke, he said, as an old-time Westerner, not as a politician. But as an old-timer in the West he knew how badly the institutions of the humid regions matched Western conditions. Montana had 35,000,000 irrigable acres, 35,000,000 acres of mountains useful chiefly for their minerals and timber, and 20,000,000 acres of range. Those figures alone had profound institutional — and hence political — implications. Farmers on the irrigable acres needed to control the adjacent mountains, not merely for their timber but for their water-storage facilities, and for their potential exposure to erosion and floods and destruction of the watershed. The relations between mountains and plains was so close that the two should not be politically separated. And on the strength of that relationship and of the abiding importance of water ("all the great values of this territory have ultimately to be measured to you in acre feet") he made a set of proposals.

What he suggested was so radical that it could not possibly have any effect on the delegates, so rational that it could not possibly come to pass short of heaven, so intelligently reasoned from fact that it must have sounded to Montana's tradition-and-myth-bound constitution-makers like the program of a crank.

He proposed simply to organize the new state of Montana into counties whose boundaries would be established by the divisions between hydrographic basins rather than by arbitrary political lines drawn on the map. Such basins, already being plotted out in Montana as in other parts of the West by his survey crews, were natural geographical and topographical unities; they might be given political and economic unity as well. Within any drainage basin, timber, grazing, and agriculture were all tied together by the controlling element of water. Suppose local self-government were established within each basin; suppose the federal government ceded to each basin-county all the public lands within its limits, suppose water rights within those limits should be established by locally elected water-masters and enforced by local courts. That way, they could lessen and perhaps eliminate litigation, friction, water-wars, multiplying costs. If it chose, Montana could organize itself and set a pattern for all the still-forming states of the West.

He told them how they might do it, though he could even then have had only the smallest and most wistful hope that they or any other western territory would match their political and economic organizations to the facts as revealed by his survey and to the most economical general plan of reclamation. Somewhere in Major Powell's small, maimed, whiskery person there burned some of the utopian zeal of Brook Farm and New Harmony. His vision of contented farmers controlling their own timber, grass, and water clear to the drainage divides, and settling their problems by an extension of the town meeting, is touched with a prophetic, perhaps a pathetic, piety. Science and Reason have always been on the side of Utopia; only the cussedness of the human race has not. In Montana the race was as cussed as elsewhere. It went ahead and organized the new state according to the tried and true patterns of more than a hundred years, with county lines marking none but the political drainage basins, and county seats competitively chosen in the atmosphere of deal, coup, and horse-trade. The water that was the state's lifeblood was not neglected, but its control was left open to franchise and purchase and grab, and its management confused by four dozen illogical political dividing lines.

3. *The Long View and the Short*

THE SWING through the West with the Irrigation Committee in the summer of 1889 had little effect on the constitution-makers of North Dakota and Montana, whom Powell addressed, nor on those of South Dakota, Washington, Idaho, and Wyoming, whom he did not. Nevertheless Powell's general system of ideas did have an effect, through Elwood Mead, on the Wyoming convention which in September wrote into the constitution the principle tying water rights to land — a principle first enunciated in the *Arid Region* report — and the Wyoming action in turn ultimately influenced at least half of the other western states.[1] Aside from that victory, the summer was about as fruitless as the Committee's August 20 inspection of the El Paso damsite that was doomed never to be used. The one positive and direct result of the trip was to breed between Powell and Senator Stewart an intense and incurable dislike.

With Senators Reagan and Jones, the others on the Irrigation Committee, Powell maintained the most cordial relations; he and Stewart were a little too positive for each other's taste, and in addition they represented utterly antithetical points of view. Powell stood for an ideal of public service both dedicated and comprehensive, for the greatest good for the greatest number as disinterested intelligence determined it. Stewart's notion of public service was as intense as his partisanship, as narrow as his intelligence, and as malleable as his personal ethics. His reason for interesting himself in irrigation was to bring water to his Nevada constituents, or some of them; his grasp of the problem was likely to be bounded by the drainage divides of the Truckee and the Carson. He wanted reservoir sites reserved and irrigable lands designated at once, by rough rule of thumb and without all this time-consuming squinting through theodolites.[2] He resented delay, disliked theorists, suspected disinterestedness, and was uncomfortable in the presence of intelligence. By the time the committee returned to Washington the honeymoon was over, though it would still be some months before Stewart would stamp out of the love nest and slam the door. And during the last months of 1889 and the first of 1890 Stewart's impatience and dislike would be exacerbated by legal developments which no one, not even Powell, had foreseen.

The Joint Resolution of March, 1888, was Powell's enabling legislation; the rider to the Sundry Civil Bill of October 2, 1888, merely provided him funds to go ahead. But the Joint Resolution carried two amendments, one directing the withdrawal of all lands that the survey designated irrigable, and the other providing that these lands could be restored to settlement under the Homestead Act provisions upon proclamation by the President. The Resolution did not specify how anyone was to tell which lands were irrigable until the survey designated them, and it did not define the boundaries of the region affected.

Trouble had brewed even before the Irrigation Committee started west. In early July, 1889, the Idaho Constitutional Convention complained to the General Land Office that speculators had followed the survey crews and staked out claims within the supposedly reserved reservoir site of Bear Lake.[3] The Acting Commissioner, William M. Stone, thought things over for a few weeks and on August 5 directed local land offices to cancel all claims filed after October 2, 1888, on reservoir, ditch, or canal sites. That is, he retroactively ordered the closing of the public lands,[4] for no one yet knew where such sites were.

Instantly there was consternation. What? Close all the land offices? Invalidate claims? Refuse the American yeoman his right to free land? And in the midst of the consternation some revelation: The General Land Office according to its own recent ruling should have been out of business in the West since the authorization of the Irrigation Survey, but it had never communicated to its local offices the law closing the entries on irrigable land. Whether it had simply overlooked that detail, which is hardly conceivable, or had misunderstood the law, which was easy enough to do, or had deliberately refused to suspend its operations, it was impossible to know. The Commissioner defended himself by insisting that the Joint Resolution, which had the force of law, had never been certified to his office.

As soon as the land offices were closed by Stone's order of August 5, 1889, both speculators and bona fide filers of claims who had acted in ignorance of an obscure law cried aloud. Their Congressmen also cried aloud, and shortly they forced a flustered Land Office back into business again: the local offices were told to issue patents to claimants, with the proviso that they might later be found invalid. That expedient pleased nobody, and left both Land Office and claimants hanging in uncertainty. But that was where they were both hanging when Stone gratefully moved over to make way for a new commissioner, L. E. Groff.

Mr. Groff, caught between the law and the wrath of the Congressmen who had passed it, appealed for an opinion to the Attorney General, the Assistant Attorney General, and the Secretary of the Interior. The answer was that as soon as Congress had passed the Sundry Civil Act making funds available for the Irrigation Survey, all irrigable lands whether surveyed or in process of survey or not yet touched were reserved by the amendment to the Joint Resolution. But it was April, 1890, before Groff finally ordered the head office to approve no more title patents on claims filed after October 2, 1888 — that date whose mere mention was now enough to scald Western excitabilities.

Attorney General Taft ruled that by the terms of the Joint Resolution all claims filed after that date were invalid; in his annual message President Grover Cleveland interpreted the act in the same way. The Land Office promptly withdrew 850,000,000 acres from entry, and now everyone understood what Congress had done in its zeal for irrigation to relieve the drouthy West. It had repealed all the land laws between the 100th meridian and the Pacific, and closed the public domain. More than that, it now appeared that there was no possibility of reopening the land to entry until the Irrigation Survey was completed or until the President proclaimed the restoration of certain districts. The President would obviously not restore any lands until they were certified to him by Major John Wesley Powell. Major John Wesley Powell would not certify any lands until his survey had worked them over. And his survey was apparently going to take forever.

Consternation approached apoplexy in Stewart and others who, having in mind a quick federal look-see at irrigation problems and a quick reservation of the obvious sites, now found that by their own act they had instituted federal planning on an enormous scale, put one man in almost absolute charge of it, and totally fouled up the local water and land interests to whom they were all bound to give a polite if not an obedient ear. What Powell aimed to do, it now became clear, would take years, and while he carried out his plans he had despotic powers over the public domain. His enemies had always said he drew his considerable authority from peculiar and irregular acts of legislation. Now the most peculiar of all had made him, so far as the development of the West went, the most powerful man in the United States. He could dictate, by his location of reservoirs and canals and his selection of the lands to be irrigated, the precise pattern that future settlement would take. He could block water and land companies wanting to accumulate a domain, by holding back lands or delaying their certification until they were ready for settlement by homesteaders. He could practically distribute the nation's remaining resources of soil and water according to his own plan and philosophy. He could all but command the sun to stand still in the West until he told it to go on.

Until the Attorney General's ruling in April, 1890, it is doubtful that Major Powell suspected the full power he possessed. At least he had taken the trouble on November 9, 1889, to request the segregation of 8,000,000 acres in the Snake River drainage basin in Wyoming and Idaho [5] — and he would not have asked the withdrawal of a specific tract if he had assumed that the whole public domain was automatically withdrawn. By the spring of 1890 he knew his strength, and he had begun to understand the violence of his opposition.

Yet he seems not to have feared it as much as he might have. Pushed by a combination of accident and public urgency into a control of land policies more complete than he could ever have dreamed of having, he could appreciate the need for haste without wanting to miss the opportunity through letting himself be crowded. He not only pursued his general plan, but he practically incorporated himself in it, and of necessity, when his enemies rallied to attack him, they attacked him through those parts of the plan that were furthest out of line with popular beliefs. He was as busy as he liked to be, trying on the one hand to convert short-range politicians and short-range settlers to long-range thinking, and on the other to balk the water and land companies with plans as long-range as his own, but with somewhat more private than public interest in their success.[6] He did not know how much public support he could summon, but he hoped for enough, and for long enough, to let him complete at least the basic essentials of the survey.

The only thing that kept him from being impossibly busy was the very real efficiency of his bureaus and the high *esprit* of his collaborators. Thanks to careful organization and the combining of the clerical staffs, the Bureau of Ethnology and the Geological Survey could almost run themselves if need be; and the Irrigation Survey complemented the Geological Survey in concrete ways. The foundation of both was the topographical map. Powell accordingly devoted almost eighty per cent of his Irrigation Survey budget to topography, and moved the $200,000 allocated for that purpose in the Geological Survey budget to areas not covered by the Irrigation Survey. Shaping the map was slow, but it was essential, essential enough to justify even the stopping of a process of settlement that had begun with Jamestown. To win the support that would let him get it done, Powell intensified his missionary campaign with Congress and the public.

He explained his plan and the scientific observations upon which it was based in a series of meetings with the House Committee on Irrigation between February and April, 1890.[7] He aired it in speeches, wrote it for the magazines, repeated it in his published reports, argued it at dinners, dictated it in patient letters to angry or inquiring or plaintive correspondents. To work through that body of report and polemic is to realize how consistent, by now, his views about the arid region had become, and how widely his plan reached to embrace the related problems of land, water, erosion, floods, soil conservation, even the new one of hydroelectric power; and how behind the plan was a settled belief in the worth of the small farmer and the necessity of protecting him both from speculators and from natural conditions he did not understand and could not combat.

The key ideas [8] were hammered at over and over in an attempt to break down tradition and the feeling that it was unpatriotic in a Westerner to admit that his country was dry. The best and the safest agriculture, and the oldest, was irrigation agriculture. And it was fatal to believe that tillage altered the climate. Tillage brought no more rain than burning the prairies, or sending up balloons, or any of the other schemes. Climate depended on meteorological forces too sweeping to be changed by any local expedients.

And no one should expect to reclaim all the western lands. Twenty per cent was probably an optimistic estimate of what was reclaimable — but even that twenty per cent would total more than all the lands tilled so far in the nation. To reclaim that twenty per cent, water would have to be available, and most of it would have to come from the large rivers. Dams on these rivers would have far-reaching effects. Properly engineered, they would protect from floods instead of causing them as at Johnstown. They would allow the reclamation of arid lands on the headwaters and swamp lands near the mouths, and they would permit a controlled flow that would prevent wasteful runoff. Also, one of the first needs in the utilization of these great rivers was a legal one, for rivers were an interstate, sometimes an international, matter, and as yet there was no clear body of law covering their ownership and use.

The best way to approach that legal question was by first organizing the West into hydrographic basins which would be virtually self-governing and hence able to negotiate with other similar basins, as well as to control their own watersheds clear to the drainage divides. Inter-basin water law would offer a sound basis for the development of interstate water law, whereas to permit development of water by local franchise was to permit monopoly and waste and the peonage of the small farmer. Moreover, no individual or company could afford the enormous engineering works that were necessary for proper development of the great rivers and the maximum use of water. The ideal way was co-operation: he would have supported federal construction only as a preventive of local grabbing. But however the works were to be built, the absolutely necessary first step was a systematic and careful survey, and that was the proper function of the government's scientific bureaus.

Over and over he repeated and explained and illustrated his thesis that the new conditions of the West demanded new institutions. These he outlined in his three articles for *Century* in the spring of 1890, he incorporated them in his reports, he used them as a basis of principle from which to answer canal companies demanding to be reassured in their rights or to be told what their rights were, or coyly offering to co-operate with the survey in the selection of reservoir sites. Probably he convinced some, perhaps many. Certainly he did more than his part to air the West's peculiar problems and emphasize the need for more forethought in its settlement than had gone into the settlement of the East and Midwest. He found himself both a champion and a scapegoat, for Congress, which had closed the public domain and repudiated the myth of the Garden of the World, was looking for someone to blame. There were three House bills and one Senate bill already introduced, all aimed at canceling the Joint Resolution's provisions. A good deal of Powell's missionary work was actually self-defense.

Meantime he was doing more than missionary work. By June, 1890, in addition to the nearly 30,000,000 acres of irrigable lands he had tentatively selected,[9] he had designated two hundred reservoir sites to the General Land Office for reservation. But before any of the 30,000,000 acres could be certified to the President for restoration to settlement, the titles to all privately held parcels within the large districts had to be checked. Powell still had a dozen clerks over in the General Land Office turning pages, but by the time the appropriations committees got around to him at the beginning of June he had been unable actually to certify a single acre.

Nevertheless the request for funds and the plan of operations that he sent to Secretary Vilas in April [10] was breezily confident. He now asked grandly, on the scale that Stewart and Teller had at first proposed. By now Dutton had trained a staff of hydraulic engineers; there were people to make the survey move. So Powell asked for $720,000, plus another $70,000 for map engraving, cement research, and office rental. The total was more than three times his last Irrigation Survey appropriation. Though Dutton had been skeptical from the beginning about the propriety of devoting so much of the appropriation to topography, Powell looked upon the map as the basis of the whole plan he had submitted to the irrigation clique in 1888.[11]

He busied himself gathering ammunition for the conversion of the appropriations committees, and while he was doing so the Senate gave notice of its temper by passing a resolution demanding to know how much, if any, of the money appropriated for irrigation surveys had been diverted to topographic work, and if so, "by what authority of law where appropriations are made by Congress for several purposes the money appropriated for one purpose can be diverted and used for another purpose for which an appropriation is also made in the same statute." [12] The animus and the apoplectic turgidity of the resolution would have told Powell who had got it up. Stewart had found what he conceived to be a loose stone in the Major's wall, and he was busy digging. If he could cast doubt on the legality of the Irrigation Survey's topographic work, he would have a chance to bring the whole thing down. Actually Stewart had known from the beginning that Powell based everything upon the topographic map. But he also knew that Powell had been criticized for taking more authority on occasion than the law allowed him. Having fathered it himself, he knew that the enabling law of the Irrigation Survey was irregular and that Powell might be made to seem responsible for it. He would personally take steps in that direction.

The Resolution that Stewart and other Westerners pushed through on May 31, 1890, had as its purpose the repudiation of the irrigation legislation, at least as it presently stood, and the scotching of the man who, having been put in charge, had shown that he would fight for it. But it was not the first action of 1890 that aimed at the vilification of Major Powell. That first action had come at the very start of the new year, when the spies and whisperers, sensing another opportunity and seeing formidable forces attacking Powell from the front, came out from behind the arras with their knives in their hands.

4. Spies and Whisperers Again

ON JANUARY 12, 1890, a Sunday, the New York *Herald* was bannered with scare headlines:

SCIENTISTS WAGE BITTER WARFARE. PROF. COPE, OF THE UNIVERSITY OF PENNSYLVANIA, BRINGS SERIOUS CHARGES AGAINST DIRECTOR POWELL AND PROF. MARSH, OF THE GEOLOGICAL SURVEY. CORROBORATION IN PLENTY. LEARNED MEN COME TO PENNSYLVANIAN'S SUPPORT WITH ALLEGATIONS OF IGNORANCE, PLAGIARISM AND INCOMPETENCE AGAINST THE ACCUSED OFFICIALS. IMPORTANT COLLATERAL ISSUE. THE NATIONAL ACADEMY OF SCIENCES, OF WHICH PROFESSOR MARSH IS PRESIDENT, IS CHARGED WITH BEING PACKED IN THE INTERESTS OF THE SURVEY. RED HOT DENIALS PUT FORTH. HEAVY BLOWS DEALT IN ATTACK AND DEFENCE AND LOTS OF HARD NUTS PROVIDED FOR SCIENTIFIC DIGESTION. WILL CONGRESS INVESTIGATE?[1]

This time Cope and his cohorts had come out loaded for bear. It is doubtful that any modern controversy among men of learning has generated more venom than this one did. All the old charges were there in the *Herald's* full and delighted story, all distilled and aged but not mellowed through twenty years of hatred. Powell was not the principal object of attack, but he took some blows aimed at Marsh and he took some in his own right. He was a political boss who had built a scientific Tammany within the government, intimidated or bought off his opposition, gained control of the National Academy, and made himself head of a great scientific monopoly. His bureaus were asylums for Congressmen's sons and provided sinecures for press agents and pap for college professors, and the activities and influence of these were used in turn to milk great appropriations from Congress.

Powell's personal learning was a fake, and in supporting Marsh he supported the worst snake, fake, and plagiarist in American science. Moreover Powell had stolen or duplicated the work of the state geological surveys; had jealously blocked publication of Cope's paleontological work done for the Hayden Survey; had insulted Cope by suggesting that some of Cope's collections actually belonged to the government; had obstructed geological work which contradicted his own; had attempted to dominate scientific meetings; had neglected mining geology in his conduct of the Geological Survey; and had misused Survey funds by sending Captain Dutton to Hawaii to study volcanoes.

As for Marsh, he was an incompetent, a plagiarist, a cheat. He consistently published the work of his assistants as his own; he failed to pay his helpers; he destroyed fossils in the field so that no one else could study them; he kept the enormous collections of the Geological Survey in his Yale laboratory under lock and key and refused other scientists access to them; and he had mixed them so hopelessly with the Yale collections that no one would ever be able to sort them out. He had conspired with Powell to pack the National Academy with Geological Survey stooges. He had committed every stupidity possible to a man who called himself a scientist. He had stolen some of his work from Cope, and his celebrated genealogy of the horse was a pure theft from the Russian Kowalevsky.

Supporting this blast was an extensive collection of letters and testimonials, gathered over a period of many years, as well as Endlich's 23,000 word smear which Congress had looked at and decided to ignore in 1885.

It was not, in spite of its hysterical extravagances, an attack to be laughed off. William Hosea Ballou, the *Herald* reporter who had assembled it out of interviews with Cope, Endlich, Sterry Hunt, Persifor Frazer, a group of Marsh's disgruntled assistants, and another group of dissident and anti-Powell scientists, was obviously convinced that he had stumbled upon a good deal of fire as well as a lot of murky smoke. He did have the courtesy to bring the article to Powell and send it to Marsh before it appeared, and he ran Powell's reply in the same issue in which the charges were made.

In that reply, Powell had one great advantage over Cope: hatred had not seared his thinking apparatus, and the dignity of his defence made the attack look as hysterical as in fact it was.

> As Director of the Survey a great trust is placed upon me, and I recognize that I am responsible not only to the President of the United States, whose commission I bear, and to the Secretary who is my immediate chief, and to the Congress of the United States, to whom I make an annual report setting forth in full the transactions of the survey, but also to the people of the United States, whose servant I am. . . . I feel myself deeply responsible to the scientific men of the country also, for during a period of more than twenty years they have supported me and the work under my charge almost with unanimity. . . .

Having put Cope where he belonged, in an envious minority, Powell traced step by step, with documents at least as convincing as Cope's, the progress of almost two decades of malice, from the founding of the survey and the defeat of Hayden's forces to the Cope-Endlich attempt to smear him before the investigating committee of 1885.[2] He corrected some of Cope's figures, especially with regard to the funds annually allocated to Marsh, and he defended Marsh's scientific reputation, leaving to Marsh himself the defense of his personal honesty. He stoutly defended his arrangements with several state surveys for topographical mapping, categorically denied duplicating or stealing from any state survey, justified his press agent W. A. Croffut as the general editor of extensive survey publications, told Cope that any time he submitted a completed manuscript his paleontological volumes for the Hayden Survey would be published, and made some mildly deleterious remarks about "species fiends" that applied about as well to Marsh as to Cope. And he concluded with a touch of kindly and ironic condescension:

> I am not willing to be betrayed into any statement which will do injustice to Professor Cope. He is the only one of the coterie who has scientific standing. The others are simply his tools and act on his inspiration. The Professor himself has done much valuable work for

> science. He has made great collections in the field and has described these collections with skill. Altogether he is a fair systematist. If his infirmities of character could be corrected by advancing age, if he could be made to realize that the enemy which he sees forever haunting him as a ghost is himself . . . he could yet do great work for science.

Professor Marsh's reply was marked by no such restraint and decorum. Having been attacked with talons, he replied with claws. First he collected a series of denials from people whom Cope had quoted against him. The denials in very few instances took back anything their authors had previously said about Marsh: they merely denied that Cope had been authorized to publish anything. Still, they prepared the way for Marsh's own turn in the *Herald* on the following Sunday.

Marsh's statement was cold, controlled, furious. He denied Cope's charges of plagiarism and misuse of his assistants, and to Cope's charges of scientific incompetence he replied with counter-charges, notably with reference to Cope's achievement in articulating one skeleton backside-to. And he noted also Cope's raids on private collections, admitting that since Cope had sneaked into the Yale laboratory and stolen and published some of Marsh's uncompleted work he saw there, the Yale collections, including those of the Geological Survey, had indeed been closed to unauthorized persons, especially Professor Cope. "Little men with big heads, unscrupulous in warfare, are not confined to Africa," he said, "and Stanley will recognize them here when he returns to America. Of such dwarfs we have unfortunately a few in science."

And what of Cope's claim that Marsh had stolen his genealogy of the horse from Kowalevsky? Poppycock. Marsh had never seen Kowalevsky's work. He had convinced Thomas Henry Huxley of the true genealogy in 1876, and a few days later Huxley had cited the source of his altered opinions in a New York speech. More than that, Kowalevsky was as notorious in Europe as Cope was in America for raiding other people's museums. "Kowalevsky," wrote Professor Marsh with his teeth precisely together, "was at last stricken with remorse and ended his unfortunate career by blowing out his own brains. Cope still lives, unrepentant."

Cope had shot off all his ammunition in the first charge. He was scattered and routed by Powell's dignified immovability and by the bullwhip of Marsh's tongue. Given opportunity to make fresh statements so that the *Herald* could keep its profitable controversy going, he replied only that "the recklessness of assertion, the erroneousness of statement and the incapacity of comprehending our relative positions on the part of Professor Marsh render further discussion of the trivial matters upon which we disagree unnecessary, and my time is too fully occupied on more important subjects to permit me to waste it upon personal affairs which are already sufficiently before the public. Professor Marsh has recorded his views *aere perenne,* and may continue to do so without personal notice by E. D. Cope." [3]

But he was not to get away with any such lame and lofty curtain line. Marsh would have the last word. Cope's feeble rejoinder, he said, showed that he was now in the exact position of the boy who twisted the mule's tail. He was not so good-looking as he once was, but he knew more.

Up to a point, Marsh's cold triumph was justified. And yet, though discomfited and even discredited in the eyes of most scientific men, Cope could take a smoldering satisfaction in what he had done. It was both true and important that the "personal affairs" toward which he now expressed indifference were "sufficiently before the public." A smear never quite washes clean from a public character, and when a public character has need of all the public confidence he can muster, even a refuted charge can hurt. Cope had no interest in Powell's general plan, probably knew little about it. But his narrowly paleontological and personal attacks could damage everything that Powell had been working for. How much, Powell could not tell until he faced the committees of both houses in the spring.

5. *Triumph of the Gilpins*

"Of course I have got a great respect for scientifically educated gentlemen, and I am always very much interested in their researches and all that, but you can not satisfy an ordinary man by any theoretical scheme or by any science. . . . 'One man can see in the ground no farther than another, unless there is a hole in it.'" (Senator Moody of South Dakota before the House Appropriations Committee, June 4, 1890.)[1]

THEY WERE LAYING for him when he appeared before the House Appropriations Committee at the beginning of June. Though he had stout friends as well as enemies, he faced a general Congressional disappointment that the survey had not achieved more in its nearly two years of life, and a specific Western irritation at the closing of the public domain. Somewhere in the room, too, was an echo of Cope's charges of power grabbing and incompetence, an air of personal mistrust that Powell had rarely met before. On the whole, he had enjoyed Congressional confidence, but the committee which had summoned him now was not reassuring. It was watchful. And in the room, present as guests at their own request, were the whole Irrigation Committee of the Senate, headed by Stewart.

What he gave them was a set of facts, but the facts had been selected in the full knowledge that he would be sharply questioned, and that the questions would center on topography. He outlined the history of the legislation and the preliminary plans which he had on request furnished before any legislation was passed, and he took pains to note that Stewart and Teller had been central in that agitation. From the beginning, Powell's estimates of cost and duration had been based on the necessity of the topographic map: the Public Lands Committee, the Appropriations Committees, and everyone else concerned had discussed and approved his estimates in the full knowledge of what they implied. He quoted them their own approval from the printed record. He outlined the relationship between the topographical work of the Geological Survey and that of the Irrigation Survey, showed them his budgets in each case, showed them how he had kept his Geological Survey mapping to eastern states and mining regions and his Irrigation Survey topography to western agricultural and water-storage lands. The two operations, he insisted, had been kept scrupulously separate, though in the long run they would be combined to produce the master atlas of the country. He showed them on skeleton maps what he had done and what he expected to do, and when the visiting Senators could contain themselves no longer they interrupted the committee proceedings and threw questions at his head. The two who came at him hardest were Stewart and Gideon Moody of South Dakota.

They wanted to know who had defined the "arid region," and implied that it was a fiction of Powell's own, designed to get him extra powers.[2] They were bitter about Representative Symes' amendment to the 1888 Resolution, which authorized the withdrawal of all arid lands. South Dakota, said Senator Moody, was not arid land. He denied rainfall statistics and resented slurs against what had from its first settlement been a rich and productive wheat belt.

They doubted the necessity of his maps. Why must a pressing need for irrigation works wait years for the completion of a fussy preliminary survey? Why couldn't the obvious reservoir sites be selected at once, a decent allowance being made for error, and the topographical survey be completed at leisure by the Geological Survey's crews?

Also, what did he say to the fact that both Dutton and Nettleton, two of his own experts, had testified before the House Irrigation Committee that a topographical map was not necessary for selecting reservoir sites? That one hurt, because Dutton, one of Powell's closest friends and collaborators for fifteen years, his left hand, his heir to the Grand Canyon study and his director of hydrography now,[3] had from the beginning doubted Powell's right to use Irrigation Survey funds for topography, and on questioning had reluctantly said so. The tight loyalty of the bureau had been cracked, the Table Round had produced its Gawain, the Twelve their Judas. That defection was ominous, but Powell could not have known it yet, with the Senators still after him.

What, they asked, did he know about the West? What did he know about South Dakota? Had he ever been there? When? Where? For how long? Did he know the average rainfall of the James River Valley? Of the Black Hills? They refused to understand his distinction between arid and subhumid, they clamored to know how their states had got labeled "arid" and thus been closed to settlement.

And what about the artesian basin in the Dakotas? What about irrigation from that source? So he gave it to them: artesian wells were and always would be a minor source of water as compared to the rivers and the storm-water reservoirs. He had had his men studying artesian wells since 1882; they were incapable of doing a tenth as much as hopeful Dakotans said they would. If all the wells in the Dakotas could be gathered into one county they would not irrigate that county.

Senator Moody thereupon remarked that he did not favor putting money into Major Powell's hands when Powell would clearly not spend it as Moody and his constituents wanted it spent. We ask you, he said in effect, your opinion of artesian wells. You think they're unimportant. All right, the hell with you. We'll ask somebody else who will give us the answer we want. Nothing personal. "Our people in the West are practical people, and we can not wait until this geological picture and topographical picture is perfected." Nothing personal.

Senator Stewart had already made it personal in the morning session. "Every representative of the arid region — I think there is no exception — would prefer that there would be no appropriation to having it continue under Major Powell."

Nevertheless, that opening round was Powell's. On June 9 he was able to write with full optimism to Elwood Mead, then state engineer of Wyoming, "The Appropriations Committee of the House of Representatives have given me my full estimate for the Irrigation Survey. I have reason to believe that the appropriations made this year will be several times greater than they were last, but, of course, until the bill finally passes I cannot state this positively. Whatever the appropriation is, however, I am expecting to have you on the work in accordance with the plan already understood by us both. I write this simply to let you know that the prospect for a large appropriation is good and I hope to have the work prosecuted with vigor." [4]

Hunting for any stick to hit him with, Stewart and Moody tried to get the whole Irrigation Survey transferred to the Department of Agriculture, but could not muster sufficient support. Meanwhile, confident that most of his opposition had been aroused by the slowness of his survey, and sure that as soon as lands began to be certified and returned to settlement the clamor would subside, the Major marshaled his arguments and awaited the second round before the Senate Appropriations Committee. He was a tough man for a committee to discountenance, an urbane and cool and well-informed witness, and he was without doubts either about the rightness of his program or of its ultimate acceptance. Still, he could hardly have stepped into that Senate committee room on July 2, 1890, without his neck hairs prickling. The subcommittee on the Sundry Civil Expenses Bill — Chairman Allison of Iowa, Gorman of Maryland, and Hale of Maine — he knew of old, and did not fear. But also in the room were the visitors from the arid region: Allen of Washington, Carey of Wyoming, Moody of South Dakota, Paddock of Nebraska, Power and Sanders of Montana, Reagan of Texas, and Stewart of Nevada. They might have struck even the cool and intrepid and hopeful Major Powell as perilously like a hanging jury.

The tone of the meeting[5] was set by the earliest questions. Both Hale and Allison examined the propriety of Powell's being "the source and fountain of information" for the Presidential proclamations that would sometime return land to settlement. Their clear implication was that his powers were excessive, that he was in a position to tell the President what to do and that he had taken over the proper duties of the General Land Office. Powell replied that his survey had no effect on the duties of the Land Office except to suspend them temporarily. He justified the delay while the survey was completed because only accurate advance knowledge could prevent mistaken, impossible, or monopolistic irrigation schemes, inefficient use of water, confusion between upstream and downstream rights to rivers, and the failure of thousands of small homesteaders. He had not asked for the powers the law gave him. Congress had presented him with a job.

But where, they asked, did such a survey as he was conducting lead? Government science for informational purposes was one thing, but Senator Hale in particular was dubious about the government's segregating land unless it intended to take over the whole business of irrigation. Powell replied that according to present law (the Desert Land Act) a homesteader must irrigate before he could obtain title, but couldn't irrigate because he had neither the knowledge nor the money to build the works. Government must go at least to the point of assuring such a homesteader that irrigation was possible where he settled, and that the terms of the law could be lived up to.

Yet even that, as Allison forced Powell to admit, went a long way in the direction of government interference. Government would have to legislate the uses of water on those segregated lands, and would perhaps be forced into the construction of irrigation works and the full control of water. How *could* you control the water unless you built and operated the dams and canals? Major Powell thought control could be exercised if the government simply refused to sell or release lands unless they were irrigable according to the findings of the survey. No sane settler would take a chance out on the plains, far from the mountains and far from any actual or proposed irrigation works. That was how settlement could be controlled.

And that control of settlement, that exercise of supervision over the individual citizen, was what they had been coming at. Up to now, the land had been settled by unsupervised men in an almost unsupervised environment.

"Do you conceive that there is any risk or doubt," Hale asked, "in the government's assuming that relation and undertaking to deal with the flow and use of water in the great streams? Do you think it is better than to leave it to nature and the common incidents of human life?"

Powell's answer was as blunt as he could make it. "You ask me the question, and I will answer. I think it would be almost a criminal act to go on as we are doing now, and allow thousands and hundreds of thousands of people to establish homes where they cannot maintain themselves."

So the issue was clarified at its most statesmanlike level: the alternatives were uncontrolled settlement and the devil take the stragglers, or controlled settlement aiming at the elimination of the heartbreak and the casualties — Spencerian social evolution or willed evolution à la Lester Ward. The committee did not pursue the question, and did not examine the possible limitations and extensions of governmental and scientific direction of people's lives, but they raised it. Or more accurately, the whole development of governmental science had already raised it earlier. Alexander Agassiz had testily attacked government patronage of science five years before,[6] and he had had a clear idea of what he was attacking. The concept of the welfare state edged into the American consciousness and into American institutions more through the scientific bureaus of government than by any other way, and more through the problems raised by the public domain than through any other problems, and more through the labors of John Wesley Powell than through any other man. In its origins it probably owes nothing to Marx, and it was certainly not the abominable invention of Franklin Delano Roosevelt and the Brain Trust. It began as public information and extended gradually into a degree of control and paternalism increased by every national crisis and every step of the increasing concentration of power in Washington. The welfare state was present in embryo in Joseph Henry's Weather Bureau in the eighteen-fifties. It moved a long step in the passage of what Henry Adams called America's "first modern act of legislation," when the King and Hayden Surveys were established in 1867. It had come much farther by the time Powell answered Hale's questions on July 2, 1890, and it would assume almost its contemporary look in the trust-busting and conservation activities of Theodore Roosevelt at the dawn of the next century. But what Powell and the earlier Adams and Theodore Roosevelt thought of as the logical development of American society, especially in the West, was by no means universally palatable by 1890 — or by 1953. It looked dangerous; it repealed the long habit of a wide-open continent; it recanted a faith.

Question: Why do both agricultural and irrigable lands have to be tied up while the survey is prosecuted?

Answer: No agricultural lands are tied up. Nothing east of the 102nd meridian is withdrawn in Kansas and Nebraska, and anything west of that line is arid. Reservation of all these arid lands is actually a benefit, not a hardship, for if they were not withdrawn the settlers on the North and South Platte would see all their water appropriated by upstream users, and no help for it.

Question (with senatorial bitterness): Do you really know anything about irrigable lands in the Three Forks country in Montana?

Question: Do you really expect us to believe that the survey — once it begins to produce results — can designate irrigable lands faster than settlers will take them up?

Question: How are settlers going to derive any benefits from "that beautiful map of the Major's" when no reservoirs or canals are actually to be built?

Answer: No homes are possible in the arid region anyway until irrigation works are built, yet the law demands that a settler build one. He should at least be assured that water is *possible* where he wants to set his house. And there is another thing: the subhumid zone is actually a more pressing problem than the arid lands, and irrigation works are just as necessary there. If irrigation is developed, the economic farm unit could be cut to 80 acres, or even to 40. The possibilities of water storage are shown on this map . . .

Question (by Senator Stewart): Can't you state it independently of the map?

Having come growling out of his den, he mauled Powell around for a good hour. The survey, he said, had proved nothing that wasn't already well known; the topographical work was useless because boundaries of reservoir sites and irrigable areas were not marked out on the ground and a settler could not tell whether he was on reserved or open ground (the Land Office maps would tell him, said Powell). Said Stewart, the maps were of no use to the hydraulic engineers, as both Dutton and Nettleton had testified. Results were a long way from justifying expenditures. Incompetents had been given responsible jobs on the survey. . . .

What had been a grilling became a tirade. At one point, after Stewart had interrupted all of his attempted answers for fifteen minutes, Powell told the Senator sharply either to stop interrupting his answers or to quit asking questions. They glared at each other.

Stewart: Now you have the whole country reserved . . .

Powell: Senator . . . You make a statement which you do not mean to make to me — that I have got the whole country reserved. . . . I have not done it. I never advocated it. That reservation was put into the law independently of me. Yet you affirm here and put it in the record that I had it done. . . .

Stewart: Are you in favor of its repeal?

Powell: No, sir. I think it is wise.

Stewart: Have you not insisted that it be maintained?

Powell: I have not insisted upon anything, but when asked my opinion as you ask it now, I have expressed it.

Eventually Allison observed that Brother Stewart had been at Powell long enough, and was keeping the other brethren from their rights. The other brethren came in strong, most of them to secede from the arid empire, to challenge Powell's rainfall figures, to attack his low opinion of artesian wells, and to shake their heads over the governmental paternalism he seemed to approve. They did not want individual initiative interfered with, they wanted the West taken care of by means of "natural conditions and natural enterprise." Montana, the Dakotas, Idaho, Washington, denied his premises. Only Senator Reagan of Texas gave him strong support, citing the attempted water-grabs in New Mexico as reason for federal control, and proposing legislation based on Powell's notion of the unified drainage basin. Powell had had a rough time, but he might have felt that he had held his own. Only Stewart and Moody had really crowded him, though the subcommittee proper had all been skeptical of too much extension of federal power, and Sanders of Montana had kidded Reagan, and hence by association Powell, with being a disciple of Henry George.

Against Stewart's hostility, Senate suspicion of his too-great powers, and Western irritation at the freezing of land, he might even have won if his missionary campaign had paid off. But he got less public support than he expected. Apparently he underestimated the capacity of the plain dirt farmer to continue to believe in myths even while his nose was being rubbed in unpleasant facts. The press and a good part of the public in the West was against him more than he knew. His revolutionary proposals for arid-belt institutions had found only scattered supporters like Reagan and Elwood Mead. The American yeoman might clamor for governmental assistance in his trouble, but he didn't want any that would make him change his thinking.

Another year, another appropriation, would convince them, Powell thought. But he didn't get the year, he didn't get the appropriation. By the same side door through which it had come into existence — by an amendment to the Sundry Civil Expenses Bill — Powell's General Plan was pushed out. A Senate Amendment eliminated all the clauses dealing with reservation of irrigable lands, and thus threw the public domain open again, to the utter confounding of Powell's hopes for reasonable planning. All entries made in good faith — and good faith was fairly easy to prove to most Land Offices — since October 2, 1888, were declared valid, though the number of acres a man could acquire under all existing land laws was dropped to 320. Hydrographic work was pointedly not mentioned, and since this appropriations bill was the sole authorizing legislation for the survey, hydrographic work was completely eliminated unless the Geological Survey wanted to undertake it.[7] The appropriation, instead of the $720,000 Powell had asked, was $162,500.

To some it might have seemed only a temporary check, a sign of Congressional impatience with the Irrigation Survey alone. At least the chastisement was qualified, for the appropriation of $719,000 voted for the Geological Survey proper made it the best-supported scientific organization in the world. Powell was still Mr. Science, the High Priest.

And yet the reduction of the Irrigation Survey from a comprehensive and articulated General Plan to an ineffectual and aimless mapping of reservoir sites was the major defeat of his life, and the beginning of the end of his public career. Everything that happened to him from this point on was documentation of a decision already made, corroboration of his public decline from the peak of 1890.

For this General Plan that Congress had just stomped to death for the second time incorporated his whole knowledge and experience and faith. The possibility that sometime events would converge toward an opportunity was the end and excuse of many of his political alliances and fights and deals and all the interlocking activities of his bureaus from 1877 on. All science must eventually be practical; the Science of Earth and the Science of Man led to the same end, the evolving and developing of better political, artistic, social, industrial, and agricultural institutions, "all progressing with advancing intelligence to secure justice and thereby increase happiness."[8]

The General Plan had been his vision of the way in which, by the help of science, justice and happiness could be guaranteed for the people and the region to which he was most attached. The opportunity had come unexpectedly, but it had opened up the dazzling possibility that the whole thing could be realized: that the waste could be stopped, the random and ill-advised mob of settlers directed by scientific knowledge and planning and steered into becoming colonists and communities.

But they hadn't given him time. They had beaten him when he was within a year of introducing an utterly revolutionary — or evolutionary — set of institutions into the arid West, and when he was within a few months of saving that West from another half century of exploitation and waste. It was the West itself that beat him, the Big Bill Stewarts and Gideon Moodys, the land and cattle and water barons, the plain homesteaders, the locally patriotic, the ambitious, the venal, the acquisitive, the myth-bound West which insisted on running into the future like a streetcar on a gravel road.[9]

6. *Coup de Grâce*

A SUCCESS which left Powell still in possession of power was unsatisfactory to Senator Stewart. Completely incapable of understanding either the scope or the meaning of Powell's General Plan, he could have no notion of the damage he had done his enemy by restricting the Irrigation Survey to a little topography west of the 100th meridian. He would not rest until he damaged him a great deal more.

With the Irrigation Survey pulled down, he turned his attention to the Geological Survey, which, created by the kind of law that was jammed through in the frantic last days and nights of a session, was vulnerable to the same tactics in reverse. Much might be made of the fact that Powell's budget was not itemized. In some instances, simply to forestall criticism, he had designated specific sums for specific purposes, but his general immunity from Congressional control was complete. His budgets showed no knobs or irregularities that could be whittled off by the watchdogs of the Treasury. And the spies and whisperers had made much of his arbitrary powers without producing any change, principally because Powell's personal integrity was as unquestioned as the efficiency of his bookkeeping. But his freedom of expenditure could be made to look bad: the malice of the Cope crowd and the persistent hatred of Stewart could work at that structural weakness like ice at a crack in a wall.

In 1891 the Stewart forces hung on relentlessly until they turned back the steady curve of appropriation increase for the Survey. The cut of $90,000 that they succeeded in getting [1] was the first reduction Powell had suffered since his fight for survival in 1877. But more alarming than the reduced budget was the fact that this appropriation designated specific salaries and allocated specific sums to different branches of the bureau.

That was more than ominous; it amounted to a vote of no-confidence. It meant that the whispers about the scientific Tammany had found hearers; that Powell's power, even though no one had ever proved it abused, troubled more and more Congressmen; and that his indefatigable enemies were starting to weaken the front of support on which he had been able to count through the years.

Since 1878, when Representative Patterson of Colorado had thundered denunciations of "this revolutionist," there had always been an opposition to the Survey in Congress, and the opposition had from time to time distinguished itself for bombast and ignorance and bad faith. It had been anti-science, anti-control, anti-reform. To it, planning was insufferable, intelligence an insult to free Americans. "Do not shackle us with this folly," Patterson had bellowed in the debate over the National Academy's proposals in 1878. "Allow the people of the West . . . that scope and opportunity which our present wise system of land laws afford and in a few years you will have peopling the vast interior of our country as numerous, thrifty, enterprising, patriotic, and happy a population as is now the boast of the most powerful states of the Union." [2]

Since then, some towns in Kansas and even in Patterson's own state of Colorado had been settled and abandoned as much as three times. The wise system of land laws had marched the West swiftly and directly toward homesteader failure and land and water monopoly by corporations and individuals. The farming population of those plains where the Pattersons and the Gilpins saw visions, and where settlers dug for firewood and drilled for the dependable artesian water, was already defeated by conditions that the Pattersons and the Gilpins would never admit. There would be fewer of Patterson's thrifty, enterprising, and happy farmers in large parts of Kansas, Nebraska, Colorado, Oklahoma, and the Dakotas in 1940 than there were in the peak year of 1890.[3]

Now in 1892 Patterson was long gone, and with him Page of California, Maginnis of Montana, Haskell of Kansas, Dunnell of Minnesota, and other tub-thumpers of homestead settlement. Gone were some of those who had suspiciously sniffed at the heels of government science in 1885. But Congressmen often have a long life, and some, like Jukeses, leave worthy successors. In 1892 Hilary Herbert was still in the House, Wolcott and Stewart and Power and Carey still in the Senate. Their grievances differed but their object was the same: to get Powell.

Again, as in the newspaper attack of January, 1890, it was Marsh whose flank was turned to expose Powell's position. This time the group which was opposed to government science and was hunting a way to reduce Powell's size discovered that the Geological Survey had published a study by Marsh on the Odontornithes, or Toothed Birds.[4] A man whose reputation had been gained and kept by shaving and denying and cutting things in budgets, Representative Herbert could grow as caustic about birds with teeth as he had about Elliot Lord's history of the Comstock or Powell's frivolous addiction to topography. Representative Wilson of Washington was picked to introduce the ridicule of the toothed-birds book into the House. Herbert then expanded that opening into a full public airing of all the whispers and slanders of 1890, 1885, 1878–79, 1874, and all the years between.[5] It may have been significant that Eugene Smith, the State Geologist of Herbert's state of Alabama, was one of Cope's crowd.[6] At any rate, Cope and Endlich were dragged out and dusted off, Agassiz found his letters against government science read again into the record. The topographical atlas of the United States on which Powell had spent close to half of the six millions he had received in appropriations over the past thirteen years was pawed over and revealed to be only half completed.

There was no end to any of it, they cried. It was all a gigantic scheme to perpetuate in power and plush the director and his henchmen. His "scheme of geology," Herbert said, was "the most ambitious ever conceived by the human mind"—and he was not far wrong. If geology conceived on that scale was a fit concern of government, why did we not expand into physics, chemistry, biology? (By now we have, and to a degree that would appall Mr. Herbert.) Multiplying researches, topographical maps that never got done, birds with teeth, waste, expense, featherbedding—Herbert made his charges aggressively and in detail, and every charge he made found supporters who hated Powell, supporters who feared government sponsorship of science, supporters scared of government control of irrigation, supporters who were simply economy-minded. Herbert said with horror what Powell would have said with pride: that the United States government spent more in promoting science than any other nation in the world.

The General Plan was a whole; since Stewart had managed to knock off one of its corners in 1890, it was only a question of time until the whole structure was brought down. Herbert and his cohorts brought it down in 1892. Admitting that the only way they could get at Powell was through the "pure science" branches of his immune bureau, Senator Wolcott of Colorado joined with Herbert, Wilson, and others in the House in a concerted attack. Herbert moved the eliminination of paleontology from the bureau and the appropriation—a move that paralleled the earlier action of the California legislature in destroying the Whitney Survey when Clarence King, fresh out of Yale, was one of its surveyors. Moved by the same arguments of impracticality, the House Appropriations Committee cut the budget. Powell's supporters rallied in the Senate Appropriations Committee and restored everything the House committee had cut. When the bill came before the Senate, Wolcott proposed an amendment cutting the appropriation from $541,000 to $400,000. Powell's supporters defeated him. But the Westerners who were after Powell's hair did a little horse trading with the South, and got through by a vote of 26 to 23 Senator Carey's amendment cutting the sum even more, to $335,000. That amendment also specified the size and salaries of the staff: two geologists at $4000, one at $3000, one at $2700, two paleontologists at $2000, and so on. A desperate sortie by Powell forces lifted the total sum to $430,000, but lost the two paleontologists and fourteen other staff jobs.[7]

That brought the house down, and with it much of the structure of government science that Powell had labored with for more than twenty years. All of the scientific bureaus felt Herbert's axe; even the Smithsonian suffered. And when the temple came down the High Priest of Science was in it, a maimed man, in constant pain from the regenerated nerves of his stump, a man getting on toward sixty and in trouble with a wife who over the years had grown into something of a shrew. He was tired and he was licked. Curtly, almost insultingly, he fired Marsh, reduced his staff, cut down his work to the topography which was almost all they had left him, and subsided. After a decent interval of two years he would retire and pass his Geological Survey on to Charles D. Walcott, who impressed him as the member of his staff most likely to bear up under the wear and tear of fighting the bureau's battles in Congress.

For himself, he was done. The whisperers and spies could subside, and the Senatorial warriors could stop striking the body, the medicine men could resume the chanting that denied the West's ills or would cure them with invocations of the Jeffersonian gods or the artesian waters.

But one more repudiation awaited him before the gulf between intelligence and wishfulness, fact and fable, would be ultimately clear. It came in October, 1893, when Powell was invited to address the International Irrigation Congress meeting in Los Angeles. The Congress was Powell's natural ally. It had been born out of the same flurry of public alarm that had created his Irrigation Survey, and its purpose was to make a million forty-acre farms by means of vast irrigation works throughout the West. It represented one form of public response to the persistent drouth of the late eighties and early nineties, and to the extent that it was a spontaneous uprising of citizens determined to do for themselves what neither private companies nor government seemed able or willing to do,[8] it matched perfectly with the democratic and co-operative bias of Powell's thought.[9] Through numbers and persistence and pressure upon political representatives it might be able to inaugurate some such program as Powell himself had suggested, and might rescue some if not all of the reclamation aspects of his General Plan.

But when he got to Los Angeles Powell found the delegates talking as if the whole billion acres of the remaining public domain could be irrigated, as if the whole West could be reclaimed. The ancient myth of the Garden of the World, dimmed by drouth and hot wind and dust storms, came back green and lush at the first irrigation of hope. It was not a program that the delegates backed, but an illusion, the unchastened illusion of William Gilpin. This was close to the irrigation which was as simple as fencing, and these acres now parched and dusty wasteland or skimpy range were to be the future homes of more people than had thronged the Roman Empire under the Antonines.

Major Powell put aside his planned speech and told them that they were mad. The highest percentage of reclaimable land that he had ever ventured, in the first flush of his Irrigation Survey optimism, had been twenty per cent. His more confirmed guess now was around 100,000,000 acres, about twelve per cent of the 850,000,000 acres still remaining in federal hands. He knew the limitations of artesian waters, his engineers had measured the capacity of the streams. "I tell you gentlemen," he said into their heckling and the rising clamor of their indignation, "you are piling up a heritage of conflict and litigation over water rights for there is not sufficient water to supply the land."

He told them, and they booed him.[10]

So a transition in society had been attempted and — at least as a unit and for the time being — had failed. Science had gone down before credulity, superstition, habit. And in a curious way the conqueror of scientific planning was not only ignorance and credulity and a crowd of stupid and venal Senators and Representatives, but that very Republickism by which according to Powell's faith the will of the people was delegated to its responsible representatives. At the time when they whipped him, the anti-planning, anti-science people in Congress were more representative of American and especially of Western thinking than Powell was.

It might have seemed by 1893 that every sort of education led to failure. Henry Adams, grandson and great-grandson of Presidents, born to public responsibility and high intellectual and ethical effort, trained in diplomacy, in journalism, in history, in social intercourse, companion and friend of his country's best and brightest, felt a decade later that 1893 showed them all how little education mattered. William C. Whitney, one of those who "owed their free hand to marriage, education serving only for ornament," seemed to Adams typical of what the world called successful. "Already in 1893 Whitney had finished with politics after having gratified every ambition, and swung the country almost at his will; he had thrown away the usual objects of political ambition like the ashes of smoked cigarettes; had turned to other amusements, satiated every taste, gorged every appetite, won every object that New York afforded, and, not yet satisfied, had carried his field of activity abroad, until New York no longer knew what most to envy, his horses or his houses." ". . . Clarence King, whose education was exactly suited to theory, had failed; and Whitney, who was not better educated than Adams, had achieved phenomenal success."

Allow for Adams' persistent and not always honest negativism; still the spectacle of Clarence King's failure was impressive. His fortune, once close to a million, had been dissipated in years of indulgence abroad and annihilated in the Panic of 1893. His art collection was mortgaged to his friend John Hay, who accepted it as security for his loans not so much because he wanted any security as because of a wish not to hurt King's pride. King himself, leaving behind him a clandestine Negro wife and five unacknowledged children, one of them defective, in an obscure Brooklyn street, was in the Bloomingdale Asylum, victim of a complete breakdown.

But it was not his education that had brought King there, nor outrageous ill fortune. What had brought him there was a lack of what Adams himself conspicuously possessed: character. Though Adams' life had been, as he said, snapped in two with his wife's suicide in December, 1885, yet he had grimly, almost as a memorial to that happiest of marriages, finished the nine-volume *History of the United States during the Administrations of Jefferson and Madison,* and completed their publication in 1891. They put a period to that section of his life; he thought of himself as finished and cut adrift. But the twenty-seven long, lonely, wandering years that followed proved, almost against his will and in the teeth of his insistent pessimism, more productive of humanly valuable observation and thinking and writing than the whole lifetimes of any but the best. What he called failure and retirement would have triumphantly justified the lives of most men.

Something similar can be said of Powell. A period of his life too came to an end with his defeat by Stewart and the others in 1890 and again in 1892; his hope to accomplish a major work in the West was killed. His education, incomparable for the jobs he had set himself, seemed to have failed the most important test. In 1894, while Adams was chaperoning the convalescent and restless King in Cuba, Powell was withdrawing from his former position of power and settling into the relative obscurity of the Bureau of American Ethnology. He wore the scars of two dozen years in Washington. But he was not defeated and damned as Clarence King was; and with as much unexpended intellectual vigor left as Adams himself possessed, he had less cause to mask it behind an apparent ennui and bitterness. He was never touched in the slightest by the cynicism that tinged all of Adams' long later life.

7. *Consequent Drainage*

POWELL RESIGNED from the United States Geological Survey in May, 1894. His outward excuse was physical disability: the stump of his arm, twice-operated-upon, was painful and difficult to live with. But he was careful to select as his successor the durable Walcott rather than the scholarly Gilbert, and in his last year he had the satisfaction of a partial restoration of his mutilated budget.[1] He left the Survey with hope for its future and a markedly paternal pride in its achievements. His bureaus had from the beginning had a high *esprit de corps;* in that, they established models for the later Forest Service, National Park Service, Soil Conservation Service, and other government agencies, mainly under Interior and Agriculture, which have been notable for the disinterested effectiveness of their work. But the Geological Survey had had more than *esprit*. It had had brilliance. "In this severance of our relations," said Powell's last report, ". . . I cannot refrain from an expression of profound gratitude for the loyal and loving aid which they have given me, ever working together with zeal and wisdom to add to the sum of human knowledge. The roster of those honored men is found in ten-score volumes of contributions to knowledge and fifty-score maps familiar to the scholars of the world."[2]

They had been dedicated to a high purpose, and the revenue of their new discoveries had enriched them individually and collectively. From the initial exploration of the last American Unknown they had extended their work across the nation; their isostatic force had raised whole continents of knowledge into the light. But certainly one of the saddest parts of Powell's general defeat was the defection of Dutton, one of the earliest and the best, the inheritor of Powell's geological labors, whose testimony had become a weapon in Stewart's hands. Dutton was gone before Powell was, back into his regular army duties.

An aging, tired man, one might think, gave up his administrative power in 1894. The last years of a man whose reach had so far exceeded his grasp might be bitter. But Powell had filled his life with such a variety of interests that even the defeat of the General Plan left him much. Long ago he had given up geology. He had been forced to give up land reform. Now he had given up administration except for the relatively minor administration of his Bureau of American Ethnology. His public career was so reduced that it could be said to have ended. But his intellectual career went on. Mental force, like water, can be dammed, but its immediate reaction is to pond behind the dam until it breaks over into a new channel. Powell's last eight years might be described in his own geological terms as an example of "consequent drainage."

What he had left to him was the Science of Man, and now he could devote himself to it. There is even some indication that he entertained ambitions to build the Bureau of American Ethnology into a great organization for anthropological research on the scale of the Geological Survey. If he did, the feeling against government science, the personal hostility of a part of Congress, and the position of the Bureau of Ethnology within the Smithsonian where it was safer but also had less freedom, all combined to thwart another piece of major bureau building. His friend W J McGee said that the failure to expand his anthropological organization embittered Powell's late years and shortened his life;[3] there is no indication other than McGee's statement that it really did so.

For even without that opportunity, he had another ambition, this one completely out of the hands of Congressional committees. He wanted to summarize human knowledge, the history of the human experience, the history of mind, from the savage level through Plato and Aristotle, Bacon and Linnaeus, and beyond those to the triumph of science in his own time. His *novum organum* was planned in three volumes. But though the synthetic rewriting of human history which Adams had foreseen as the result of geological and anthropological discoveries tempted him as it had tempted Marx, Ward, Spencer, Sumner, Morgan, he was less historian than analyst. History provided the illustration for his epistemology. All human progress led toward science, error gave way slowly to truth. And "most of the literature of the past," Powell had said in 1885, "is a vast assemblage of arguments in support of error."[4]

To point out those errors, cut away the accumulated web of argument and disputation masking mythology or thaumaturgy or unverifiable belief, to establish the knowability and verifiability of the properties of phenomena, to map the progressive stages of development of human organization and intelligence — those were jobs enough for his declining years. Also, he was as good a man as any to take the jobs on. By common consent among all but his personal enemies he was one of the foremost scientists in America, one of the foremost in the world. This farm boy with the homemade education held honorary degrees from several universities including Harvard and Heidelberg. In 1891 he had been awarded the Cuvier Prize, given every three years for "the most remarkable work either on the Animal Kingdom or Geology," in recognition of the combined work of the Geological Survey. He was a member of a dozen national and international scientific societies, and he had not been boasting when he said that the work of his bureau — which was to a large but indeterminable extent his own — was known to the scholars of the world. Among anthropologists he was quite as well known. Perhaps he did not, as Spencer Baird said, know "more about the live Indian than any live man," but he was outranked in the Science of Man by no more than three men, dead or alive — if Gallatin, Morgan, and Brinton could really be said to outrank him. Age and retirement were the proper time for memoirs: the appropriate memoir for John Wesley Powell was a summary of human growth, the "larger synthesis" which Henry Adams had long sought and finally lost hope of.

With his philosophy of science, his epistemology, this book has nothing to do. It was the late, cherished, cranky, highly original, wildly abstract, and characteristically unfinished culmination of his years of scientific education. No one who couldn't formulate and hang on to an abstraction, he said, had any business psychologizing.[5] He himself formulated and hung on to a complexity of abstractions that bewildered his contemporaries, dazed his most loyal friends, and has apparently influenced as yet not one philosophical thinker.

His friend Lester Ward, who had dedicated to Powell his *Dynamic Sociology*[6] and to whom Powell dedicated his first philosophical volume, called *Truth and Error,* accused Powell of being a little touched on the five-fold properties of matter;[7] Powell replied with dignity that he was not making numbers-magic as Ward thought he was, but was simply reporting what long and verified observation had taught him. Gilbert confessed frankly that he did not understand the Major's philosophical writings. Powell would have told him, and perhaps did, that his difficulty was not the complexity of the ideas in *Truth and Error,* but their dazzling simplicity. It was only the accumulation of centuries of error, metaphysics, and idealism, the reification of various voids, the confusion of abstraction with analysis, that made Powell's system seem difficult. His system reduced the complexities of the world, if not to unity, at least toward simplicity;[8] the philosophers of the past had built the simplest things into complexities until at length matter itself disappeared and Reality, as in the Idealists, became Illusion.

Powell believed in objective reality, and he did not trouble himself overmuch with the "supersensual chaos" that frustrated Adams' search for Unity. He thought he knew the essential properties of matter — number, extension, speed, persistence, and consciousness. He thought he could tell the difference, as few philosophers had been able to, between these inherent and concomitant and irreducible "properties" and the subjective "qualities" which human consciousness had read into them and confused with them. Upon these five properties of matter he built his whole system, and logic led him to find the fifth of them — consciousness — as certainly in the particles of a molecule as in the human brain. The force that made hydrogen atoms seek always a certain arrangement and structure, or that made minerals arrange themselves in definite patterns of crystals, or that led a watermelon seed to extract from soil and water precisely those chemicals that would build new watermelon vines and fruit, was *choice,* and this choice could be tracked back to the smallest particles of matter as definitely as could speed, persistence, extension, or number.

On the evolutionary scale, the highest choice, the most complicated relationship, was that in which the human intelligence was conscious of itself: the consciousness of consciousness, the knowledge of knowledge, the perception and apprehension of mind. It was mind toward which all evolution moved, and since Powell believed with Lamarck that long exercise of an organ increased its use and function and size and efficiency, evolution for him was no longer blindly biotic, but mental. When he died he had a bet on with W J McGee that his brain was bigger and heavier than McGee's. For whatever it mattered, it was.[9]

Knowledge of knowledge, method of method, perception of perception, a philosophy of mind. What do you want to do all that thinking for, Doña Ana's father asks Don Juan in Shaw's *Man and Superman.* Why don't you just relax and enjoy yourself? Ah, says Don Juan, without the mind you only enjoy yourself. You do not know the fun you are having.

Epistemology is not our province. If there is any virtue in the Major's five-fold systematizations, if he succeeded in making any sort of coherent and enduring structure out of the ideas he ransacked from chemistry, physics, geology, astronomy, biology, anthropology, psychology, personal experience, philosophy, and the accumulated mass of human error, some philosopher will eventually discover the first volume of his *novum organum* and the scattered essays which were to make up the second. The fact that he does not appear in the discussions of modern philosophers or get himself quoted in the symposia which aim, as he did, to synthesize scientific knowledge, may mean much or little. Powell does not appear importantly in the social and political histories either, or has not until recently, when Walter Webb, Henry Nash Smith, and Joseph Kinsey Howard all discovered him. Oberholtzer's massive *History of the United States since the Civil War* does not mention him in text or bibliography. Allan Nevins in *The Emergence of Modern America* gives him a few paragraphs. Fred A. Shannon's otherwise admirable volume on post-Civil War agriculture, *The Farmer's Last Frontier,* ignores him completely, though he was one of the most potent influences both in the West and in Washington in those postwar years, and he proposed and almost put into effect a program that would have altered all the agricultural history that Professor Shannon wrote about. George Wharton James' *Reclaiming the Arid West* in 1917 gave Powell credit for being the father of reclamation, and Louise Peffer, in *The Closing of the Public Domain,* traced back to him a number of contemporary land policies. Yet the Truman Water Resources Commission's report in 1952 never mentioned his name.

Still, comparative neglect does not necessarily mean unimportance: importance has been overlooked in other cases than his. It is possible, though hardly probable, that his epistemology will be dug out by someone less dazed than Gilbert and less captious than Lester Ward, and shown to have as much validity in the half-mapped terrain of the philosophy of science as his plan for the conservation and reclamation of the arid regions has in the drouthy West.

Of the validity of that Western blueprint, which is our concern here, there is not the shadow of a doubt. He was not merely an explorer, an opener, and an observer, he was a prophet. And yet by the law of motion (and hence of history) which he himself accepted, his motion as a particle in the jar and collision of American life was bound to be spiral. His reforms have taken effect, his plans have been adopted, but partially, belatedly, sidelong, as a yielding resultant of two nearly equal stresses.

VI

THE INHERITANCE

1. Resurrection Morn, with Reservations

DURING THE EIGHTEEN-NINETIES Hamlin Garland, busily interviewing everyone who had ever served with Grant, in preparation for his biography of the late President, was sometimes a visitor at the "literary evenings" at the Powell house on M Street.[1] He admired the Major as a student of the Indian and as the explorer of the Colorado: the nature and implications, and even the fact, of Powell's attempted Western reforms seem never to have struck him, though the rebellious plowboy novelist and the scientific bureaucrat were one in their democratic optimism, their loyalty to the small farmer, their mistrust of monopolies, their firsthand knowledge of both Midwest and West. Powell would have made a reasonable facsimile of a Populist; his General Plan could have been dovetailed with the Populist platform of 1892 without serious conflicts. Certainly its purposes of relieving and preventing agricultural distress, extending scientific government aid to farmers, and protecting small landholders against monopolistic practices and the inequalities or inadequacies of the laws, were completely in harmony with what Garland had preached from soapboxes in Nebraska and Dakota. It is an index of how little Powell's ideas had been able to enter the public consciousness, and how intracongressional a matter his defeat really was, that even an aware and militant and experienced agrarian like Garland had apparently never heard of them.

Nevertheless Garland admired the Major, and meeting him some years later, broken and shuffling on the arm of a colored servant, his memory gone, a palsied and dying old man, he was shocked and saddened. He thought of Powell as a trail-breaker, one of the openers of the West, and he connected him in his mind with his own Uncle William, who had chased a dream westward all his life and was now a similarly shaken wreck in San Jose. In tribute to the two Garland wrote a poem called "The Stricken Pioneer." Its theme is admiration for the courage and leadership of the westward seeker — "Our velvet way his steel prepared" — and it concludes:

Then bury him not here in city soil
Where car-wheels grind and factories spill
Their acrid smoke on those who toil:
Bear him far away — to some high hill
That overlooks the mighty stream
Whose thousand miles of pathway through the corn
Blazons his progress. There let him dream
And wait his resurrection morn!

It would be an injustice to Major Powell to let so lame a verse be his epitaph, or for that matter to bury him beside the Mississippi, which is apparently the "mighty stream" that Garland had in mind. But let us, with permission, imagine that the mighty stream is the Missouri, and let us imagine Major Powell buried there, perhaps seated on his horse like the Omaha chief Blackbird so that he can look out up and down the river by which white civilization first came watchfully into the West. From there he will have a view of all that the years have done or will do with ideas he bequeathed his country.

He will already have seen some curiously mixed evidences of human cussedness, contradiction, belatedness, and failure to see straight, along with some equally human persistence, growth, and ability to learn. He will see some ground that he thought successfully taken lost again, or fought over with as much viciousness as if his own battles had never been; and the repetitiveness of that struggle, the similarity of the antagonists both individual and institutional to those he knew, may impress him with the unlikelihood of the evolved human perfection he once dreamed of. He will not have seen resurrection morn yet, but he will have seen some streaks that look a little like dawn and some clouds that may perhaps indicate rain for the great day.

If Major Powell were to return and study the map of reclamation activities, present and proposed, that was published by the Bureau of Reclamation on January 1, 1951,[2] he might get the impression that resurrection morn had really dawned. All the great river systems — Missouri, Columbia, Colorado, Rio Grande, Sacramento–San Joaquin, and every tributary branch and twig — have been surveyed and mapped in even greater detail than he intended. Blue river lines are strung with the irregular blue beads of reservoirs or projected reservoirs, and the storage dams, as well as the map symbols that record them and the topographic base map on which they are superimposed, are part of the heritage that Powell left. The wide flood-plain of the Missouri from Gavin's Point to the mouth of the Musselshell shows as an almost-continuous lake on this map which indicates both what is and what will be, and the sarcastic questions of Senator Gideon Moody about how water will be got out onto the fields from the sunken riverbed have their not-too-difficult answer.

From approximately the 95th meridian all the way to the Pacific, in fact, reclamation has already remade the map of the West. It has had an effect on the very shape and tension of the earth: reservoirs such as Lake Mead have redistributed so much weight in water and silt that seismological stations watchfully record the settling and shifting of the crust, and the isostacy which Powell and Gilbert and Dutton established as a physical force has been affected by the work of men's hands. The whole Western future is tied to the multiple-purpose irrigation-power-flood-control-stream-management projects built to specifications first enunciated by Powell's bureaus, and the West's institutions and politics are implicit in the great river plans.

Some of the wildest water that Powell's boats ran will someday soon be silted mudflats, as Separation Rapid, except during an occasional scouring flood, is a mudflat now. Intense blue water may some day fill the inner gorge of the Grand Canyon whose dark rock the boat parties hated and feared; blue water may lap the feet of the Rainbow Bridge on the flank of the mountain that

Powell first named for the Howlands; blue water may extend — unless another group of conservationists is successful in preventing it — from the junction of Yampa and Green up both river canyons. On every little creek and tributary the runoff water is already or will be ponded and diverted and fed out and controlled, or run through turbines to create the power for a Western empire. Colorado River water has permitted the mushroom growth of Los Angeles and the full use of the Coachella and Imperial Valleys. A project like the Deer Creek Reservoir on the Provo insures the growth for decades of the Salt Lake Valley, where the first Anglo-American irrigation on the continent began a little over a hundred years ago.

Within the seven great reclamation regions, planning has increasingly come to be by coherent river basins and drainage basins, as Powell foresaw that it must. The responsibility for long-range planning that Powell thought belonged to the federal government, since no one else could or would assume it, has been assumed. The Bureau of Reclamation which came into being with the Newlands Act just a little before Powell's death in 1902 is such a bureau as Powell himself might have proposed, devoted to purposes which his own Irrigation Survey began.

And the effect of long-range planning has indeed been what Powell said it would be: the reclamation of arid land in Montana has a direct relation to the reclamation of swamps in Louisiana; the control of waters on the tributaries does indeed not only check floods below and provide a regulated flow for navigation, but it has cleaned out of the channel of the Missouri and Mississippi many of those snags and sawyers and window-makers that used to peril navigation all the way to New Orleans. Without the dams already installed, the 1952 floods on the Missouri would have been very much worse than they were — would have been unmitigated disaster from the Milk River to the Gulf.

Major Powell was never primarily interested in the forests: those were to be Gifford Pinchot's peculiar province.[3] But he would approve the reservations that by the middle of the twentieth century totalled 139,000,000 acres, plus another 21,000,000 in Alaska. He would approve the National Parks which add another 12,000,000 acres to the reserved public lands. He would approve of the steady liberalizing of the homestead laws and the increase in the size of grazing homesteads through the early years of the century. Most of all, he would approve the Taylor Grazing Act which in 1934 practically closed the public domain to further homestead settlement.

The reservation of those same arid lands by the Irrigation Survey resolution in 1888 had been both accidental and temporary; but Powell from the very beginning[4] thought much of the West ought to be permanently retired from farm settlement. The drouth of the late eighties and nineties had only corroborated what the Major already knew. But it took other drouths and other disasters, specifically the dust bowl disaster of the early 1930's, to convince the country at large. Another panicky retreat from the edge of the arid plains, another abandonment of the plowed and wind-eroded fields, another collection of dry tanks, weatherbeaten shacks, sand-pitted corrals, was necessary to bring a solution. When solution came, it followed from the same inescapable conditions that had led Powell in 1878 to hurry his *Arid Region* report into the hands of Carl Schurz, and in 1889 to plead his ideas before the Montana and North Dakota Constitutional Conventions.

Powell's accidental suspension of the historical process of homestead settlement had brought on his defeat by Congress in 1890. More than forty years later Representative Edward Taylor of Colorado, for years a rabid States' rights enemy of Washington bureaus and federal meddling, and an advocate of cession of the public lands to the states, drafted, introduced, and fought through Congress a grazing bill that might conserve not only the natural resource of the range, but the industry built on it.[5] Congressman Taylor may be taken as a striking example of the deflection of path when forces collide. Or rather, he should perhaps be taken as showing the ultimate teachability of a people, for he began pure Gilpin, he ended pure Powell.

"I fought for the conservation of the public domain under Federal leadership," he said later, "because the citizens were unable to cope with the situation under existing trends and circumstances. The job was too big and interwoven for even the states to handle with satisfactory co-ordination. On the western slope of Colorado and in nearby states I saw waste, competition, overuse, and abuse of valuable range lands and watersheds eating into the very heart of western economy. Farms and ranches everywhere in the range country were suffering. The basic economy of entire communities was threatened. There was terrific strife and bloodshed between the cattle and sheep men over the use of the range. Valuable irrigation projects stood in danger of ultimate deterioration. Erosion, yes even human erosion, had taken root." [6]

One may query the geological or metaphysical propriety of an erosion that takes root, but one may not doubt Congressman Taylor's sincerity or the validity of his observations. He had finally learned what an earlier and abler student of erosion had fruitlessly taught for half a lifetime. A good part of that learning process involved the brushing aside of a mythic figure: "The praises and eulogies upon the American homesteader will continue as long as our Republic survives. The West was built, and its present proud development rests most largely upon the courage, privations, and frightfully hard work of the pioneer homesteaders . . . But my dear sirs, if those hardy pioneers had had to go onto the kind of land that is contemplated within this bill, the West would still be a barren wilderness." [7]

If they had listened to Powell fifty years earlier they would not have had so hard a lesson to learn in 1934. For while Taylor's bill was before the Senate, winds from the West carried soil from the dustbowl states clear to the east coast and the air of the capital was thick with the presence of what one Senator called "the most tragic, the most impressive lobbyist" that had ever come to Washington.

The bill which was eventually passed by Congress and signed by President Roosevelt created an authority, the National Grazing Service, to organize grazing districts in which established stock interests could obtain grazing leases of specified acreages at specified nominal fees. Its effect in practice was to provide the unfenced common range — carefully supervised — that Powell had proposed as a co-operative device in 1878 and as a part of the drainage-basin local control in 1889.[8] The innovation — with which again Powell would probably have agreed — was the application to the range of the leasing principle that had already been devised for grazing areas within the national forests and for certain kinds of mineral and oil lands owned by the government. (The Mineral Leasing Act of 1920.) With the Taylor Grazing Act, a historical process was complete: not only was the public domain virtually closed to settlement, but the remaining public land was assumed to be continuing Federal property, income-producing property to be managed according to principles of wise use for the benefit of the whole nation.[9]

On any composite map showing the modern use and management and reclamation of western lands, that is, it would appear as if almost every suggestion Powell made has been finally adopted, and every type of western land is being put to the kind of use Powell advocated. Time and loud debate have effectively classified the lands as he began to classify them in 1875. Grazing land is cropped in large unfenced ranges, irrigation farms under Reclamation Bureau dams are limited to 160 acres.[10] The development of hydroelectric power from the multipurpose dams has created a source of continuing income which can be devoted to new projects and to the federal supervision and management of the public's enterprises. States such as those on the Colorado have edged closer to Powell's drainage-basin organization by compacts establishing the several rights to water. The principle of tying water rights to land titles is accepted through much of the West.

And yet what seems, on the maps and on the record, to be a progressive triumph for the Major's ideas is not quite so complete as it seems. The forces that he fought all during his public life are, as of 1953, not only still there but active and aggressive. The agencies that he helped consolidate still persist in division and antagonism. The private interests that he feared might monopolize land or water in the West are still there, still trying to do just that. And the scientific solutions to western problems are still fouled up by Gilpins, by the doubletalk of Western members of Congress, by political pressures from oil or stock or power or land or water companies, by the obfuscations of pressagents and the urgings of lobbyists. In 1953 a public land policy that a few years before had looked reasonably consistent and settled was in danger of complete overturn.[11]

Take it back to the first real struggle in which Powell engaged — the jurisdictional dispute between civilian and military agencies over who should survey the unopened West. That row between Powell, Hayden, and to a degree King on one hand, and Lieutenant Wheeler and the Army Engineers on the other, was apparently settled with the establishment of the United States Geological Survey in 1879. But within limits the army could still allocate funds for survey work of a specifically military character, and it could, across a long span of years, succeed in establishing its right to navigational and flood-control projects on the western rivers. The policies which Henry Adams' "first modern act of legislation" pointed toward have never fully come about.

The Missouri Valley development which by logic and public demand should already be well under way is reduced to piecemeal improvisations by that same jurisdictional dispute between the Department of the Interior and the War Department that hampered the early Western surveys. Where does irrigation leave off and navigation and flood control begin? On a river like the Missouri, which purpose is paramount? And if neither bureau trusts the other, and both have powerful political backing, and each has its fixed prerogatives, how shall they be compelled to compromise and work for the realization of a systematic river-development plan? A degree of co-operation necessarily exists, but the full authority to harness the Missouri as the Tennessee has been harnessed is blocked by interbureau jealousies and overlappings, and these jealousies are exploited by enemies of the public land policies.

Or look farther West. One of the really massive and hopeful reclamation developments is the Central Valley Project which the state of California turned over to the Bureau of Reclamation after a special referendum election in 1933. The state turned it over because it realized its inability to carry out its own admirable and coherent plan for use of the waters of the Sacramento, American, San Joaquin, and other valley rivers. Turning over the plan meant putting the individual projects under reclamation law. And reclamation law, completely in the spirit of Major Powell and of all those who for many decades tried to make the land laws fit the needs of the small farmer, carried specific restrictions. It limited the public land that could be homesteaded under a reservoir to 160 acres; it limited existing private owners under such reservoirs to the water that would irrigate 160 acres. And it gave preference to public and co-operative agencies in the distribution of power generated at the dams.

Locally the Bureau of Reclamation has not always lived up to the letter of the Newlands Act, though the administrators of the bureau have generally tried to carry out its terms. But the Engineers, whose purposes are flood control and navigation, are not bound by reclamation law, and when (as usually happens) the waters impounded by an Engineers dam can be used for irrigation, no legal compulsion except the orders of the President as Commander in Chief can make them conform to Reclamation Bureau policies. On occasion, the Corps of Engineers has ignored even the orders of the Commander in Chief. And when in 1944 the land companies of the lower San Joaquin Valley put on a campaign against reclamation restrictions, one of the net effects was that the Corps of Engineers was squeezed into the very middle of the coherent — and approved — Central Valley Project and authorized to build *flood-control* dams on the American, the Kings, and the Kern.[12]

Major Powell, who had been irritated by Lieutenant Wheeler's duplications and interferences in 1871 and after, would be a little depressed to see one of the few examples of sound regional water planning broken wide open by those same Engineers whose principle public justification is that they train engineers for combat duty. He might even see resemblances on that point: in Wheeler's parties, most of the scientists, geologists, topographers, and skilled men were civilians. In 1948, when the Hoover Commission took a look at the Corps, it found among its personnel 200 army engineers against 9000 civilian engineers and 41,000 other civilian employees.[13]

Its critics insist that the Corps of Engineers got its finger into the bung of the pork barrel at the very beginning and nobody has ever been able to get it out, though the actual military justifications of the Corps' work in the West practically ceased with the subjugation of the Plains and Mountain Indian tribes. The Engineers-Reclamation struggle, like the similar wrangle between Interior and Agriculture over the national forests,[14] has been damaging and could be fatal to the kind of articulated planning that Powell's proposals and the Newlands Act envisaged, looking toward the "greatest good for the greatest number for the longest time."

Were there land-hogs trying to corral grazing empires in Powell's time, and not above barefaced trespass on the public domain? They are still there, only now they are trying to bite out of national parks and national forests chunks of grazing land, oil land, timberland, that they covet. The conservation forces swamped such a foray in 1947;[15] they will have others to fight, and they may never be able to restore the full effectiveness of the Grazing Service which Senator McCarran — a Senator Stewart come again, and from the same state — all but ruined by the profoundly Stewart-ian tactics of investigating and then cutting the budget.[16]

The nation will listen to a good deal more of the doubletalk about "returning" the public lands, especially the Taylor Grazing District lands and some of the rangelands within forests and parks, to the states. Those lands, of course, never did belong to the states, which relinquished all claim to them on being admitted to the Union and would in most cases have to pay more for their management than they could take in in taxes if they were "returned." There will be a good deal of anathema against "absentee landlordism" in Washington, and little about the fact that the lands now in government hands have almost all been rescued from private exploitation or neglect, disastrous exploitation and disastrous neglect, and have in many cases been returned to productive use.

There will be a good deal of talk too about giving private companies a bigger share in the distributing of public power, and even of giving private companies some reserved sites for the generating of power below government dams. That talk will overlook the fact that the government dam is absolutely necessary for the utilization of the sites on the lower streams — a stream must be tamed before it can be utilized for power production. And the taming of the stream by Bureau of Reclamation or Corps of Engineers may be worth literally millions to the private company granted a franchise to build a generating plant below it.

Major Powell did not live long enough to learn fully the potential of hydroelectric power as a force in Western life or as a source of income for federal projects. But he would have recognized the techniques of those eager to take it over.[17]

He would recognize a lot of things, grown vastly bigger but not changed in their essentials. The issue would seem to him the same now as it was during his years in Washington: the application of federal science, know-how, money, in the general public interest, and against that the belief that the West would develop better and in more "American" terms if left, as Senator Hale suggested, "to nature and the common incidents of human life."

There is always that question, and probably it would trouble the Major, for he was a democrat to the marrow and he knew enough about Washington to know that federal controls could have their dangers too. He might see, as many conservationists believe they see, a considerable empire-building tendency within the Bureau of Reclamation,[18] an engineer's vision of the West instead of a humanitarian's, a will to build dams without due regard to all the conflicting interests involved. He might fear any bureau that showed less concern with the usefulness of a project than with its effect on the political strength of the bureau. He might join the Sierra Club and other conservation groups in deploring some proposed and "feasible" dams such as that in Echo Park below the mouth of the Yampa, and he might agree that considerations such as recreation, wildlife protection, preservation for the future of untouched wilderness, might sometimes outweigh possible irrigation and power benefits. He would probably be with those who are already beginning to plead for conservation of reservoir sites themselves, for reservoirs silt up and do not last forever, and men had better look a long way ahead when they begin tampering with natural forces.

He would see all this; he was always one to take the long view, and he was a bureaucrat before the name got either familiar or unpopular. His bureaus set a pattern that was duplicated with little change in later years, and he trained a lot of the men who later ran them.[19] But along with the bureaucrat dwelt a democratic idealist with a peculiarly unselfish and devoted notion of public service. And both the bureaucrat and the idealist knew that private interests, whether they dealt in cattle or sheep, oil, minerals, coal, timber, water, or land itself, could not be trusted or expected to take care of the land or conserve its resources for the use of future generations. They could be trusted or expected to protect neither the monetary nor the nonmonetary values of the land: even in his day Americans had the passenger pigeon and the buffalo, the plowed and eroded plains, the cutover forests of Michigan, to tell them where "nature and the common incidents of human life" would lead us. Later years have added the Dust Bowl and the eroded watersheds to the evidence.

He would have said, undoubtedly, in 1953 as in 1889, that there are values too critical and resources too perishable to be entrusted entirely to private exploitation. He would have said there is a difference between using a resource and mining it. He would have said the future has a claim on us. He would have said that on the evidence of several generations of exploitative freedom no one could guarantee the future its share of the American earth except the American government. If that government contained quarreling and jealous bureaus, that was too bad; if it sheltered grafters as it did so spectacularly during the time of Grant, too bad. If it was too far from the resources in question to make every decision right, too bad.

Too bad. But the alternative was worse. The alternative was creeping deserts, flooded river valleys, dusty miles of unused and unusable land, feeble or partial or monopolistic utilization of the available land and water. The alternative was great power and great wealth to a few and for a brief time rather than competence and independence for the communities of small freeholders on which his political economy unchangeably rested.

The Jeffersonian agrarian 160-acre freeholder ideal was already beginning to wither against the arid front of the West in Powell's own day. Powell himself, observing and admitting the conditions that would wither it, had taken a hand in the correction of some of the ideal's more mystical aberrations. The attempt to preserve that ideal in the Newlands Act, and the labor to save it since, might look mistaken to a tired and soured observer like Henry Adams. Trusts and corporations, Adams thought, accounted for the largest part of the power that had been generated in America since 1840.[20] They were, to be sure, "obnoxious because of their vigorous and unscrupulous energy," and they called for some counter force, some new man. Either that or they simply corroborated one's notion that the world rocketed with a measurable acceleration toward its own destruction, and one's guess that the meteor-head of historical motion was already near perihelion.

2. *The Corkscrew Path of Progress*

EVEN ADAMS, disillusioned and sad over the death of John Hay, thought he saw some signs of the new man, the counter-force, when he returned to New York from Europe in 1904. Theodore Roosevelt was busily busting trusts with the only corporate instrument big enough to deal with them: government. A little later he would be applying through that same corporate instrument a good many checks to the greed that was gobbling the West. Behind him would be Gifford Pinchot with a coherent plan of conservation and a bureaucratic aggressiveness and daring even greater than Powell's. Behind Pinchot would be Powell's friend and one-time employee, W J McGee, "the brains of the conservation movement," and these three — Roosevelt, Pinchot, and McGee — would so effectively sell the conservation idea in all its manifold shapes to the American people that the Conservation Congress in 1907 may be taken as the end and the beginning of an era.

But behind W J McGee, and behind most of the ideas which he brought to the conservation movement and which were embodied in legislation and in public opinion through the practical genius of Pinchot and Roosevelt, was a little man with wild whiskers and one arm. The program that the Conservation Congress accepted and adopted and fought for was essentially Powell's "General Plan" of 1878, amplified and particularized to fit a later generation's knowledge and needs.

In the doctrines of evolution and of progress Henry Adams came to have no faith at all. Science's attempts at the larger synthesis, he felt, brought us no closer to the discovery or recognition of that Unity which was man's whole object of search on earth. The larger synthesis was bounded by the limits of the senses and the sense-extending instruments, by the inadequacies of observation and experiment; and beyond even the larger synthesis lay the "super-sensual chaos" which asserted not Unity but Multiplicity as the law of Nature. Radium denied its gods; matter was motion, motion matter, and the kinetic theory of gas, which seemed as sure a starting point as any for the philosopher of matter and force and hence of history, merely underlined the implications of chaos. "In plain words, Chaos was the law of nature; Order was the dream of man." [21]

Like Adams, Powell built his philosophy upward from the kinetic theory of gas, and like Adams he made no scruple about applying laws of physics, by analogy, to the study of history. Like Adams, again, he inevitably chose to apply those laws of physics which corroborated his own ingrained beliefs, his temperamental and perhaps ultimately regional reactions to phenomena and events. Adams, product of a class and a region whose importance was fading, might have been expected to fall upon the second law of thermodynamics, with its demonstrations of the dissipation of energy, and make it a metaphor for the world and for man, a parable of the decay of civilizations. Powell accepted the jar and collision of molecules in every scrap of matter, but he seems to have accepted without question also a second motion, a forward thrust which was social, evolutionary, human, rather than physical, and which was in keeping with the West's incurable optimism. The supersensual chaos did not tempt him; in spite of his wild addiction to abstraction, he was a practical man, a doer, a pragmatic manipulator of forces. For Adams, evolution in its social and economic aspects was illusory; for Powell, it was merely incomplete. For Adams, matter was motion, and motion was energy which could be used up; for Powell, motion was perpetual, the binding principle of the universe.

"Even Newton," Powell wrote in *Truth and Error,* "thought light to be corpuscular. The doctrine that motion as speed emanates from one body as a substance or substrate and passes to another, comes from this source. This relic of ancient philosophy clings to much of modern physics, and is the foundation of a body of speculation in which scientific men indulge when they theorize about the dissipation of motion, the exhaustion of the heat of the sun, and the general running down of the solar system into a state in which life will be impossible." [22]

Scientific men or historical gentlemen. For physics or for history the error was the same, Powell would have said. The speed of any particle of matter, molecular or molar or stellar, was constant, and if one reduced everything to force or motion as Adams did, then the speed of a thought was likewise constant. So was collision constant, and collision neither accelerated nor decelerated the particles; it only deflected them. Ideas, institutions, human society too, viewed in long perspective, neither heated nor cooled off, went faster or slower. They only changed direction, and the large, riverlike forward movement of evolution contained all smaller motions and deviations, and swept them ahead as a river sweeps its eddies and currents. If choice was a property of even the smallest particle of matter, and he believed it was, there was no reason to believe that choice was not also a property of the largest units, of the universe itself. Powell was an evolutionist in every cell. He never despaired, apparently, of that final Perfection that to Adams was a mirage, and he was sure of the method that must be used to find it: experimental science.

Nevertheless, he could not have believed that the world marched toward Perfection by a series of regular and predictable steps. Though he repudiated Herbert Spencer and his accidental, laissez faire evolution of society, he was not so naive as to believe that a social motion such as John Wesley Powell, a particle possessing both energy and choice, could move toward its willed goal like a bullet shot out of a gun. Collision was as certain a law of nature as motion, and the product of collision was deflection.

In practical terms, over a span of seventy-five years and within the dynamics of the expanding West, Powell's law of deflection could hardly have been better demonstrated. Social and economic forces have not faded, nor have they accelerated beyond the strength of the machine, as Adams sometimes thought they might. The human race has not yet blown itself off the planet, though it has made a good try. Instead of expending itself or running out, force has begotten new force. And even the ideas, even the characteristic personalities, that collided in Powell's time still are present, and still collide.

In seventy-five years, the program that Big Bill Stewart thought he had utterly defeated in 1890 and 1892 has collided with the private greeds of the Stewarts and the myths of the Gilpins to such purpose that Western economics, Western institutions, even Western character, have been bent and changed. Powell's program itself has been bent; it has had to swerve and sometimes backtrack; it has succeeded only partially, or in changed proportions; its motion has sometimes whirled around a vortex of failure. But it persists, and moves. So do the Stewarts and the Gilpins. Lieutenant Wheeler and the Corps of Engineers are still present, though slightly changed; Senator Stewart is born again, with slight modifications, in Senator McCarran. The objections of an Alexander Agassiz have their parallels, the Gilpins are not dead.

Order is the dream of man. It was the dream of John Wesley Powell more than of most, and he never questioned that an order could be discovered, or perhaps to some degree created, by the human mind and the scientific method. The larger syntheses that he attempted in several areas — in the mapping of the continent, in the organization of the Science of Man, in the history of intellection, in the planning for the settlement of the arid West — turned out to be always working syntheses only, sure to be periodically discarded and replaced.

Even so, he would probably have said that the energy of the colliding particles was constant. Even so, he would have said that despite temporary defeats, and shocks that rattled a social mover to his ultimate particle, the large motion was always, like that of a comet — or a glacier — forward.

Even with his apparent defeats, he would have had to count his efforts successful. When he died in Haven, Maine, on September 23, 1902, he did not die as Clarence King did, penniless and alone in an Arizona hotel, still chasing a rainbow with dollar signs on it, and leaving behind him a record of such waste and loss of magnificent energies as might have corroborated Henry Adams' theory of history. Powell died with at least one evidence of the persistence of his ideas: the session of Congress just finished had passed the Newlands Act putting the United States government in the business of reclaiming the arid region according to principles that Powell himself had first suggested. And it had testified to the persistence of myth, though in changed form, by writing that Act in the interest of the Jeffersonian yeoman and the 160-acre farmstead. Powell had helped both to preserve and to change that mythical figure, who had come a long way from the form that Representative Patterson or William Gilpin had found him in.

The fate of all leaders who go too far ahead, and of all thinkers who think straighter than their contemporaries, was Powell's. Attempting to lead his own time in accordance with the principles of order and science that he believed in, he was almost, though not quite, deserted. But from the river bluffs where we have symbolically planted him, looking over the West that was his province, he can perhaps contemplate the truly vortical, corkscrew path of human motion and with some confidence wait for the future to catch up with him.

NOTES

BECAUSE POWELL'S WORK proliferated in so many directions and influenced in so many ways so many kinds of people, not only during his lifetime but since, a proper list of writings consulted in the preparation of his biography would be enormous. It would, ideally, cover everything of importance on the physical history and development of the West after the Civil War; and through its extension into the history of exploration, of the Indian, of the earth sciences, and of irrigation and reclamation, it could be indefinitely lengthened back into the past and on into the future. I have therefore omitted any formal bibliography from this book.

All titles directly utilized or specially germane are cited in the notes. There are some which have been used and quoted so consistently throughout the text that they deserve a summary listing:

Adams, Henry, *The Education of Henry Adams* (Modern Library ed.).
Bell, William A., *New Tracks in North America* (London, 2nd ed., 1870).
The Century Association, *Clarence King Memoirs* (New York, 1904).
Clawson, Marion, *Uncle Sam's Acres* (New York, 1951).
Darrah, William Culp, *Powell of the Colorado* (Princeton, 1951).
Dellenbaugh, Frederick, *The Romance of the Colorado River* (New York, 1902).
DeVoto, Bernard, *The Course of Empire* (Boston, 1952).
Garland, Hamlin, *A Son of the Middle Border* (New York, 1925).
Gilbert, Grove Karl, et al., *John Wesley Powell, a Memorial* (Chicago, 1904).
Malin, James C., *Grasslands of North America* (Lawrence, Kansas, 1947).
Peffer, Louise, *The Closing of the Public Domain* (Palo Alto, Calif., 1951).
Schuchert, Charles, and C. M. LeVene, *O. C. Marsh, Pioneer in Paleontology* (New Haven, 1940).
Shannon, Fred A., *The Farmer's Last Frontier* (New York, 1935).
Smith, Henry Nash, *Virgin Land* (Cambridge, Mass., 1951).
Stanton, Robert Brewer, and J. M. Chalfant, *Colorado River Controversies* (New York, 1931).
Webb, Walter, *The Great Plains* (Boston, 1931).

In addition, the Reports of the United States Geographical and Geological Survey of the Rocky Mountain Region, J. W. Powell in Charge, especially

G. K. Gilbert, *Report on the Geology of the Henry Mountains* (Washington, D. C., 1877); J. W. Powell, *Report on the Geology of the Eastern Portion of the Uinta Mountains and a region of country adjacent thereto* (Washington, D. C., 1876); Powell, *Report on the Lands of the Arid Regions* (Washington, D. C., 1878); and Clarence Edward Dutton, *Report on the Geology of the High Plateaus of Utah* (Washington, D. C., 1880).

Also the Annual Reports and Bulletins of the United States Geographical and Geological Survey of the Territories, which accumulated into a bulky library between 1867 and 1878.

Also the Annual Reports of the United States Geological Survey, as well as the valuable series of Geological Survey Monographs, especially C. E. Dutton, *The Tertiary History of the Grand Canyon District,* with Atlas (Washington, D. C., 1882).

Also the Annual Reports of the Bureau of Ethnology, especially those between 1879 and 1902; and certain publications of the Smithsonian Institution, especially J. W. Powell, *Report on the Exploration of the Colorado River of the West* (Washington, D. C., 1875).

For other government publications, particularly those bearing upon the history of the several bureaus considered here, see the notes to the chapters in question.

I. THE THRESHOLD

1

1. The best short discussions of William Gilpin are in Henry Nash Smith, *Virgin Land,* (Cambridge, Mass.), pp. 35–43; and in Bernard DeVoto, "Geopolitics with the Dew on It," *Harper's Magazine,* CLXXXVIII (March, 1944), 313–23. So far as I am aware, the only biography is that by Hubert H. Bancroft, *History of the Life of William Gilpin. A Character Study* (San Francisco, 1889).

2. An extraordinarily provocative study of the whole notion of a Great American Desert, together with the opposed myth of the West as the "Garden of the World," is Smith's *Virgin Land,* cited above. It will be apparent throughout this book that I have drawn heavily upon Mr. Smith's scholarship and conclusions. A summary of the travelers from Pike on who contributed to the belief in such a desert between the 100th meridian and the Rocky Mountains may be found in Ralph C. Morris, "The Notion of a Great American Desert East of the Rockies," *Mississippi Valley Historical Review,* XIII (1926–27), No. 2, 190–200. Mr. Morris' list is representative, though it might be almost indefinitely expanded. In fact, until settlement began to creep out into the semi-arid plains in the sixties, there was little attempt to controvert the notion of a desert; the principal opposition to the notion came from immigrant brochures or as a result of local patriotism. One of the most effective gestures in this direction was Henry Worrall's cartoon, "Drouthy Kansas," first printed on the cover of the *Kansas Farmer* for November, 1869, and later reproduced in C. C. Hutchinson's *Resources of Kansas,* 1871, an immigrant come-on. Even as early as 1866, when Bayard Taylor visited the Colorado mountains, the debate between disparagers and local patriots was on, and Taylor, like many other travelers, felt himself called upon to cast a vote. He sidestepped the issue and closely

approximated the truth by seeing not a desert but a steppe, eminently suitable for grazing and with arable oases. Powell's position in this continued debate, which involved great questions of policy, law, and planning, was absolutely central. At the same time, as Mr. Smith points out, it was one of Powell's scientific contemporaries and later employees, Dr. Cyrus Thomas, who noted the cyclic increase in rainfall and stream flow following the first settlement and gave official sanction to the folk belief, strenuously promoted by town builders and speculators, that tree planting and sod breaking altered the climate in man's favor. For Thomas' cautious and apparently justified statement, see the *Preliminary Field Report of the United States Geological Survey of Colorado and New Mexico, 1869.* (Hayden Survey, *3rd Annual Report, 1868.*)

3. The furious destruction of the buffalo after the coming of the railroad needs no copious documentation. It is one of the shameful memories of the nation. Colonel Henry Inman, in *The Old Santa Fe Trail,* p. 203, estimated on the evidence of Sante Fe freight reports that the haul of buffalo bones during the seventies and eighties from Kansas alone was 300,000 tons, which represented approximately 31,000,000 buffalo. Colonel Dodge estimated that in 1872 a half million and in 1873 three quarters of a million hides went east by the three western railroads. Amplification of these statistics may be found in E. P. Oberholtzer, *The History of the United States since the Civil War* (New York, 1917–37), II, 488, and Dan Elbert Clark, *The West in American History* (New York, 1937), pp. 587–90. Clark mentions a pile of buffalo bones twelve feet high and a half mile long beside the Santa Fe tracks.

4. James C. Malin, in *The Grasslands of North America.* Malin rightly treats Powell as one of the pioneers in understanding the true problems of the plains, but seems even at this date to bristle at Powell's "deficiency terminology," and he puts himself in the awkward position of applauding both Powell and Gilpin for their vision of plains resources and possibilities. Professor Malin, in fact, seems almost as intent upon proving that there is no desert in Kansas as was Reuben Gold Thwaites, who summarized the feeling of the turn of the century in his *Brief History of Rocky Mountain Exploration* (New York, 1904). "Pike," wrote Mr. Thwaites, "appears to have been the first to describe the fine grazing plains of Nebraska and western Kansas as a 'desert' — 'a barrier,' he says, 'placed by Providence to keep the American people from a thin diffusion and ruin.' It took over half a century to destroy this myth of a Great American Desert, for which Pike was responsible. When more gigantic systems of irrigation than now exist shall slake the thirst of these parched plains lying upon the eastern slope of the Rockies; when what is at present being done for comparatively narrow districts at the base of the hills shall be extended as far east as the rainy belt, this desert shall everywhere blossom as the rose. The cattle ranches are fast being subdivided into homesteads, and the cultivable area is rapidly growing before our eyes. We hear now and then the cry of the alarmist; that the limit of settlement in the great West is clearly in sight; but there is still room for tens of millions of vigorous colonists in the upper valleys of the Missouri, the Platte, and the Arkansas, and the great plains stretching north and south between them. The Great American Desert of our childhood may yet become the garden of the land."

There could not be a more perfect demonstration of Henry Smith's "garden of the world" syndrome, and in fact Thwaites in talking thus is uncritically repeating the optimism and repudiation of facts that marked William Gilpin. Professor Malin, resenting deficiency terminology and insisting that dust storms are a natural and by no means alarming part of plains life, and have occurred since before settlement and the breaking of the sod, seems to be straining toward the same defensiveness that made Kansas break its neck to put on a gaudy show at the Philadelphia Centennial in 1876, two years after drouth and grasshoppers had cleaned the whole state down to the grassroots. And Thwaites' faith in larger and larger irrigation works presupposes an indefinite amount of water, which is against the facts, or some Martian system of reservoirs and canals like that proposed by Cyrus Thomas in the seventies. This called for a dam from the Platte to the Arkansas, parallel with the Rockies, so as to impound a lake forty miles wide and more than two hundred long against the foot of the mountains. See the U. S. Geological and Geographical Survey of the Territories, *3rd Annual Report, 1868,* pp. 140–41.

2

1. Henry Adams, *The Education of Henry Adams,* p. 52.

2. The thesis of Frederick Jackson Turner is of course peculiarly applicable to education. Education on the frontier was less a matter of schools than of books and men, and especially of men's attitudes toward books, and men's hunger for what books contained. Part of the essential background for a home-made education was deprivation, and this was a condition that successive frontiers all provided.

3. I have made no attempt to cover in any detailed way the early years of Major Powell's life, or to track down his personal relations with his family, his Civil War record, his genealogy, or any of the routine data of the biographer. Since I am attempting only the biography of a *career,* and that because of the way in which it heightens the typical, I have chosen to deal only with the quality of Powell's education, which is where both his personal distinction and his typicalness are rooted. Details of his boyhood and youth and war service are available in William Culp Darrah's useful *Powell of the Colorado;* in Grove Karl Gilbert, et al., *John Wesley Powell, a Memorial;* and in W. M. Davis, *Biographical Memoir of John Wesley Powell,* National Academy of Sciences Biographical Memoirs (Washington, February, 1915).

4. On frontier education, see Meredith Nicholson, *The Hoosiers,* especially Chapter III, "Bringers of the Light"; also Edward Eggleston's novels *The Hoosier Schoolmaster, The Circuit Rider,* and *The Hoosier Schoolboy;* further light is shed by many of the striking autobiographies of men who grew up out of a frontier background: John Muir, *The Story of My Boyhood and Youth;* John Burroughs, *My Boyhood;* William Dean Howells, *A Boy's Town;* Hamlin Garland, *A Son of the Middle Border.* It would be unwise to omit Mark Twain's accounts, either fictional or otherwise, of a boyhood on the Mississippi, or to neglect later, imported documents such as Ole Edvard Rölvaag's *Peder Victorious,* or Marie Sandoz's *Old Jules,* or Willa Cather's plains novels, especially *O Pioneers* and *My Ántonia.* Lincoln's boyhood is of course part of American folklore; it is given magnificent treatment in Sandburg's *Lincoln, the Prairie Years.* The documentation, in fact, is endless; the way the frontier American boy and girl got their education is still so close to our memory and so entangled with our habits of thinking and believing that even after the basic condition of deprivation is outgrown we continue to act and believe in many things according to patterns established in the backwoods of Indiana or the prairies of Illinois or the windy plains of Dakota a hundred or seventy five or fifty years ago.

5. For this first experience in promotion of a scheme within a political context, see Darrah, *Powell of the Colorado,* pp. 73–82; Lindley Morris, "John Wesley Powell," unpublished M.A. thesis, Illinois State Normal University (Bloomington, Illinois, 1947); *Proceedings,* Illinois State Board of Education (1858–75); and the 25th Illinois General Assembly, "An Act concerning the board of education and the Illinois Natural History Society," Illinois Laws (1867), pp. 21–22.

6. An application to the Smithsonian during this visit brought only the loan of scientific equipment, in exchange for the data Powell's party should collect. In the following April Powell went again, and again approached Grant, this time with a request for free rations for twenty-five men. Grant approved, but General Eaton, then commissary general of subsistence, disapproved on the ground Powell was neither a member of the army nor a civilian employee of the government. He suggested a special enactment of Congress as the only recourse, which meant calls on Senator Trumbull and Representative Cullom, as well as on Professor Henry, who introduced Powell to Garfield. After numerous objections, and a spirited support from Trumbull, the Senate authorized the drawing of rations for twenty-five men. The principal justification urged in Powell's behalf was his proposed exploration of the unknown Colorado River and his intention of studying irrigation possibilities in the mountain region.

What Powell actually got out of Congress before 1870 was meager; they looked upon this unknown with suspicion, apparently afraid that he would set an expensive precedent, though for the past two years they had given F. V. Hayden a budget of $5000 to conduct a geological survey of Nebraska, and the year before had embraced Clarence King's proposed survey of the 40th parallel.

7. See Schuchert and LeVene, *O. C. Marsh, Pioneer in Paleontology.* It was the discovery of *Protohippus parvulus,* a veritable missing link in the history of the horse, that conclusively clinched the theories of Darwin and Huxley. What diggers thought were human bones, dug out of a well, Marsh seized upon with a sure and trained comprehension only possible to a thorough professional.

3

1. Accounts of the 1868 Powell expedition have been consulted in the following sources: *Rocky Mountain News,* August 19, 20, 25, and September 1, 1868, and August 9, 1873; Denver *Post,* September 7, 1935; four letters from Sam Garman to Gertrude Lewis, preserved in the Milner Library, Illinois State Normal University; the diary of William N. Byers for 1868, in the Western History Division of the Denver Public Library; William N. Byers, "First Ascent of Long's Peak," *The Trail,* VII, No. 5 (October 1914); L. W. Keplinger, two articles with the same title as that of Byers, in *The Trail,* VII, No. 8 (January, 1915), and XII, No. 1 (June, 1919); Thomas F. Dawson, "Lost Alone on Bear River Forty Years Ago," *The Trail,* XI, No. 2 (July, 1918); *Bloomington Daily Pantagraph* (August 27, 1868); and the diaries of Lyle Durley and Rhodes Allen, both of these last available to me through the kindness of William Culp Darrah of Gettysburg, Pennsylvania. There is additional information, though somewhat garbled by bad memory and personal animosity, in the recollections of Jack Sumner and Billy Hawkins, cited in Note 3, below, and some refutation of the Sumner-Hawkins accounts in a letter from L. W. Keplinger to Robert Brewster Stanton, November 1, 1919 (Box II of the Stanton Papers, New York Public Library). The Sumner-Hawkins version is developed in R. B. Stanton and J. M. Chalfant, *Colorado River Controversies.* Some of the party's activities

are reported in Samuel Bowles, *The Switzerland of America: A Summer's Vacation in the Parks and Mountains of Colorado* (Springfield, Mass., 1869), pp. 81 ff.; and in Bowles, *Our New West. Records of travel between the Mississippi River and the Pacific Ocean* (Hartford, Conn., 1869), pp. 502–3.

2. The status of natural science in the Rockies in 1868 was still remarkably uncertain. Collections and observations had been made by Lewis and Clark, Pike, Long, Emory, Frémont, Gunnison, Captain W. W. Anderson, Captain W. L. Carpenter, Lieutenant C. A. H. McCauley, Lieutenant Colonel T. C. Henry, and others, but the peculiarly hazardous conditions of early collecting had caused the loss not only of many of the collections but of notes as well. Lewis and Clark's collections were never used as effectively as they might have been; Maximilian of Wied lost practically all of his 1833–34 collections in the burning of the steamboat *Assiniboine* on the Missouri; Pike's account is scientifically undocumented; Say and James, scientists with Long's expedition, suffered constant loss from the wetting and spoiling of specimens, and some of their notes were carried off by deserters; Frémont's collections were mainly lost. Especially in the region of the Colorado Rockies, there was little that could be called scientifically definite until about 1850, and not too much afterward until the late sixties, when Meek, Hayden, Powell, Marsh, and others had begun their expeditions. See Joseph Ewan, *Rocky Mountain Naturalists* (Denver, 1950), pp. 1–12 and *passim.*

3. Sumner's grudge has been taken up and exploited by several people, notably in Stanton and Chalfant, *Colorado River Controversies,* and W. W. Bass, *Adventures in the Canyons of the Colorado* (Grand Canyon, Ariz., 1919). Sumner's reminiscences are reprinted in *Colorado River Controversies;* they constitute a revision and slight alteration in detail, though not in tone, of a spiteful letter he wrote from Hanksville, Utah, to the Denver *Post* on October 13, 1902, after Powell's death. The original letter is in the Colorado Historical Society archives. Hawkins' account is reprinted in the Bass booklet and in *Colorado River Controversies.* Both the Sumner and Hawkins recollections are full of egregious errors of fact, as is a letter from Jack Sumner's son to Clyde Eddy summarizing his father's experiences and grievances, which is now in the files of the Utah State Historical Society. The whole controversy is a melancholy and spiteful affair. I have discussed it in detail, hoping thereby to scotch a good many persistent misconceptions, in "Jack Sumner and John Wesley Powell," *Colorado Magazine,* XXVI (1949), 61–69.

4. Taylor comments on Sumner's skill and daring in *Colorado: A Summer Trip, 1866* (New York, 1867).

5. At least the somewhat boastful and tainted testimony of his reminiscences. Sumner's later tendency was to take credit for all invention, all good management, and all resolution that were demonstrated on the expedition.

6. Because of the grab-bag methods of his early expeditions, and because of confusion that later arose between Illinois State Normal University, the Natural History Society, and the Smithsonian as to who owned parts of the collection, and most of all because of Powell's own failure to label and catalogue the specimens he brought back, neither the first nor second Rocky Mountain Scientific Exploring Expedition did much to clarify natural science in Colorado. Powell left the Normal museum before he had time to tidy it up, so that whatever the botanical activities of the ladies, they remain unrecorded. But Nellie Thompson later, while living at Kanab with the Powell Survey party, contributed plant specimens to Asa Gray (1872), and there is an *astragalus*

thompsonae that Sereno Watson named for her, as well as a *Pentstemon pumilus* var. *thompsoniae* that records her association with Gray. See Ewan, *Rocky* Mountain Naturalists, p. 321.

7. These constitute a series, on August 19, 20, and 25, and September 1, and reproduce in ampler form the notes in his diary for the same period. My account of the ascent of Long's Peak is taken from these letters, from Garman's letters to Gertrude Lewis, and from Keplinger's articles in *The Trail.* The Byers article in *The Trail* is a reprint of his September 1, 1868, letter to the *Rocky Mountain News.*

4

1. An account of this junket appears in Samuel Bowles, *The Switzerland of America* (Springfield, Mass., 1869), pp. 82 ff., and in essentially the same form in his *Our New West* (Hartford, Conn., 1869), pp. 502–3. See also O. J. Hollister, *Life of Schuyler Colfax* (New York, 1886), pp. 325 ff.

2. Hollister reports that the wedding ring for Nellie Wade was made from gold dust presented to Colfax in the mountains by a Colorado miner (p. 327, note).

3. Bowles' trip was part of the extraordinary rush of journalists and editors and artists who after the end of the war began interpreting the opening West, its natives, flora, fauna, scenery, resources, and opportunities, for eastern readers. Horace Greeley, John Hanson Beadle, Samuel Bowles, and L. P. Brockett among the editors; Frenzeny and Tavernier, Alfred Waud, Theodore Davis, Alfred Mathews, Joseph Becker, and Henry Worrall among the artists; Alexander Gardner, T. H. O'Sullivan, W. H. Jackson, among the photographers, were only a handful among hundreds. The popular journals of the time, especially *Leslie's Illustrated Newspaper, Harper's Weekly, Scribner's Monthly,* and *Century,* show a heavy proportion of Western articles and illustrations, and the flood of books by transcontinental travelers can never be said to have ceased entirely. An extremely informative study of the illustrators who made up part of this journalistic gold rush is Robert Taft, *Artists and Illustrators of the Old West: 1850–1900* (New York, 1953).

4. The map upon which Powell depended was apparently a General Land Office map drawn by Gorlinski, which was in turn based, presumably, upon various Army reconnoissances and upon the rectangular surveys of the General Land Office so far as they had been extended. The most detailed maps of the region he was planning to enter may or may not have been available to Powell. Clarence King's maps of the Uinta region were not yet completed, and Macomb's expeditionary map, drawn by F. W. von Egloffstein in 1859 when Macomb attempted to reach the junction of Green and Grand, would not be published until 1876, though the map bears the date 1860 and may have circulated in the sixties. I have seen no evidence that Powell was yet acquainted with John Strong Newberry, Macomb's geologist, though the two later became close friends. Unless he had Macomb's map, Powell thus had to rely on the Gorlinski map (see Darrah, *Powell of the Colorado,* p. 108, note), the reports of Frémont, Ives, and Berthoud, and the *Pacific Railroad Reports,* especially those of Lieutenant Gunnison and Lieutenant Beckwith (*Reports of Explorations and Surveys to Ascertain the Most Practicable and Economical Route for a Railroad from the Mississippi River to the Pacific Ocean,* made under the direction of the Secretary of War, in 1853–54, II [Washington, 1855]).

The map to accompany Beckwith's report was published in Vol. XI. It was drawn by von Egloffstein from notes by Richard Kern, and perpetuated several early misconceptions, notably in calling what was later known as the Gunnison River the Grand, and calling the Grand above its junction with the Gunnison, the Blue. It left just as blank as the Gorlinski map that tantalizing region along the Green and Colorado between the Uinta Valley and the mouth of the Little Colorado.

5. In spite of the fact that every mile of the canyons has been surveyed and resurveyed, this sort of tale is common even today. The appetite for the marvelous dies hard.

6. The evidence that Powell had talked to White comes only from the journal of George Y. Bradley, though Sumner's journal also mentions the White claim (with derision). I have not encountered anyone who has run the Colorado canyons, or knows them well, who credits White's tale. Robert Brewster Stanton painstakingly traced the story down, interviewed White and others, and came to the conclusion that White was sadly mistaken, though he may not have deliberately lied. Stanton believed that White had run only the final minor stretch of canyons, now part of Lake Mead, from the Grand Wash Cliffs to Callville, and was never in the Grand Canyon proper at all. (*Colorado River Controversies,* pp. 70–93.) Yet as late as 1917 there were champions of White's claim to the glory of first running the river. See Thomas F. Dawson, "The Grand Canyon," an article giving the credit of first traversing the Grand Canyon of the Colorado to James White, a Colorado gold explorer, who it is claimed made the voyage two years previous to the expedition under the direction of Major J. W. Powell in 1869. 65th Cong., 1st Sess., Senate Document No. 42. Dawson makes much of the fact that Powell knew of White's voyage, and so gained courage to run the river. There is no doubt, from the evidence of Bowles, Bradley, and Sumner, that Powell did know of White, and had perhaps talked to him. Neither is there any doubt that both he and his men thought White's yarn a fable. Years later, Powell told William H. Brewer of Yale that he was convinced before he ran it that the Colorado had no falls. His reason was not White's story, but the scientific conclusion that a river so loaded with silt would very soon scour its bed down to something like an even grade. See Wm. H. Brewer, "John Wesley Powell," *American Journal of Science,* XIV (November, 1902).

7. A search of the archives of the Denver Public Library's Western History Division, as well as those of the Colorado Historical Society, has produced little on any of these mountain men except Sumner and O. G. Howland. What little is known of each of them is summarized by Darrah in *Utah Historical Quarterly,* XV (1947).

5

1. Sources for this part of the 1868 expedition are the Allen and Durley diaries; Garman's letters to Gertrude Lewis; Dawson, "Lost Alone on Bear River Forty Years Ago;" and to some extent Sumner's letter to the *Denver Post* and his reminiscences in *Colorado River Controversies.*

2. Powell Bottoms is a mile or two below the Rifle Junction, about three miles below Meeker. Nathan Meeker, when he was made Indian agent to the White River Utes in 1878, utilized as agency buildings some of the cabins erected by Powell's party. A letter from Meeker to Powell dated December 12, 1878, nine months before Meeker and all his men were massacred, shows not

the slightest premonition that the Utes were restive. On the contrary, Meeker optimistically outlines the improvements he is making, and invites Powell back to observe the changes that have been made. (National Archives, Powell Survey, Letters Received, VIII, No. 50.)

6

1. Captain Macomb, working down the incredibly cut-up sandrock country toward the junction, had got close enough to see from a high point what he thought must be the confluence of the canyons of the Grand and Green, but had been unable to get down to the rivers. As I have pointed out (Chapter 4, note 4) Newberry's geological report, though earlier in time than Powell's exploration, was not published until 1876, the year after Powell's *Exploration of the Colorado River of the West* appeared. Macomb's map may have been available to him, though he never mentioned it, as one might have expected him to do if he knew of it. In modern maps the Grand is called the Colorado.

2. As it turned out, the river party was kept much too busy to pan the sandbars, and the loss and spoilage of provisions kept them from loitering in the canyons. Later Jack Sumner spent several years prospecting in the area. It was while he was working a river placer that Robert Brewster Stanton ran across him on December 13, 1891, and got the first intimations of the ill will with which Powell's former helper regarded the Major. (*Colorado River Controversies,* p. xli.)

3. Here too Sumner, and after him Stanton and others, have misstated or misinterpreted facts. Sumner, in conducting his campaign of sour grapes and vilification, claimed that through Senator Trumbull Powell had obtained a government appropriation of $10,000 for the 1869 expedition. He bitterly charged that the boatmen were not paid, that supplies were stingily bought, and so on. Actually Powell had no appropriation whatever aside from the right to draw rations. For a full and specific statement of how his expedition was financed, see his letter to the Chicago *Tribune,* dated from Green River, Wyoming on May 24, 1869, and published on May 29. It is reprinted with other documents of the expedition in *Utah Historical Quarterly,* XV, (1947).

4. Now the University of Illinois.

5. The wages paid, or not paid, to the boatmen is one of the most angrily debated details of the expedition. Sumner and Hawkins, in their late attacks, charged Powell with turning them loose all but penniless at the mouth of the Virgin. As he points out in his May 24 letter to the Chicago *Tribune,* the only money he had for wages was obtained by commuting some of the meat ration into cash. The $75 he is said (*Colorado River Controversies,* p. 211) to have given Sumner, as well as the few dollars he distributed among the others, probably represented all he had beyond what was necessary to get himself and Walter back east. He gave the two remaining boats to Sumner, Hall, and Bradley. (See Stegner, "Jack Sumner and John Wesley Powell.") The whole controversy about wages seems to have arisen after Sumner got the erroneous impression that Powell had a government subsidy and was holding out on the men. That it was not something immediate and incurable, a result of the river trip itself, is indicated by the fact that Sumner would have gone on the 1871 expedition if deep snows had not held him up in Colorado, and by the further fact that Hawkins, the other irreconcilable, was for several years after 1870 a packer with Powell Survey parties in southern Utah. There are letters from him to Powell, dated as late as January, 1879, which show him full of friendship

and camaraderie — and anxious for a continued job with the survey. Powell Survey, Letters Received, II, No. 33; IX, No. 240.

6. Otis Marston of Berkeley, California, an intense student of the Colorado River and its expeditions, is contemptuous of Powell's boats. It is impossible not to agree that the craft were clumsy, heavy, and ill suited to the actual conditions on the river, but it may be argued in defense of Powell that those conditions were not known when the party started from Green River. The relative importance of strength and maneuverability would have been easy to misjudge.

7

1. Eventually, steamers went upriver as far as the mouth of the Virgin.

2. I have put the Adams story together out of a number of sources: the reminiscences of Billy Hawkins, in W. W. Bass, *Adventures in the Canyons of the Colorado* — lively but unreliable; "Petition of Samuel Adams praying compensation," Senate Miscellaneous Document No. 17, 41st Cong., 2nd Sess.; "The Colorado River Expeditions of Samuel Adams," House Miscellaneous Document No. 37, 42nd Cong., 1st Sess.; "Report submitted by Mr. Washburn for the Committee on Claims, February 17, 1875," Senate Report No. 662, 43rd Cong., 2nd Sess.; letters from R. M. McCormick to J. W. Powell, April 20, 1872, and from Powell to McCormick, same date, Powell Survey, Letters Received, I, Nos. 59–66, 67.; a collection of newspaper references noting Adams' activities at various times, kindly furnished me by Otis Marston of Berkeley, California; eleven letters from Adams to the San Francisco *Chronicle* beginning March 8, 1872; and Adams' own manuscript journal, which exists in two versions in the Henry E. Huntington Library. I have carefully examined and transcribed this journal and compared it with its printed version. It is contradictory and full of plain lies, which grow more extravagant with each editing. The letter from Powell to McCormick and the report of Senator Washburn for the Committee on Claims are basic documents. The first especially summarizes all of Powell's contacts with Adams, establishes the fact that Hawkins' "young scientific duck" at Green River was the good captain, and disposes of Adams' "claims" point by point.

3. On Dickson, see Bernard DeVoto, *Across the Wide Missouri,* Chapter X; there is a short account of Gibson in Wallace Stegner, *Mormon Country* (Duell, Sloan, and Pearce, 1942), pp. 128–35.

4. Captain Johnson's activities on the lower Colorado are summarized in Frederick S. Dellenbaugh, *The Romance of the Colorado River,* pp. 144–55. The official account of the Ives expedition is the *Report upon the Colorado River of the West, explored in 1857 and 1858* (Washington, 1861).

5. A copy of this letter, together with one from General Humphreys to Secretary of War Belknap and three from Adams to Congressman Austin Blair and J. I. Burns about his claims, is preserved with the Adams journal in the Huntington Library.

6. Letter, J. W. Powell to R. M. McCormick, April 20, 1872. Powell Survey, Letters Sent, I, Nos. 59–66.

8

1. The most recent and most authoritative accounts of the 1869 Powell expedition down the Colorado are Darrah, *Powell of the Colorado,* and the *Utah His-*

torical Quarterly, XV (1947), in which most of the original documents are published and to which several scholars, including Mr. Darrah and Dale L. Morgan, have contributed introductions and notes. The sources include the diary of George Y. Bradley, the partial diaries of Powell and Sumner, and letters of Powell, Walter Powell, and O. G. Howland. Mr. Darrah's account is based entirely upon these original sources; its weakness is that Mr. Darrah does not personally know the river and its canyons. In my own account I have utilized — some of them through his kindness — the sources known to Mr. Darrah, plus one that has come to light since the publication of Mr. Darrah's book. This is the first part of Jack Sumner's journal, covering the stretch from Green River to the mouth of the Uinta. Otis Marston, who discovered it in the files of a St. Louis newspaper, is properly the one to discuss it first. It is enough here to remark that it is rather fuller, and with more literary flourishes, than the long-known second half, and that it corroborates the Bradley journal and the Howland letters on the details of the wreck at Disaster Falls. None of the original journals indicates any of the wrangling, bad feeling, or failure of command that have been later charged against Powell by Sumner, Hawkins, Stanton, and others. Not even Sumner's does; his newly discovered journal, in fact, contradicts some of his later statements.

2. Beckwourth, in *The Life and Adventures of James P. Beckwourth* (1856), says that he rescued General Ashley from this cataract, which he seems to have located either at the foot of Brown's Hole or at the mouth of Flaming Gorge — in Beckwourth's words, "where the river enters the Utah mountains." Actually, Ashley's journal, long supposed to be that of William Sublette, and now in the Missouri Historical Society archives, indicates that Ashley's near-drowning occurred in what Powell would name Split Mountain Canyon, and Beckwourth's own account indicates elsewhere that when Ashley's detachment ran the canyons of the Green, Beckwourth was clear over on the other side of the Uintas with Clyman's and then with Fitzpatrick's brigade. The whole story of the "Suck," as well as that of the rescue of Ashley, is fable based on hearsay, and its only purpose was the glorification of Beckwourth.

3. On the Risdon affair, see *The Rocky Mountain News,* (July 5, 6, and 7, 1869). There are echoes, of varying degrees of gullibility, in many newspapers of the time. *The Rocky Mountain News,* because of Byers' close connection with the Powell party, was harder to fool than most; but the whole Risdon episode, in itself a half ghoulish, half amusing piece of backwoods effrontery, is a convincing testimonial to the lack of public knowledge about the area into which Powell was penetrating.

4. On the Hook Expedition, see Dellenbaugh, *The Romance of the Colorado River,* p. 249, and *The Rocky Mountain News* (July 16, 1869).

5. Records of the river trip as far as the mouth of the Uinta are thus Howland's two letters to the Rocky Mountain News, Powell's five to the Chicago *Tribune,* Walter Powell's one to the Chicago *Evening Journal,* and the first part of Sumner's journal, all of these published shortly after being written; in addition, letters from Major Powell to Henry Wing and Richard Edwards, President of Normal University, were sent to the papers by their recipients. Of the records not immediately published there were a letter from Andy Hall to his brother, Powell's own journal and field notes, and the journal which George Bradley kept secretly throughout the journey and which is now in the Library of Congress. All of these except the first part of Sumner's journal and the letter from Hall are in the *Utah Historical Quarterly,* XV (1947). It is significant that

as the hardships increased, and the expedition went deeper into the wilderness, there were no more communications to the press. Not even after the successful conclusion did any member write up his experiences for the papers, though Powell the following winter made numerous lecture appearances, and wrote a preliminary and important account of the whole expedition which appeared in an English publication, William A. Bell's *New Tracks in North America.* Bell talked him into doing this article when they met in the cars on the trip home. The first part of Powell's field diary has never been found, and is not likely to be of great value if it ever is, unless it is much more full and detailed than the surviving notes. The "official" record of the voyage, though as we shall see subject to much doubt in details, is of course Powell's *Exploration of the Colorado River of the West.* It has been reprinted twice, once as *The Canyons of the Colorado* (Meadville, Penn., 1895, with additions and alterations), and once as *First Down the Grand Canyon,* in Nelson Doubleday's Outing Adventure Library, 1915. In this the second and more scientific section is omitted.

6. If, as is probable, Powell had read the classic accounts of western explorations, he would have found plenty of precedent and justification for caution. The most spectacularly successful exploration in all our history, that of Lewis and Clark, was notably sober in its methods. By contrast Zebulon Pike, plunging recklessly over the Colorado Rockies in winter, brought his expedition to near-disaster, crippled some of his men for life, and made himself a sitting duck for the Spaniards to take into custody. Frémont too, in 1848, through his own recklessness underwent the most ghoulish of trials in the San Juan Mountains, and some of his survivors survived by falling back upon man-meat. Frémont was just as reckless, though in the second instance more successful, when he crossed the mountains westward in midwinter in 1853. On the other hand, the expedition of Major Long in 1820 had suffered if anything from a lack of resolution. It seems clear that Powell did not lack resolution; it is just as clear that he did not intend to fail for lack of reasonable precaution.

7. A distorted version of Ashley's river explorations, that in *The Life and Adventures of James P. Beckwourth,* was for many years the only one. With the publication of Ashley's papers, which did not occur until 1918, guesswork about Ashley's movements was largely eliminated. He made the trip by bull-boat through all the Uinta canyons, but left the river after a short attempt to go on through Desolation Canyon below the Uinta Valley. From there he went overland following the Strawberry to its source and thence north and finally east to his rendezvous on Henry's Fork. See Harrison Clifford Dale, *The Ashley-Smith Explorations and the discovery of a central route to the Pacific, 1822–1829, with the original journals.* (Revised edition, Glendale, Calif., 1941.)

8. See particularly *The Education of Henry Adams,* pp. 309–13, and David A. Dickason, "Henry Adams and Clarence King, the Record of a Friendship," *New England Quarterly,* XVII, No. 2 (June, 1944).

9. William Lewis Manly, in *Death Valley in '49* (San Jose, Calif., 1894), tells the story of his trip down the Green in an abandoned barge. He too, like Ashley, left the river in Uinta Valley, discouraged by the Ute chief Walker from trying to go farther in the attempt to reach California by water. Considering the kind of boat they started in, and the rafts they ended with, it was a blessing that they ran into Walker's band and that Walker, thinking them "Mormonee" as distinguished from "Mericats," gave them good advice.

10. For the diamond swindle, see The Century Association, *Clarence King Memoirs,* and James H. Wilkins, ed., *The Great Diamond Hoax, and other*

incidents in the life of Asbury Harpending (San Francisco, 1913). In this, as in other matters relating to King, I have leaned heavily on the findings of Harry Crosby, in "So Deep a Trail: A Biography of Clarence King" (Stanford University unpublished Ph.D. dissertation, 1953).

11. Chicago *Tribune,* July 19, 1869.

12. Sumner, Journal, June 20, 1869.

13. In his letter to *The Rocky Mountain News,* July 17, 1869.

14. J. W. Powell, *Exploration of the Colorado River of the West,* p. 25.

15. One contributing cause of the wreck, as of a lot of their later trouble, was the sluggishness and lack of maneuverability of the boats.

16. Later experience on the river has demonstrated that a free-running boat, especially if unloaded, will generally halt of itself in an eddy or reversing current. The Powell party, without means of knowing this, had every apparent reason to think the *Maid of the Canyon* was lost.

17. Dated June 18, 1869; published August 20, 1869.

18. *Rocky Mountain News,* July 17, 1869.

19. Renamed, on the second expedition, Split Mountain Canyon.

20. The mouths of White and Uinta have changed their relative position since 1869. The Uinta (now called the Duchesne) now enters the Green nearly opposite the mouth of the White.

21. Sumner, Journal, July 6, 1869.

22. Captain Pardon Dodds, the agent, was away at the time, and Powell dealt with an assistant named Lake. Dodds was later employed as a guide and packer by Powell's survey, and for a while was a partner with Powell in a Uinta Valley cattle ranch.

23. Letter to the Denver *Post,* October 13, 1902. See also Stegner, "Jack Sumner and John Wesley Powell."

24. The amount of actual dislike for Walter Powell is hard to assess. The late and unreliable reminiscences of Sumner and Hawkins make much of it, and ornament their tales with instances of near-fights, always heroically broken up by Hawkins or Sumner, between Walter Powell and Dunn, or Dunn and the Major. Bradley's journal, aside from reporting an increasing dissatisfaction as supplies dwindled and danger grew, makes no specific recording of such incidents; neither does Sumner's journal, and neither do any of Powell's several versions of the trip. But Walter Powell, hurt mentally by the war, was not asked to accompany the second expedition, and according to Darrah (*Utah Historical Quarterly,* XV, 89) was by the early seventies so unstable that he could not work regularly. He never recovered from his derangement. It is entirely probable that he was a difficult companion on such a tense and strenuous trip as this one.

25. The original of this letter is in the library of the Grand Canyon National Park. It is published in the *Utah Historical Quarterly,* XVI–XVII, 506–7.

9

1. Accounts differ on the character of this stretch of river. Sumner's journal mentions on July 7 that there is no timber in the canyon, though there is on the summits. The expedition was led to name the stretch Desolation Canyon, and Bradley speaks of the especially desolate view from the rims. But E. O. Beaman's photographs taken in 1871 show straggling trees, and Otis Marston, one of the most experienced of modern river boatmen, has found cotton-

woods and greenery all the way along Desolation — perhaps grown since 1869, since cottonwoods are short-lived and fast-growing trees. The natural bridges, he says, are two: one high on the skyline, and one at the head of a side gorge.

2. This rescue, which is the subject of one of the more imaginative illustrations in Powell's 1875 *Scribner's* articles about the voyage, might well have been thought somewhat colored and dramatized if it were not for the corroboration of Bradley's journal entry for July 8: "In one place Major having but one arm couldn't get up so I took off my drawers and they made an excellent substitute for rope and with that assistance he got up safe."

3. Here again Marston disagrees with the 1869 journals. Bradley's journal for July 9 speaks of "a succession of rappids or rather a continuous rapid with a succession of cataracts for 20 miles." Sumner's journal for the same date records "20 miles with that number of rapids, some of them very bad." Marston, in a note to the author on February 6, 1953, says, "If they found 20 miles of continuous cataracts the river must have changed. I can find no evidence of a change that marked." Powell's own field journal is missing the entries from July 7–19, inclusive. The records of the second Powell Expedition are of little value for comparison because the second expedition ran this stretch more than a month later in the season, and in very low water.

4. Some of Powell's later detractors, notably Stanton and Chalfant, have made much of the fact, established first in Hawkins' reminiscences, that Powell wore a life preserver, as if this fact somehow reduced the heroism of his exploration. It is hard to see how the wearing of a life preserver by a one-armed man is in any way shameful, or why Powell's failure to mention the existence of the preserver in his *Exploration* constitutes deliberate suppression of facts.

5. See *Reports of Explorations and Surveys to Ascertain the Most Practicable and Economical Route for a Railroad from the Mississippi River to the Pacific Ocean,* made under the direction of the Secretary of War, in 1853–54, Vol. II (Washington, 1855).

6. As has been indicated before, Macomb's map does not seem from any outward evidence to have been known to Powell. It was published in Captain J. N. Macomb, *Report of the Exploring Expedition from Santa Fe, New Mexico, to the Junction of the Grand and Green Rivers of the Great Colorado of the West, in 1859* (Washington, 1876).

7. Sumner, Journal, July 16, 1869.

10

1. My account of Adams' journey down the Blue and the Grand is taken from his manuscript journal. Though there is no real reason for giving much credence to any single detail in either of the versions, I have in general stuck to the original draft, as likely to be somewhat closer to what Adams thought he saw at the time. A dressed-up version, prepared in connection with Adams' claim for compensation from the United States, is in *Colorado River Expeditions of Samuel Adams,* House Miscellaneous Document No. 37, 42nd Cong., 1st Sess.

2. Adams, Journal, July 12, 1869.

3. There is some reason to believe that Powell's first plan was to explore the Grand rather than the Green. At least there is an item in the *Rocky Mountain News* for November 6, 1867, which reports Powell's departure for

the east, and continues: "He will return to the territory next spring to prosecute his scientific labors, and will go down the Grand to its junction with the Colorado River."

4. Adams, Journal, August 1, 1869.

5. Fragmentary second version of Adams' journal bound in with the first; single page numbered 17.

11

1. The writing of this report and the vexed question of its reliability is discussed in Part II, Chapter 5.

2. Powell, *Exploration*, pp. 7–9.

3. Bradley, Journal, July 23, 1869.

4. See Bass, *Adventures in the Canyon of the Colorado.*

5. Bradley, Journal, July 29, 1869.

6. *Ibid.*, July 30, 1869.

7. *Ibid.*, July 31, 1869.

8. See Powell, Journal, August 4, 1869, where he calls the Paria "Ute Creek." Sumner's journal reads, for August 4, "Pulled out early and made a run of 38 miles, that brought us to the old Spanish Crossing between Salt Lake and New Mexico, called the Escalanta 'El vade de los Padres.'"

9. The modern highway or rail crossings of the Green-Colorado canyons are precisely where the crossings were in Powell's time — at Green River, Wyoming; at Jensen, in the Uinta Valley; at Greenriver, Utah, the old Spanish or Gunnison's Crossing; and at the mouth of the Paria where the ferry has been superseded by the Navajo Bridge. There have been none added except the ferry at Hite, the old Dandy Crossing, at the upper end of Glen Canyon, which permits an undependable connection between Hanksville and Blanding, Utah. A bridge was scheduled to be built at Hite in the summer of 1953.

10. Bradley, Journal, August 4, 1869.

11. For the story of the Brown-Stanton Expedition, see Robert Brewster Stanton, "Through the Grand Canyon of the Colorado," *Scribner's,* VIII (November, 1900), 591–613; and F. A. Nims, "Through Mysterious Cañons of the Colorado," *Overland Monthly* (March, 1892), pp. 253–70. There are secondary accounts in Dellenbaugh's *Romance of the Colorado River* and in Lewis R. Freeman, *The Colorado River, Yesterday, Today, and Tomorrow* (New York, 1923). The Stanton papers, including Stanton's diaries and notebooks, are in the New York Public Library.

12. Lieutenant Ives, after fighting his way upriver as far as the mouth of Diamond Creek, led a party overland across the Colorado Plateau to the Hopi towns and across the Navajo country to Fort Defiance. It was a side excursion from this land party that tried unsuccessfully to reach the mouth of the Little Colorado.

13. Bradley, Journal, August 10, 1869.

14. *Ibid.*

15. Sumner, Journal, August 10, 1869.

16. Bradley, Journal, August 11, 1869.

17. Though the name "Grand Canyon" was in use before his expedition, Ives used the name "Big Canyon" in his report and map. Powell chose to return to "Grand Canyon," and his choice has stuck.

18. Powell, *Exploration,* p. 80.

19. Jacob Hamblin, Henry Miller, and Jesse Crosby, three Mormons, took a sixteen-foot skiff from the foot of Grand Wash Cliffs to Call's Landing, later Callville, in 1867. In his *Exploration,* Powell says (p. 102) that he had the manuscript journal of that two-day trip with him on his own, so that he had fairly accurate information about the river below the Grand Wash. No copy of the Hamblin-Miller-Crosby journal is now known to exist. All of this stretch of river, which before Powell had been traversed by Ives, Hamblin, and probably James White, is now under Lake Mead. See *Utah Historical Quarterly,* XV, 71, note.

12

1. In practice, the moving power of a stream is conditioned by numerous unpredictable factors such as the smoothness of the bed, the straightness of the course, and so on. An early and extremely lucid discussion of the corrasive and moving power of streams is in G. K. Gilbert, *Report on the Geology of the Henry Mountains,* in which Gilbert develops many observations first made by Powell himself.

2. Evidence of the morbid effect of being confined in the dark and narrow inner canyon is contained in most of the river journals. The *imaginary* effects upon people who have not been there or who let their imaginations run free are much more extreme, as in many of the early canyon illustrations, where towering height, acute narrowness, and cavernous darkness are wildly exaggerated. In this key, simply as random examples, see the picture of James White losing his companion, George Strole, in Bell, *New Tracks in North America;* or the illustrations made by F. W. von Egloffstein for the Ives report — the first pictures made of the Grand Canyon — which are reproduced elsewhere in this book; or Frederick Dellenbaugh's painting, "Running the Sockdologer," reproduced in his *Romance of the Colorado River,* p. 329; or many of the Thomas Moran woodcuts illustrating Powell's *Exploration of the Colorado River of the West.*

3. Bradley, Journal, August 22, 1869. Bradley several times remarks how much farther it is from the Little Colorado to Grand Wash than they expected it to be from Mormon estimates. The reason is simply that through the plateaus into which it has cut the Grand Canyon the Colorado runs a very tortuous course. At its junction with the Little Colorado it is flowing almost due south; it shortly swings west, then northwest, then almost south again, then north, then again west, then southwest, then south, and then, with many minor twists, northwest to its break out of the Grand Wash Cliffs.

4. They seem to have had no special trouble with Dubendorff Rapid, a mile below the end of the Middle Granite Gorge, though it is held by modern boatmen to be one of the twenty stiffest on the river.

5. Stanton thought this rapid the worst on the entire Colorado, but Julius Stone, on his excursion in 1909 (Julius F. Stone, *Canyon Country* [New York, 1932]), found it neither so rough as Powell's report had led him to expect, nor obscured by any turns. Except for a brief time when a flood scoured it out in 1952, the rapid has long been buried under Lake Mead silt, but photographs taken before the lake filled in show it as a straight reach with a creek coming in on each side to form an almost perfect cross. It was up the northern cross canyon that the Howlands and Dunn made their way out onto the Shivwits

Plateau. Powell's statement that after running the rapid they were out of sight of the three men is certainly an error — an error which is perhaps less damning if we remember that Powell's notes by this time were almost in code, and that he never saw this rapid again, since the second Powell expedition left the river at Kanab Wash. Stone, a contentious and literal-minded man, was undoubtedly right in rejecting some of Powell's detailed statements of fact; he was undoubtedly wrong in others, for he was himself deceived by the profound changes that a difference in water level can make in the canyons. Otis Marston's investigations of river history have indicated that Separation, while it existed, capsized more boats than any other on the river. (Letter of February 6, 1953.)

6. Bradley, Journal, August 27, 1869.

7. The only corroboration for this dramatic story of Powell's is in Hawkins' reminiscences, notoriously unreliable and written down years later, after he could have read the Powell report and could easily have confused details in it with things actually remembered. Nevertheless, Hawkins does report that Powell got stuck on a cliff and had to be rescued by oars pressed into crevices so as to afford him a foothold. The difficulty is that Hawkins places the incident far back in the Canyon of Lodore, on the day when Powell was on the cliff and the camp was swept by a flash fire, the day when Hawkins lost most of the messkit in the Green. It is conceivable that Hawkins was right, and that Powell deliberately moved the story for dramatic effect to a more climactic place in his narrative. But Hawkins within two lines of telling this story has jumped from Lodore to the junction of Grand and Green, and is so obviously scrambling his memories that his account is worth very little.

8. Bradley, Journal, August 27, 1869.

9. *Ibid.*

10. Powell, *Exploration,* pp. 98–9.

11. Bradley, Journal, August 28, 1869.

12. There is little point in dragging a reader through the dreary controversy over the precise status in history of the three who left the party. Powell himself never called them deserters, and in his report spoke of them as "faithful men." Much of the debate was stirred up by the omission of the names of the three from the Powell monument on the south rim of the Grand Canyon — an omission which, however unfortunate, can hardly be blamed upon Powell, since he had been a dozen years dead when the monument was unveiled.

13. Powell's detractors, concentrating on the details, in which he was sometimes unmistakably inaccurate, have questioned his statement that the party waited and shot off guns to see if the three would not rejoin them. Both Powell's account in Bell's *New Tracks in North America* and his *Exploration* say that they waited two hours. Sumner's journal mentions no wait. Bradley's, probably the most reliable, says, "The three boys stood on the cliff looking at us [while the party was bailing out after running Separation Rapid] and having waved them adieu we dashed through the next rapid and then into an eddy where we stopped to catch our breath and bail out the water from our now nearly sunken boats." It was perhaps to this second wait, still within range of the three if they wanted to rejoin the boat party, that Powell referred, though from Bradley's record it would not seem to have lasted anything like two hours.

14. Powell, Journal, August 28, 1869.

15. This was Lava Cliff, which according to Otis Marston was briefly uncovered in 1952 by the same flood that scoured out Separation Rapid. It seems to have been more scary than dangerous. (Letter of February 6, 1953.)

16. Omaha *Republican*, September 16, 1869.

II. THE PLATEAU PROVINCE

1

1. In attempting to appraise the relationship of Washington as scientific center with the West as scientific frontier I have naturally relied heavily upon the many series of government scientific publications of the eighteen-seventies and eighteen-eighties. These include the reports, monographs, and bulletins of the King, Hayden, Powell, and Wheeler Surveys (see L. F. Schmeckebier, *Catalogue and Index of the Publications of the Hayden, King, Powell, and Wheeler Surveys,* United States Geological Survey Bulletin 222 [Washington, 1904]); the Annual Reports, beginning in 1879 in each case, of the United States Geological Survey and the Bureau of Ethnology; the *Contributions to North American Ethnology* begun under the Powell Survey and completed under the Bureau of Ethnology; the monographs of the Bureau of Ethnology and the United States Geological Survey; the Annual Reports of the General Land Office; and certain reports of the Office of Indian Affairs, especially J. W. Powell and G. W. Ingalls, *Report of Special Commissioners on the Condition of the Ute Indians of Utah; the Paiutes of Utah, northern Arizona, southern Nevada, and southeastern California; the Go-si-utes of Utah and Nevada; the northwestern Shoshones of Idaho and Utah; and the western Shoshones of Nevada, and report concerning claims of settlers in the Mo-a-pa Valley, southeastern Nevada.* Washington, 1874. The same Washington in which these reports and monographs and bulletins were prepared and published is reflected in Henry Adams' *Education* and in his letters of the period (see Worthington Chauncey Ford, ed., *Letters of Henry Adams, 1858–1891* [Boston, 1930], and Harold Dean Cater, *Henry Adams and His Friends* [Boston, 1947]), as well as in his novel *Democracy* (New York, 1908) and in the letters of his wife (Ward Thoron, *Letters of Mrs. Henry Adams, 1865–1883* [Boston, 1936]). I have found extremely useful Allan Nevins' *Hamilton Fish, the Inner History of the Grant Administration* (New York, 1936), and a number of other biographies and autobiographies, especially: Schuchert and LeVene, *O. C. Marsh, Pioneer in Paleontology;* Allan Nevins, *Abram S. Hewitt: with Some Account of Peter Cooper* (New York, 1935); The Century Association, *Clarence King Memoirs;* G. R. Agassiz, ed., *Letters and Recollections of Alexander Agassiz, with a Sketch of His Life and Work* (Boston, 1913); Simon Newcomb, *Reminiscences of an Astronomer* (Boston, 1903); N. S. Shaler, *Autobiography* (Boston, 1909); G. R. Brown, ed., *Reminiscences of William S. Stewart of Nevada* (New York, 1908); Carl Schurz, *Reminiscences of Carl Schurz,* 3 vols. (New York, 1908); Joseph Schafer, *Carl Schurz, Militant Liberal* (Evansville, Wis., 1930); U. S. Grant, *Personal Memoirs of U. S. Grant* (New York, 1885–86); T. C. Smith, *The Life and Letters of James Abram Garfield,* 2 vols. (New Haven, 1925). The general history of the period is best summarized in Allan Nevins, *The Emergence of Modern America,* in *A History of American Life, Vol. VIII* (New York, 1927); and E. P. Oberholtzer, *The*

History of the United States since the Civil War (Toronto, 1917–37). There is a very useful brief article, "Science in Washington: A Historical Survey," by Paul H. Oehser of the Smithsonian, in the American Association for the Advancement of Science Centennial Program (Washington, August 26, 1948). And perhaps most revealing of all sources, though they are cited here only piecemeal as they happen to be used, are the extensive letter files of the various western surveys, the United States Geological Survey, and the Bureau of Ethnology, all in the National Archives, and other manuscript and letter material preserved in the libraries of the United States Geological Survey and the Bureau of Ethnology. Across a period of two or three decades, these letters give a peculiarly intimate cross-section of the ideas and personalities of American science.

2. Mark Twain, Letter to an unidentified person, 1890. In Bernard DeVoto, ed., *The Portable Mark Twain* (New York, 1946), p. 775.

3. Henry Adams, *Democracy, an American Novel,* p. 10.

2

1. John Wesley Powell, *Report on the Geology of the Uinta Mountains,* Chapter I.

2. The Plateau Province which Powell delimited was more precisely defined by Captain Clarence Edward Dutton in the course of his geological studies under Powell's direction. See especially Dutton, *Report of the Geology of the High Plateaus of Utah,* Chapter I.

3. The history of the Spanish Southwest is a separate and extensive field of learning — almost a separate religion — whose bibliography is far too large even to sample here. For Father Escalante's diary, the document which most centrally touches the region of Powell's interest, see Herbert E. Bolton, *Pageant in the Wilderness* (Salt Lake City, 1950).

4. Harrison Clifford Dale, *The Ashley Smith Explorations.* One of the most vivid accounts of the mountain-man breed, though the book does not touch more than the fringes of the Plateau Province, is Bernard DeVoto's *Across the Wide Missouri.*

5. In Vol. XI of the *Pacific Railroad Reports,* published in 1861.

6. It might be said to have begun with Columbus or even with Columbus' predecessors, for as Bernard DeVoto brilliantly demonstrates in *The Course of Empire* (Boston, 1952), it is possible to look upon the opening of America as an episode in the search for the Great South Sea or the Northwest Passage, and the events of America's westering as milestones on the road to Asia. He thus takes the Lewis and Clark expedition not so much as the beginning of something as the final act of a long historical drama.

3

1. Testifying before a House investigating committee in May, 1874, when the question of the consolidation of the surveys was up for consideration, Powell said that a member of the Appropriations Committee which had given him his first appropriation had been the cause of this error. "A member of that committee asked me what was done with the collections. I told him that they went to the Smithsonian Institution, and I said that if there was any question about it, it might be inserted in the law. He said that he would have that attended to and he made a memorandum of it. It seems that afterwards,

seeing this memorandum, that the collections were to go to the Smithsonian Institution, he accidentally sent my whole work there." (House Report No. 612, 43rd Cong., 1st Sess., testimony on May 20, 1874). There is no reason to believe that Powell ever tried to correct the error, but one result of the 1874 investigation of the Western surveys was to send his outfit back to the Department of the Interior and make it a second but autonomous division of Hayden's Geological and Geographical Survey of the Territories. It remained under Interior until 1879, when the surveys were finally consolidated in the United States Geological Survey.

2. Bell, *New Tracks in North America.*

3. J. W. Powell, "The Personal Characteristics of Professor Baird," *Annual Report* of the Board of Regents of the Smithsonian Institution, 1888 (Washington, 1890), pp. 739–44.

4. There are brief biographical sketches of all these early members of the Powell Survey in the *Utah Historical Quarterly,* XV, XVI, and XVII — the volumes in which many of the known journals of both river expeditions are reproduced. See also Frederick S. Dellenbaugh, *A Canyon Voyage* (New York, 1908), a detailed account of the second trip. This was for many years the only published account of that trip except for Beaman's series of articles entitled "The Cañon of the Colorado and the Moqui Pueblos," *Appleton's Journal,* XI (April–May, 1874).

5. For a summary of the history and work of all these early surveys, see G. P. Merrill, *The First One Hundred Years of American Geology* (New Haven, 1924), and C. L. and M. A. Fenton, *The Story of the Great Geologists* (New York, 1945). There is also much information as well as a judicious evaluation of the work of many western geologists in Herman LeRoy Fairchild, *The Geological Society of America, 1888–1930* (New York, 1932). Fairchild concludes (p. 47), "The explorations of the western part of America during the years 1867–1890, with the wonderful discoveries in structure, dynamics, and in the evolution of the vertebrates, probably make the most brilliant chapter in the entire history of geology." Actually it was Powell, with his co-workers Gilbert and Dutton, who did the most enduring work in pure science, especially in physiography and geophysics. The geological work of both King and Hayden has suffered much more than theirs with time.

4

1. Darrah, *Powell of the Colorado,* p. 152.

2. From the beginning he expressed his confidence that the three could not have been guilty of the atrocity the story charged them with — a fact which in itself may be taken as evidence that his feelings towards the Howlands and Dunn were not vindictive. See Chicago *Tribune,* September 28, 1869.

3. Jacob Hamblin's journal up to the year 1858 is in the Church Historian's Office, Salt Lake City. His reminiscences are incorporated in James A. Little, *Jacob Hamblin,* Faith Promoting Series (Salt Lake City, 1881). He has been the subject of two full-length biographies: Paul Bailey, *Jacob Hamblin, Buckskin Apostle* (Los Angeles, 1948), and Pearson Corbett, *Jacob Hamblin, the Peacemaker* (Salt Lake City, 1952).

4. The most objective account of the Mountain Meadows Massacre, written from within the Church but free of all impulses to whitewashing, evasion, and scapegoating that earlier "official" accounts have had, and without the im-

placable anti-Mormonism of the Gentile accounts, is Juanita Brooks, *The Mountain Meadows Massacre* (Palo Alto, Calif., 1950).

5. Otis Marston believes that they took him to the river somewhere near the mouth of Whitmore Wash, and points out that for some reason, either mistrust of Powell or fear that prospectors and others might learn of the route and use it, they carefully refrained from revealing to him the comparatively easy horse trail down the Parashont. (Letter of November 15, 1952.)

6. Powell, *Exploration,* p. 129. The pictures which Powell's photographers, especially Jack Hillers, took among these plateau bands in the next few years constitute one of the more valuable parts of the Bureau of American Ethnology's collection of Indian pictures. They have been discussed by Julian Steward, "Notes on Hillers' Photographs of the Paiute and Ute Indians Taken on the Powell Expedition of 1873," *Smithsonian Miscellaneous Collections,* XCVIII, No. 18 (Washington, D.C., July 21, 1939).

7. It is instructive to compare Powell's approach with that suggested or advocated by more "orthodox" members of his generation. For example, the editor of the Topeka *Weekly Leader* remarked on June 27, 1867, his opinion of "Lo, his squaws and papooses, and his relatives and tribe, a set of miserable, dirty, lousy, blanketed, thieving, lying, sneaking, murdering, graceless, faithless, gut-eating skunks as the Lord ever permitted to infect the earth, and whose immediate and final extermination all men, except Indian agents and traders, should pray for." (Quoted by Robert Taft, *Artists and Illustrators of the Old West,* p. 66.) Compare also Lieutenant George Wheeler, who lost three men from his 1871 expedition in the Wickenburg stage massacre, and who wrote in his *Geographical Report,* not published until 1889: "One cannot approach the subject of the Indian without reverting to the Stage Massacre near Wickenburg, Arizona (where three members of the expedition were murdered), long proven to have been committed by Indians professedly friendly, and being fed at the expense of the Government. Maimum, one of the Mohaves of the river trip, who had formed a great fondness for the ill-fated Loring, was largely instrumental in ferreting out these red-skinned assassins, and some of their number were finally found and punished by General Crook's first command of the Military Department of Arizona. This is one of the evidences of the mistaken zeal, of the then peace-at-any-cost policy, that for so long a time applied to settlement of the Indian problem. Unfortunately, the bones of murdered citizens cannot rise to cry out and attest the atrocious murders of the far-spreading and wide-extending border lands of the Great West, and while the fate of the Indian is sealed, the interval during which their extermination as a race is to be consummated will doubtless be marked in addition to Indian outbreaks, with still many more murderous ambuscades and massacres." *Report upon the United States Geographical Surveys West of the One Hundredth Meridian, in charge of Capt. George M. Wheeler, Corps of Engineers, U.S. Army, Vol. 1, Geographical Report* (Washington, 1889), p. 35.

8. Powell, *Exploration,* p. 129.

9. Some of his experiences among the Hopi are told in "The Ancient Province of Tusayan," *Scribner's Monthly,* XI (December, 1875), 193–213.

10. For the peace conference with the Navajo, see Paul Bailey, *Jacob Hamblin, Buckskin Apostle,* pp. 317–25. The sad tale of Tuleta is told in the journal of W. C. Powell, *Utah Historical Quarterly,* XVI–XVII, 481–82. Clem Powell was a little uneasy about meeting Tuleta in 1872 for fear he would have held a grudge against the Major.

5

1. See discussion of Powell's juggling of facts in his report, in Part II, Chapter 6, *post.*

2. Beaman's equipment on the second river trip was said to have weighed a ton. The lamentations of Clem Powell, who as photographer's assistant had the job of packing the portable dark room, fill his journal. It was to some extent the weight and clumsiness and difficulty of the wet-plate equipment which led to experimentation with dry-plate methods. William Bell, photographer with Wheeler's Survey in 1872, experimented with dry-plate negatives, though Powell's men, viewing his negatives when the parties met near Kanab, were not impressed by the results. James Fennemore, in 1935, told me that he had invented the dry-plate camera while with Powell on the Colorado in 1872. His claim is not quite accurate, as an examination of the histories of photography will show; it is evidence only of the eagerness that stronger and heartier men than Fennemore had to rid themselves of the incubus of wet-plate equipment in the field. So far as I know, the first dry-plate equipment used in the West was that taken by T. H. O'Sullivan on the King Survey in 1868.

3. Dellenbaugh's book is lively and is based upon more than his own journal, but it is inaccurate in some details and suffers from a not unlaudable desire to protect Powell against the charges that had by that time been leveled against him. Since 1908 other diaries and other records have come to light, and we can document every day of the second voyage with considerable precision. The journal of Almon Thompson, edited by Herbert Gregory, was published by the *Utah Historical Quarterly,* VII, Nos. 1, 2, and 3 (1939). It contains a number of unfortunate editorial errors of fact, but the text itself, since Thompson was for long periods in command of the expedition, is of first importance. The journal of F. M. Bishop, edited by Charles Kelly, appeared in the *Utah Historical Quarterly,* XV (1947), along with a collection of his letters. (Many of Bishop's papers, including the original journal, are now in the archives of the Utah State Historical Society.) Volumes XVI and XVII of the *Quarterly* are devoted to the journals of Stephen V. Jones, John F. Steward, and W. C. Powell, with notes by Dale Morgan, Dr. Gregory, Charles Kelly, and William Culp Darrah. These three volumes of the *Quarterly,* plus the earlier one containing Thompson's journal, brought together materials previously widely scattered and to some extent unknown. Since I have not seen fit to describe the second river trip in detail, I have rarely indicated specific sources. All the above journals, as well as Dellenbaugh's two books and his early account of the voyage published in eight installments in the Ellenville, New York *Journal* in 1886, plus Beaman's serialized story entitled "The Cañon of the Colorado and the Moqui Pueblos," *Appleton's Journal,* XI (April–May, 1874), have provided material for this chapter.

4. Thompson's diary scolds him for this.

5. For C. R. Savage, a Mormon convert who became one of the West's great photographers, see Robert Taft, *Photography and the American Scene* (New York, 1938), pp. 272–73, 491.

6. Still known as Potato Valley. In it, now, is the little town of Escalante, on the spectacular road that links the Bryce Canyon country with the Capitol Reef National Monument by way of the Aquarius Plateau.

7. See C. E. Dutton, *Geology of the High Plateau of Utah,* pp. 1–5. With regard to the historical extension of the name Wasatch, Dale L. Morgan writes me, "There is a curious paradoxical irony to this [Dutton's] determination of

where the 'Wasatch proper' ends. For it was Frémont who first applied the name, on Joe Walker's authority, in 1844, and as originally bestowed, the name applied to the mountains lying south of the great bend of the Sevier. It was only in the fifties that the name migrated north. Now geographers deny the name entirely to its place of origin." (Letter of April 21, 1953.) In other words, the "Wasatch Mountains" were originally the chains of high plateaus; now they are the range which overlaps the plateaus at Mount Nebo, near Nephi, Utah.

8. Diary of Almon Harris Thompson, June 6, 1872.

9. Powell and Thompson had distinguished precedent for missing the mouth of a tributary. Lewis and Clark overlooked the mouth of the Willamette, which they called the Multomah, both going and coming on the Columbia, and Clark had to go back down river a second time before he satisfied himself that there was really a river where the Indians said there was. I have not myself seen the mouth of the Escalante, and cannot comment on the reasons why it was twice overlooked. Dellenbaugh, passing it in the *Cañonita* after Thompson's party finally reached the Colorado at the mouth of the Dirty Devil, said "it was narrow and shallow and would not be taken at its mouth for so important a tributary." (*A Canyon Voyage,* p. 210).

10. Diary of Almon Harris Thompson, June 9 and June 10, 1872.

6

1. Dutton testified that the exchange of ideas among the three of them had been so complex, and his debt to Gilbert and Powell so immense, "that if a full accounting were demanded it would bring me to bankruptcy." ("Mount Taylor and the Zuñi Plateau," United States Geological Survey *Annual Report VI,* 1885.)

2. Julius Stone, in *Canyon Country,* and Stanton and Chalfant, in *Colorado River Controversies,* have attacked these discrepancies in detail, with the general aim of discrediting Powell. These attacks are intertwined with the Sumner-Hawkins attacks; the fact that the names of the Howlands and Dunn were left off the Powell Monument at Grand Canyon after Powell's death has been made, by some alchemy, Powell's fault, and added to the evidence of his failure to give credit to the men of the second expedition, until the whole body of charges begins to give a picture of Powell as a publicity-mad egoist willing to suppress either individuals or the truth to gain his ends. As this present chapter attempts to show, there is a legitimate criticism to be made of Powell's treatment of his report; it is not true that there was any such sinister conspiracy against his men as his critics maintain, or that he was so culpably careless with the truth. The one reference to the second expedition in the *Exploration* is a statement of intention: "We have determined to continue the exploration of the cañons of the Colorado. Our last trip was so hurried, owing to the loss of rations, and the scientific instruments were so badly injured, that we are not satisfied with the results obtained, and so we shall once more attempt to pass through the cañons in boats, devoting two or three years to the trip."

3. "Report on the Survey of the Colorado River of the West, April 30, 1874." House Miscellaneous Document No. 265, 43rd Cong., 1st Sess.

4. By 1873 Wheeler's parties had already run foul of Hayden's in Colorado, and had nudged into territory that Powell might well have considered his own by right of prior exploration. Wheeler took boats up the Colorado as far as

the mouth of Diamond Creek in 1871, and announced in his report that "the exploration of the Colorado River may now be considered complete" — though Powell's boats had gone down that stretch two years earlier, and Ives had gone up it twelve years before Powell. Wheeler's field parties of 1872 were working in the Kanab area when Powell's were. And since, with the King Survey closing up its work, Wheeler had the full weight of the War Department behind him, Powell might, like Hayden, have been uneasy about the possibility of being shouldered out. The feud, in other words, began almost with the inauguration of the Powell and Wheeler Surveys; it erupted in a congressional investigation in 1874, and came to a head in the consolidation proposals of 1877 which two years later resulted in the formation of the United States Geological Survey. See Part III, Chapters 1–5, for discussion of this consolidation.

5. An indication of popular interest in the canyons is the fact that John W. DeForest's novel *Overland* contains an episode in which the protagonists, like James White, take to the river to escape Indians while on a westward journey from Santa Fe. The book was published in 1871, and presumably written the previous year. It could thus have been inspired either by newspaper accounts of White's tale, or similar accounts of Powell's exploration. Since Powell's first report, that in Bell's *New Tracks,* did not appear until 1870, and then only in England, it does not seem that DeForest could have had any very detailed information on Powell's trip. Clem Powell in his journal, June 26, 1871, reports reading in the March *Galaxy* "a story called 'Overland' taken from the Maj's lecture of his going down the Grand Cañon." Whether this represents supposition or information it is hard to say. DeForest's reputation as a pioneer realist, gained from his *Miss Ravenal's Conversion from Secession to Loyalty,* could not have been increased by *Overland,* which is a romantic and sensational yarn.

6. In 1895 it was reprinted (though only after a considerable period of shopping around by Powell) as *The Canyons of the Colorado* (Meadville, Pa.). In 1915 its first half was reprinted, with an introduction by Horace Kephart, in Nelson Doubleday's Outing Adventure Library. Besides the *Scribner's* version, and the short account in Bell's *New Tracks,* parts of what later became the second half of the official report were published as "The Physical Features of the Colorado Valley" in *Popular Science Monthly,* VIII (1875), 385–99, 531–42, and 670–80.

7. On the success of this venture, which was purely personal and separate from the official duties of his Survey, see Darrah, *Powell of the Colorado,* p. 182. After Beaman's abrupt departure from the expedition, Powell bought up his rights to the views he had already taken; later he negotiated an agreement with Hillers similar to that which he had had with Beaman, which split the proceeds 40–30–30 among Powell, Thompson, and the photographer.

8. See Thompson's and W. C. Powell's journals, February 1 through 8, 1872.

9. Powell Survey, Letters Received, II, No. 36.

10. *Ibid.,* No. 60.

11. *Ibid.,* No. 88.

12. *Ibid.,* No. 89. Alden's reason was that there was not enough completed to make a book.

13. *Ibid.,* Nos. 190–192.

14. "Some Remarks on the Geological Structure of a District of Country Lying to the North of the Grand Cañon of the Colorado," *American Journal of Science and the Arts,* 3rd ser., V, 1873, 456–65.

15. "John Wesley Powell, Proceedings of a Meeting Commemorative of His Distinguished Services," February 16, 1903, *Proceedings of the Washington Academy of Sciences,* V (1903), 99–187.

7

1. See, for example, Holmes' comments in his report on the San Juan Division, *10th Annual Report of the Geological and Geographical Survey of the Territories, 1876.* Also G. P. Merrill, *The First One Hundred Years of American Geology* (New Haven, 1924), p. 546.

2. G. K. Gilbert, *Lake Bonneville,* United States Geological Survey Monographs, I, Washington, 1890.

3. Gilbert's career is most thoroughly treated in William M. Davis, *Biographical Memoir of Grove Karl Gilbert, 1843–1918,* Memoirs of the National Academy of Sciences, XXI (1927).

4. See Journal of W. C. Powell, November 20, 1872.

5. Many of Powell's associates testified to the extraordinary open-handedness with which he gave away his ideas. See Dutton, "The Geological History of the Colorado River and Plateaus," *Nature,* XIX (1879), 247, 272; also G. K. Gilbert, "Powell," *Science,* October 10, 1902: "He was extremely fertile in ideas, so fertile that it was quite impossible that he should personally develop them all, and realizing this he gave freely to his collaborators. The work which he inspired and to which he contributed the most important creative elements, I believe to be at least as important as that for which his name now stands directly responsible. . . ."

6. G. K. Gilbert, et al., *John Wesley Powell: A Memorial to an American Explorer and Scholar.* Reprinted, with slight changes, from *The Open Court,* Vols. XVI and XVII (Chicago, 1903).

8

1. There is no biography of Dutton. A discussion of whatever literary interest he may possess is in Wallace Stegner, "Clarence Edward Dutton," unpublished University of Iowa thesis, 1935, and in Stegner, *Clarence Edward Dutton, an Appraisal* (Salt Lake City, 1936). See also Yale University, *Biographical Record — Class of Sixty* (Boston, 1908), pp. 95–100.

2. Though Dutton worked with the Powell Survey, the Public Lands Commission, the United States Geological Survey, and the Irrigation Survey for more than fifteen years, he never relinquished his commission, having each year to be "loaned" by an elaborate routine of requests from Interior to War Department, special orders, and special acts of Congress. He returned to army duty in the autumn of 1890.

3. On April 17, 1906, he read before the National Academy of Sciences a paper entitled "Volcanoes and Radioactivity." It was published at Englewood, New Jersey, as a pamphlet, and appeared also in the *Journal of Geology,* XIV, 259–68, and in *Popular Science Monthly,* LXVIII, 543–50.

4. Gunnison in 1853, and Frémont a few months later in the same year, and with many variations from Gunnison's route, made their way from Gunnison's Crossing up through Castle Valley and over the Wasatch Plateau into the valley of the Sevier, but they did so with great labor, and no highway engineers have yet seen fit to follow them, though it is possible to trace their route by back roads.

5. C. E. Dutton, *Report on the Geology of the High Plateaus of Utah,* pp. 208–9.

6. C. E. Dutton, *The Tertiary History of the Grand Canyon District,* United States Geological Survey Monographs, II (Washington, 1882), 26.

7. *Ibid.,* pp. 153–54.

8. *Ibid.*

9. See Thomas Hornsby Ferril, "Rocky Mountain Metaphysics," *Folksay* (Norman, Okla., 1930).

10. Henry Van Dyke, "Daybreak in the Grand Canyon of Arizona," *Scribner's,* LIV (September, 1913), 275–78.

11. John Gould Fletcher, "The Grand Canyon of the Colorado," in *Breakers and Granite* (New York, 1921), pp. 95–99.

12. Harriet Monroe, "The Grand Cañon of the Colorado," *Atlantic,* LXXXIV (December, 1899), 815.

13. Joaquin Miller, "Grand Canyon of the Colorado," *Overland,* n.s., XXXVII (March, 1901) 786–90.

14. The original letter, which is apparently not preserved, drew an amused reply in a letter from King to Dutton, October 12, 1880. In King Papers, Huntington Library, King MSS — Letter Book, 1879–82, pp. 154–56.

15. Dutton was not the only one. Indeed, I do not recall a single report of western exploration, from Lewis and Clark to Powell and Dutton, which does not fall back upon architectural terminology the moment it encounters horizontal strata and bare rock.

16. Now called the Navajo Sandstone.

17. The term is still in use, though it is more precisely applied.

18. Dutton, *Tertiary History,* pp. 58–59.

19. *Ibid.,* pp. 141–42.

20. Thomas Moran and William Henry Holmes, discussed in Part VI, Chapter 9.

9

1. The problem is discussed, with relation to both the land and the types of Western hero and heroine, in Smith, *Virgin Land,* pp. 81–120.

2. The words are those of Moran's friend W. H. Jackson, in "With Moran in the Yellowstone," *Appalachia, XXI* (December, 1936), 149.

3. The best accounts of this summer are those of William Henry Jackson, in *Time Exposure* (New York, 1940), and in the article "With Moran in the Yellowstone," cited above.

4. Letter from Hayden to Moran in the possession of Miss Ruth Moran; quoted by Fritiof Fryxell, "Thomas Moran's Journey to the Tetons in 1879," *Augustana Historical Society Publications,* No. 2, 1932.

5. The originator of the project seems to have been Harry Fenn, a well-known illustrator who himself made the drawings for a number of chapters. The book is a valuable pictorial and textual record of what America knew and thought about itself in the seventies. It represents part of that same centennial curiosity that resulted in books like L. P. Brockett's *Our Western Empire: or The New West beyond the Mississippi* (Philadelphia and Columbus, 1882). The widespread interest in the Philadelphia Exposition of 1876, when the nation got another sort of graphic look at itself, is a further indication of public curiosity about the state and nature of the United States during this decade.

6. This mountain, and the first pictures of it — the painting by Moran and the photographs by W. H. Jackson — excited a peculiar and almost superstitious

wonder. Like the wonders of the Yellowstone, it existed for years in a state of fable and rumor before it was actually pictured.

7. For the work of these and other artists in the West following the Civil War see Robert Taft, *Artists and Illustrators of the Old West.*

8. Diary of Almon Harris Thompson, July 4, 1873.

9. *The National Cyclopedia of American Biography* (1932 ed.), XXII, 24–25.

10. In G. W. Sheldon, *American Painters* (New York, 1879), p. 125. Quoted in Taft, *Artists and Illustrators of the Old West,* p. 250.

11. Stone, *Canyon Country,* especially pp. 55, 82.

12. Thomas Moran, *The Yellowstone National Park, and the Mountain Regions of Idaho, Nevada, Colorado, and Utah.* Described by Professor F. V. Hayden of the U.S. Exploring Expeditions to the Yellowstone. There are 15 chromolithographic reproductions of water-color sketches by Thomas Moran, artist to the expedition of 1871 (Boston, 1876). The last quotation I have seen of this in a bookseller's catalogue lists it at $275.

13. Henry Adams, *Democracy, an American Novel,* pp. 113–14.

14. "William Henry Holmes, 1846–1933," *Cosmos Club Bulletin,* V, No. 5 (March, 1952).

15. Many of these are bound together in Vol. XI, *Pacific Railroad Reports.*

16. Some but not all of the illustrations for *Bulletin* articles were reproduced in the *Annual Reports.*

17. *9th Annual Report of the Geological and Geographical Survey of the Territories, 1875,* p. 22.

18. William Henry Holmes, "Journal of the Grand Canyon trip in 1880." Bound with *Random Records,* Vol. V, a collection of Holmes' papers preserved in the Bureau of American Ethnology, Smithsonian Institution, Washington.

19. By inference from a letter from King to Dutton, October 12, 1880. In King MSS, Letter Book, 1879–82, pp. 154–56.

20. Dutton, *Tertiary History,* p. 144.

21. These are reproduced in Wheeler, *Geographical Report, 1889.*

22. Joseph Pennell, *The Adventures of an Illustrator* (Boston, 1925), pp. 82–83.

10

1. There is as yet no adequate study of Utah place names; the only work I know — and it is of limited usefulness and often of dubious accuracy — is the Utah Writers Project, *Origins of Utah Place Names,* Salt Lake City, 1940. For Arizona I have used Will C. Barnes, *Arizona Place Names,* University of Arizona Bulletin No. 2 (Tucson, 1935). On the whole question of names I have leaned very heavily upon George R. Stewart, *Names on the Land* (New York, 1945). The reports of early western explorations, if carefully searched, would give up very much more information about the naming of the Plateau Province than they have yet been forced to yield.

2. *Origins of Utah Place Names* lists it as of unknown origin. It is, of course, an echo of the Spanish pronunciation of La Virgin. George Stewart has pointed out in conversation that he knows of no other Spanish use of the word Virgin in place-naming, so that La Verkin may in fact be a Spanish pronunciation imposed upon an Anglo-American placename. It is also possible, but not at all probable, just to complicate the matter further, that the Virgin River was not named for the Virgin at all, but for Thomas Virgin, one of Jedediah Smith's men.

3. The Green is another river whose name is lost in controversy. The Crows called it the Seedskeedee-agie, the Prairie Hen River. Very early the Spaniards were calling it the Rio Verde, and the mountain men simply translated the Spanish name. H. H. Bancroft suggested, erroneously, that it was named after a trapper in Ashley's party. It is almost impossible that anyone seeing the upper river in low water would call it anything *but* the Green, for its color then is very marked, but the Spaniards probably named it from the green of its banks in a waste of bare rock. See Dee Linford, "Wyoming Stream Names," Wyoming Fish and Game Department Bulletin No. 3 (Cheyenne, 1944).

4. Gilbert, *Geology of the Henry Mountains,* p. viii.

5. See Wallace Stegner, "C. E. Dutton — Explorer, Geologist, Nature Writer," *Scientific Monthly,* XLV (July, 1937), 82–83, which briefly discusses and lists some of Dutton's names.

6. Dellenbaugh, who himself participated in the mapping and naming of the Grand Canyon region, wrote me in 1935, just before his death, that he had argued with Dutton without effect on the propriety of Indian names and the impropriety of Dutton's favored Oriental names. The letter is included in the Appendix to Stegner, "Clarence Edward Dutton," University of Iowa unpublished Ph.D. dissertation, 1935.

7. So at least says Charles Kelly, who is intimately familiar with the whole region and has made its history his lifelong study. Nevertheless, it is a courageous man who will assert that he knows the incontrovertible origin of any placename, much less an Indian one. And Indian informants are sometimes as confused about name origins in their own tongue as Americans are about names like La Verkin.

11

1. Letter of November 20, 1869, quoted in another letter from Humphreys to Belknap dated March 13, 1872, bound with Adams' Journal in the Huntington Library.

2. Darrah, *Powell of the Colorado,* p. 183.

3. Letter, Powell to R. M. McCormick, April 20, 1872. Powell Survey, Letters Sent, I, Nos. 59–66.

4. Letter, Samuel Adams to Rep. Austin Blair, January 20, 1873, bound with Adams' Journal in the Huntington Library.

5. *Beaver Evening Tribune,* May 15, 1915.

III. BLUEPRINT FOR A DRYLAND DEMOCRACY

1

1. By the beginning of the year 1877 Hayden had published, besides ten increasingly elaborate Annual Reports, quarto monographs by Joseph Leidy, E. D. Cope, Cyrus Thomas, Leo Lesquereux, F. B. Meek, and A. S. Packard, and two volumes of Bulletins jammed with short or preliminary studies by many men, plus eight volumes of "Miscellaneous Publications" including everything from lists of photographs by W. H. Jackson to a handbook on the birds of the Missouri region by Eliott Coues plus a hamperful of "Unclassified Publications" — pamphlets and reprints and preliminary reports — plus a good many maps. Clarence King's Annual Reports, incorporated in the Reports of

the Chief of Engineers to the Secretary of War, seldom exceeded two pages, but three of his projected seven quarto final reports were finished: James D. Hague's *Mining Industry,* Sereno Watson's *Botany,* and Ferdinand Zirkel's *Microscopical Petrography.* Also finished by 1877 were both his large folio Atlas incorporating all the topographical and geological work of the survey, and the Atlas to accompany Hague's *Mining Industry.* Wheeler, besides progress reports and Annual Reports (the latter growing like Hayden's until by 1876 it totaled 355 pages) had published two of his contemplated seven final reports, that by Gilbert, Marvine, et al., on *Geology,* and that by Yarrow, Coues, et al., on *Zoology.* In addition he had brought out a dozen or more miscellaneous publications, lists of birds, vertebrate fossils, meteorological readings, and the like, and an unspecified number of undated atlas sheets. See L. F. Schmeckebier, *Catalogue and Index of the Publications of the Hayden, King, Powell, and Wheeler Surveys* (Washington, 1904).

2. Josiah Whitney, with whose Geological Survey of California Clarence King had his first field experience, had learned early and to his sorrow how practical-minded a legislative body can be, and had had to fight for appropriations against every sort of anti-intellectual criticism. King, enlightened by Whitney's experience, took pains to see that his first publication was his most practical: Hague's Mining Industry. The "impractical" scientific activities of the United States Geological Survey, especially the paleontological work carried on by Professor Marsh of Yale, came under similar fire in 1892 when Hilary Herbert of Alabama attacked the Survey in the Senate by ridiculing Marsh's monograph on the Odontornithes, the "Birds-with-Teeth." A man conducting a bureau of government science did well not to look *too* scientific.

3. Congress on April 15, 1874, requested information from President Grant on the possibility of consolidating the surveys operating west of the Mississippi. Hayden, Powell, the Secretary of War, and the Chief of the Army Engineers, General Humphreys, were first called on for opinions by letter, and later called for questioning. Powell, who had introduced into the controversy the further question of civilian or military control of a consolidated survey, supported a civilian control, but remained aloof from the squabbling that broke out between Hayden and Wheeler. The result of the 1874 investigation was to leave things pretty much as they were before, except that Powell was moved from the Smithsonian back to the Interior Department and the official name of his survey changed to "Geological Survey of the Territories, Second Division." A secondary result was to bring into the open the antipathy between Wheeler and Hayden, an antipathy so outspoken that the committee rebuked them both; and probably to arouse Hayden's suspicion of Powell as well, since Powell had obviously come off the best of the three. See, for the testimony in the case, House Report No. 612, 43rd Cong., 1st Sess. The episode is well covered in Darrah, *Powell of the Colorado,* pp. 207–11.

4. Before the 1874 investigating committee, Dr. H. C. Yarrow, a zoologist of the Wheeler Survey, testified that Hayden had told him, "You can tell Wheeler that if he stirs a finger or attempts to interfere with me or my survey in any way, I will utterly crush him — as I have enough Congressional influence to do so, and will bring it all to bear." House Report No. 612, p. 62.

5. Henry Nash Smith, "Clarence King, John Wesley Powell, and the Establishment of the United States Geological Survey," *Mississippi Valley Historical Review,* XXXIV (June, 1947), 37–58.

6. Powell's departure from Normal was somewhat chilly. His resignation, proffered on June 26, 1872, was accepted without comment, and there was an

insistent attempt on the part of the university, through Jesse Fell, to obtain a clarification of the ownership of natural history collections which both Powell and the university claimed. Letter from Jesse Fell dated December 3, 1872, Powell Survey, Letters Received, II, No. 87.

7. Powell Survey, Letters Sent, I, Nos. 137, 139, 154–5.

8. Copies of the letters to both Garfield and Hewitt are preserved in Powell Survey, Letters Sent, I, Nos. 156–62. Newberry's dislike of Hayden evidently grew from his feeling that his student and protégé, Henry Newton, had been wronged by Hayden's interference. In his biographical memoir prefixed to Newton's *Report on the Geology of the Black Hills, 1880,* Newberry is bitter and unmistakable, though he names no names: "Mr. Newton took great pains with his report, as he had done in the accumulation of facts, and in its preparation expended about eighteen hundred dollars from his own pocket, when it was quite uncertain whether this sum would be repaid him by the government. When presented to Congress its publication would have been immediately authorized except for a selfish and heartless opposition it encountered springing from the fear that it would betray the inaccuracy of previously published descriptions of the geology of this region. This opposition cost Mr. Newton his life, for when Congress deferred action on his report till another session he determined to employ a part of the interval in revisiting the Black Hills. . . . While engaged in this work he was attacked by typhoid fever, and died at Deadwood August 15, 1877." Since Hayden's "General View of the Geology of the Missouri Valley," in the *4th Annual Report of the Geological and Geographical Survey of the Territories, 1870,* was the only real geological publication on the Black Hills region, there can be no doubt at whom Newberry's bitterness is aimed.

9. After 1871, Hayden's Annual Reports were illustrated with increasing lavishness, by woodcuts, line drawings, panoramas, maps, and lithographs, many of them made from Jackson's photographs, and some of them in color. King's finished reports were even more beautifully printed and illustrated. To compete, Powell's had to be of comparable quality. Actually, we can thank the jealousy among the various early surveys for some of the most beautiful books about the West that have ever been produced. See Part II, Chapter 9, *ante.*

10. Powell Survey, Letters Received, VI, No. 74.

11. *Ibid.,* Nos. 79–92.

12. Especially A. S. Packard and F. W. Pearson, both of Hayden's survey. Much of their correspondence is in F. V. Hayden, Personal Letters Received, National Archives.

13. Powell Survey, Letters Received, V, Nos. 308–326.

14. F. V. Hayden, Personal Letters Sent.

15. The first part of this was published as *An Introduction to the Study of Indian Languages* in 1877, and was subsequently used by all the amateur and part-time workers who collaborated in Powell's studies of the Indian languages.

16. See Powell Survey, Letters Sent, I, Nos. 1036–7 and 1082–3.

2

1. Powell Survey, Letters Sent, II, Nos. 172 and 284.
2. *Ibid.,* No. 351.
3. *Ibid.,* Nos. 111–114.

4. These tactics, actually, he could have learned from Hayden, who in 1874 had appeared before the Congressional committee armed with a petition, signed by the most formidable names in American science, supporting the notion of civilian control of the consolidated surveys. House Report No. 612, 43rd Cong., 1st Sess.

5. Fred A. Shannon, *The Farmer's Last Frontier*, p. 60.

6. See Henry Nash Smith's penetrating discussion of these folk beliefs of the West in *Virgin Land*, especially Section III, "The Garden of the World."

3

1. Thus Thomas Nuttall, pursuing his natural history studies on the frontier reaches of the Arkansas in 1819, found a surveyor running his lines on the land along the Cadron, and heard of another moving that way from the Great Prairie. At the time there were only squatters in the bottoms, and title was still being disputed among Cherokees, Osages, and the United States. Mr. Pettis, the surveyor, was laying out only the easily settled lands, ignoring the difficult and hilly sections not likely to be desired by frontier farmers. For his labors he was getting three dollars a mile. His activities, in that year and later, were being duplicated all along the western border. Thomas Nuttall, *Journal of Travels into the Arkansas Territory during the Year 1819* (Philadelphia, 1821). (Thwaites, Vol. XIII), p. 165.

2. The ordinance of May 20, 1785, before the act creating the surveyor-general in 1789, specified that "the geographers and surveyors shall pay the utmost attention to the variation of the magnetic needle, and shall run and note all lines by the true meridian, certifying with every plat what was the variation at the time of running of the lines thereon noted." But practice was never quite in step with intention, partly because of inaccurate instruments and methods, and partly because the system of contract surveying invited carelessness and venality. See Lowell O. Stewart, *Public Land Surveys, History, Instruction, Methods* (Ames, Iowa, 1935). Major Powell's testimony before several Congressional committees indicated that he had little faith in the accuracy of the General Land Office surveys, and found the Land Office maps useless for anything but land parceling.

3. *Report of the Commissioner of the General Land Office, 1876*, p. 130.

4. The classical statement of the changes compelled by the conditions of the arid West is that of Walter Webb, *The Great Plains*. See also Henry Nash Smith, *Virgin Land;* Joseph Kinsey Howard, *Montana, High, Wide, and Handsome* (New Haven, Conn., 1943); James C. Malin, *The Grasslands of North America;* and what underlies the thinking in all of these, Powell's own *Report on the Lands of the Arid Region.*

5. Despite the efforts of speculators, local patriots, and visionaries such as Gilpin to deny the Great American Desert, and despite the undoubted exaggeration in that word "desert," no one need be in doubt about the sharp change in climate that occurs somewhere between the 96th and 100th meridians. It can be felt on the lips and skin, observed in the characteristic plant and animal life, seen in the clarity and/or dustiness of the atmosphere, determined by measurements of rainfall and evaporation, tested by attempts at unaided agriculture. Practically every western traveler in the early years remarked the facts of aridity, though not all used the word "desert," especially after the Kansas boom of the sixties had made the natives sensitive to supposed

slurs. Part of the difficulty of adjustment, part of the continued misunderstanding of the facts, arose from the fact that the dividing line between subhumid and arid runs not along the state lines, but along a line about a third of the way west in Kansas, Nebraska, and the Dakotas. The well-watered eastern third of Kansas might well resent being called a desert; the arid western portion might well believe for a time that it could use the farming methods and institutions that worked perfectly well only a few miles east.

6. Allan Nevins, *The Emergence of Modern America,* in *History of American Life,* Vol. VIII (New York, 1927).

7. Bayard Taylor, despite his attempt to be judicial in *Colorado, A Summer Trip,* was close to being converted to the popular optimism: "I am fast inclining toward the opinion, that there is *no* American Desert on this side of the Rocky Mountains. . . . I remember that as late as 1859, the lowest computation of the extent of the Desert was two hundred miles; yet in the Smoky Hill route I saw less than fifty miles to which the term could be properly applied . . . time and settlement may subdue even this narrow belt . . . there may some day be groves and farms on the treeless plains . . . wheat may usurp the place of buffalo-grass, and potatoes drive out the cactus." Few people had a keener ear than Taylor for what people wanted to hear. It was only three years later that Science was corroborating the travelers, in Cyrus Thomas' report on "The Agriculture of Colorado" in the Hayden Survey's *3rd Annual Report.* Thomas did guess rather lamely that the timber supply of Colorado would prove "not inexhaustible," and his cautious tone as well as the circumspection of Hayden's letter of transmittal indicated that the Hayden Survey had already begun to feel pressure from the Gilpin tribe whenever it ventured any "deficiency" judgment of Western resources.

8. Dan Elbert Clark, *The West in American History,* pp. 592–93. The most authoritative account of the beginning of the cattle drives is in Joseph G. McCoy, *Historic Sketches of the Cattle Trade* (1874; reprinted in facsimile by The Rare Book Shop, Washington, D. C., 1932). Pictures, including photographs, record the very earliest years. There is an Alexander Gardner photograph of cattle being loaded at the McCoy pens in Abilene, and drawings of cattle drives by Tavernier, Frenzeny, and Henry Worrall. See Robert Taft, *Artists and Illustrators of the Old West,* pp. 123–25, and his *Photography and the American Scene,* p. 278.

9. Jack Sumner, Journal, June 7, 1869.

10. Oberholtzer, *History of the United States since the Civil War,* III, 380.

11. The tunnel was begun on October 19, 1869, and reached the Lode on September 1, 1878. *Ibid.,* II, 532 ff.

12. Fred A. Shannon, *The Farmer's Last Frontier,* p. 55.

13. The sagas of pioneers attempting to break and hold a homestead in the arid belt have become part of our tradition and one of the great "matters" of our literature. Hamlin Garland's *Main Traveled Roads* and *A Son of the Middle Border,* O. E. Rölvaag's *Giants in the Earth,* and Mari Sandoz's *Old Jules* are among the finest representatives of the literary type. See also Shannon, *The Farmer's Last Frontier,* and Everett Newton Dick, *The Sod House Frontier, 1854–1893* (New York, 1937).

14. The effects of the various land laws upon the individual farmer are discussed in Shannon, *The Farmer's Last Frontier,* pp. 51–75; in Paul Wallace Gates, "The Homestead Law in an Incongruous Land System," *American Historical Review,* XLI, No. 4 (July, 1936); and in *Report of the Public Lands Commission,* Senate Document No. 189, 58th Cong., 3rd Sess., Washington,

1904. This last brings up to date as of 1904 the findings of the Public Lands Commission of 1879–80, on which Powell served.

15. Shannon, *The Farmer's Last Frontier*, p. 63, quoting S. A. D. Puter and Horace Stevens, *Looters of the Public Domain* (Portland, Ore., 1908), pp. 59–66.

16. On Henry Miller, see E. F. Treadwell, *Cattle King* (New York, 1931). Miller was no isolated phenomenon. In 1883 there were twenty cattle companies, with capitalization from $10,000 to $3,000,000, incorporated in Wyoming alone. The Union Cattle Company and the Swan Land and Cattle Company were each initially capitalized at $3,000,000. Swan controlled a range fifty by one hundred miles, on which it ran more than 100,000 cattle. John Iliff, a pioneer cattle king of Colorado, controlled thirty-five miles along the Platte, thereby dominating a huge range. See Clark, *The West in American History,* pp. 596–98, and Howard R. Driggs, *Westward America* (New York, 1942), pp. 283–86.

17. After 1875 the classification of public lands was a duty charged to both the Powell and Hayden Surveys by the Secretary of the Interior. The instructions to Hayden that year read in part, "It will be borne in mind that the ultimate design to be accomplished by these surveys is the preparation of suitable maps of the country surveyed for the use of the government and of the nation, which will afford full information concerning the agricultural and mineral resources, and other important characteristics of the unexplored regions of our Territorial domain. . . . In addition thereto, you will obtain the necessary information for the preparation of charts, upon which shall be indicated the areas of grass, timber, and mineral lands, and such other portions of the country surveyed as may be susceptible of cultivation by means of irrigation. . . ." (Quoted in Hayden's Letters of Transmittal, United States Geological and Geographical Survey of the Territories, *10th Annual Report, 1876.*) Cyrus Thomas, Hayden, and Henry Gannett all reported on such land classification during the next three years. Powell was thus not the only advocate or student of land classification, though he may well have suggested the whole idea to Columbus Delano, the Secretary of the Interior. The problem was much closer to his interests than to Hayden's. Actually, Powell's *Arid Regions* was an innovation neither in its emphasis on irrigation nor in its advocacy of classification of public lands. What Powell did was to attack systematically, with an eye to the long-term public good and with the experience of a full decade, what others had approached halfheartedly or without adequate information, and he examined not only conditions, but the human consequences of conditions.

18. WPA, *Utah,* American Guide Series (New York, 1945), p. 98.

19. Though the *Report on the Lands of the Arid Region of the United States, with a more detailed account of the lands of Utah,* United States Geographical and Geological Survey of the Rocky Mountain Region, J. W. Powell in Charge, 2nd edition, Washington, 1879, contains chapters on rainfall, water supply, the water requirements of different classes of irrigable lands, and detailed studies of the lands of the Salt Lake, Sevier, and Colorado River drainage systems in Utah, the meat of the book is in its first two chapters. The first summarizes the physical characteristics of the arid region that had up to then been too much ignored, and the second outlines the land system and the institutional modulations needed for the region: a statement of observable facts, and a policy derived from them.

20. One should never forget, in estimating the truly revolutionary character of Powell's proposals, that not much more than a year before they were made,

in the Centennial year marked by the Philadelphia Exposition, the hundred-year-old democracy was at as low an ebb in public morals and public and private morale as it has ever been. As Allan Nevins says, ". . . the Grant era stands unique in the comprehensiveness of its rascality. The cities, half of which had their counterparts of Tweed; the legislatures, with their rings, lobbyists, and bribe-takers; the South, prey of unscrupulous Carpetbaggers and Scalawags; the West, sacked by railway and mining corporations; Congress, with its Crédit Mobilier, its salary grab, its tools of predatory business; the executive departments, honeycombed with thievery; private finance and trade, with greedy figures like Jay Cooke and Collis P. Huntington honored and typical — everywhere the scene was the same." (Allan Nevins, *Hamilton Fish, the Inner History of the Grant Administration,* pp. 638–9.) Supporting all this was a hectic economic boom which collapsed in 1873, and after the collapse every smelly rathole in the government began to give up its vermin. James Watson Webb's steal in Brazil, Van Buren's steal at the Vienna International Fair, Schenck's entanglement in the Emma Mine deals; the Crédit Mobilier; the Whiskey Ring; the Indian Bureau scandals that disgraced Columbus Delano — they came so fast that one was hardly out of the headlines before another appeared. Congressmen, Senators, cabinet ministers, ambassadors, presidential advisors, Vice-Presidents, Grant himself, the whole government was afflicted with a moral infection as contagious as ringworm. Directly on top of this, or in the midst of it, Powell made his proposals for the development of the West.

21. J. W. Powell, "From Savagery to Barbarism," *Transactions of the Anthropological Society of Washington,* III, 173–96.

4

1. House Executive Document No. 73, 45th Cong., 2nd Sess., Washington, 1878.

2. Henry Nash Smith has pointed out the great importance of Professor Henry's death in the events leading up to the consolidation of the surveys. See "Clarence King, John Wesley Powell, and the Establishment of the United States Geological Survey"; also *Virgin Land,* p. 197.

3. Schuchert and LeVene, *O. C. Marsh, Pioneer in Paleontology,* is a valuable biography and sheds light on many of the developments of government science during the eighteen-seventies and eighties.

4. Abram Hewitt, "Consolidating the Western Surveys." Speech in the House of Representatives on the General Appropriations Bill, February 11, 1879. In Allan Nevins, *The Selected Writings of Abram Hewitt* (New York, 1937), pp. 209–26.

5. Samuel Franklin Emmons, "Clarence King, Geologist," in Century Association, *Clarence King Memoirs.*

6. Smith, "Clarence King, John Wesley Powell, and the Establishment of the United States Geological Survey."

7. Powell Survey, Letters Sent, II, Nos. 775–6, 792–3.

8. Without making a careful check, I have noted, among the Letters Received of the Powell Survey within the one week of October 7–13, 1878, receipts for the *Arid Regions* report from the Salt Lake *Herald,* the *Rocky Mountain News,* the *Alta California,* and the San Francisco *Herald, Evening Post,* and *Chronicle.* There was evidently a concerted campaign to put review copies of the report

into the hands of influential Western editors — an indication that its importance was quite as much political as scientific.

9. Powell Survey, Letters Received, VIII, Nos. 268–9, 270–1.

10. One sample of how this campaign was conducted is contained in Dutton's letter to Professor A. G. Wetherly of the University of Cincinnati, a strong Powell supporter who had offered aid in promoting Powell into the headship of the combined surveys. Through a half dozen careful pages Dutton outlines Powell's policies. These exactly reproduce — in advance — the National Academy's recommendations. Powell Survey, Letters Received, VII, Nos. 139–45, 231. See also Powell's letter to E. W. Ayres of the Kansas City *Times* — an equally careful and detailed summary of the Academy program or of Powell's own *Arid Regions* proposals, as one wishes to read it. Letters Sent, III, Nos. 54–63. Also Powell to Wetherly, December 31, 1878, Letters Sent, II, Nos. 997–8.

11. Powell Survey, Letters Received, VIII, No. 86.

5

1. Powell Survey, Letters Received, VIII, No. 233.

2. Abram Hewitt, "Consolidating the Western Surveys."

3. F. V. Hayden, Personal Letters Received, contains numerous reports from Packard and Pearson indicating that they had their ears (very unsuccessfully) to the ground. Darrah reprints several, all showing that Hayden's scouts did not fear Powell, knew nothing of what he was up to, considered King the strongest opposition, but thought Hayden held a very strong position. Darrah, *Powell of the Colorado,* p. 247.

4. Powell Survey, Letters Sent, II, Nos. 982, 983, 984–5.

5. Smith, *Virgin Land,* esp. pp. 165–200.

6. The historical development of the garden-myth of the West, from F. V. Hayden's 1867 guess that timber would increase on the plains following settlement, to the full elaboration of the theory by Samuel Aughey and Charles Dana Wilber, both chiefs of the tribe of Gilpin, is traced in detail in Henry Nash Smith, "Rain Follows the Plow: the Notion of Increased Rainfall for the Great Plains, 1844–1880," *Huntington Library Quarterly,* X (1947), 169–93, and summarized in *Virgin Land,* pp. 179–83. It was Wilber, a speculator and townbuilder, who coined the slogan, "Rain follows the Plow," which, corroborated by Cyrus Thomas, did incalculable damage to western agricultural resources by encouraging grain farming where it should never have been attempted.

7. As I have pointed out earlier (in Part I, Chapter I, note 4), even a supposedly sober historian, Reuben Gold Thwaites, raised Gilpin to 200,000,000, as late as 1904. Malthus was not a popular scholar in the eighteen-seventies. Henry George attacked his views, Spencer Baird demonstrated that an acre of sea was ten times as productive of human food as an acre of land, the Midwest looked at its crops and bet its pile on the future.

8. Congressional Record, VIII, Part 3, 45th Cong., 3rd Sess.

9. *20 Stat.* L, p. 394, March 3, 1879.

10. Known as the Bureau of American Ethnology after 1894.

11. Pilling to E. E. Howell, March 17, 1879, Pilling to J. J. Stevenson, April 1, 1879, Powell Survey, Letters Sent, III, Nos. 379, 380.

12. Powell Survey, Letters Received, IX, No. 316.

13. *The Education of Henry Adams,* pp. 294–95, 322.

14. As late as 1885, when he published his volume *Facts Concerning the Origin, Organization, Administration, Functions, History, and Progress of the Principal Government Land and Marine Surveys of the World* (extracted from the report on the Third International Geographical Congress and Exhibition to which he was a commissioner and delegate), Wheeler was still rancorously asserting the right of the War Department to conduct western topographical surveys, a right interrupted by "the temporarily successful claim of certain geologists to the control of Government topographical map work" (p. 489).

15. This report actually took two forms. The first was the *Report of the Public Lands Commission, Created by the Act of March 3, 1879, Relating to Public Lands in the Western Portion of the United States and to the Operation of Existing Land Laws* (Washington, 1880). The second was Thomas Donaldson's *The Public Domain: Its History, with Statistics* (Washington, 1884), which utilized and elaborated the commission's findings.

16. Hilgard to Powell, December 12, 1878, Powell Survey, Letters Received, VII, No. 216.

17. On the founding of the Cosmos Club, see *The Twenty-Fifth Anniversary of the Founding of the Cosmos Club of Washington, D.C., with a documentary history of the club from its organization to November 16, 1903* (Washington, 1904).

IV. THE REVENUE OF NEW DISCOVERY

1

1. *The Education of Henry Adams,* p. 346.
2. My discussion of King is based primarily upon Harry Crosby, "So Deep a Trail," the *Clarence King Memoirs,* the letter files of the United States Geological Survey and of the King, Hayden, and Powell Surveys, *The Education of Henry Adams,* the letters of Henry and Mrs. Henry Adams, and the King Papers (Hague Collection) in the Henry E. Huntington Library.
3. *The Education of Henry Adams,* p. 311.
4. *Ibid.,* pp. 294–95.
5. United States Geological Survey, *1st Annual Report, 1880,* pp. 3–4.
6. United States Geological Survey, Letters Sent, 1879, Nos. 91, 109, 111; 1880, No. 10.
7. United States Geological Survey, *1st Annual Report,* pp. 5–6.
8. United States Geological Survey, Letters Sent, 1879, No. 91.
9. *Ibid.,* 1880, No. 30.
10. Ward Thoron, *Letters of Mrs. Henry Adams,* p. 278.
11. *The Education of Henry Adams,* pp. 312–13.
12. Harold Dean Cater, *Henry Adams and His Friends,* pp. 83–5, 86, letters to Morgan dated July 14, 1877, and June 3, 1878.

2

1. The "pentalogic" divisions of the Science of Man were first elaborated in five essays in *The American Anthropologist,* n.s., I, II, and III, (1899–1901). These were reprinted in the 19th and 20th *Annual Reports* of the Bureau of American Ethnology.

2. Developed in Lewis H. Morgan, *Ancient Society* (New York, 1877).

3. Thus the *Weekly People*, official organ of the Socialist Labor Party, devoted much of its issue of November 26, 1938, to a discussion of Morgan, and advertised *Ancient Society* as "a companion work to Marx's *Capital*."

4. In "From Savagery to Barbarism."

5. He stated and restated the "immeasurable difference" between animal and human evolution, insisting that human evolution is intellectual and no longer biotic. See "Human Evolution," *Transactions of the Anthropological Society of Washington*, II (1883), 176–208; "Darwin's Contributions to Philosophy," *Proceedings of the Biological Society of Washington*, I (1882), 60–70 (also in *Smithsonian Miscellaneous Collections*, XXV); "The Three Methods of Evolution," *Bulletin of the Philosophical Society of Washington*, VI (1884), 27–52; and "Relation of Primitive Peoples to Environment, Illustrated by American Examples," *Smithsonian Report, 1895*, pp. 625–37.

6. "On the Evolution of Language, as exhibited in the specialization of the grammatic processes, the differentiation of the parts of speech and the integration of the sentence; from a study of the Indian Languages," Bureau of Ethnology, *1st Annual Report, 1881*, pp. 1–16.

7. R. H. Gabriel, *The Course of American Democratic Thought* (New York, 1940).

8. The vital — or lethal — influence of trade upon some of the Indian cultures is traced in Bernard DeVoto, *The Course of Empire*, pp. 90–96.

9. Both Gallatin and Powell doubted the common assertion that the Indian race was being swiftly exterminated. See Powell, "Are Our Indians Becoming Extinct?" *Forum*, XV (May, 1893), 343–54.

10. Bureau of American Ethnology, *24th Annual Report, 1902–3*, p. 37.

11. It is described at length, with extensive illustration, in Thomas Donaldson, "The George Catlin Indian Gallery," *Annual Report of the Board of Regents of the Smithsonian Institution, showing the operations, expenditures, and condition of the Institution to July, 1885*, Part V (Washington, 1886). The whole subject of early Western painting, both of the country and of the Indians, is only beginning to find its students. Robert Taft's *Artists and Illustrators of the Old West* is invaluable; so is the Appendix, "The First Illustrators of the Far West," in Bernard DeVoto's *Across the Wide Missouri*. The Smithsonian Institution has published several short studies of painters of the Indian. These include David L. Bushnell's several contributions: "Drawings by A. LeBatz in Louisiana, 1732–1735," "Drawings by Jacques LeMoyne de Morgues of Saturioua, a Timucua Chief in Florida, 1564," "Sketches by Paul Kane in the Indian Country, 1845–1848," "Drawings by George Gibbs in the Far Northwest, 1849–1851," and "Seth Eastman: the Master Painter of the North American Indian," all in *Smithsonian Miscellaneous Collections:* LXXX, No. 5; LXXXI, No. 4; XCIX, No. 1; XCVII, No. 8; and LXXXVII, No. 3. See also John C. Ewers, "Gustavus Schon's Portraits of Flathead and Pend d'Oreille Indians, 1854," *Smithsonian Miscellaneous Collections*, CX, No. 7; John Francis McDermott, "Samuel Seymour, Pioneer Artist of the Plains and Rockies," *Smithsonian Report, 1950*, pp. 497–509; and Julian Steward, "Notes on Hillers' Photographs of the Paiute and Ute Indians Taken on the Powell Expedition of 1873," *Smithsonian Miscellaneous Collections*, XCVIII, No. 18.

12. Albert Gallatin, "A Synopsis of the Indian Tribes of North America," *Archaeologia Americana*, Transactions and Collections of the American Antiquarian Society, II (1836), 2.

13. Letter to G. F. Becker, April 4, 1882. King Papers, Letter Book, 1879–82.

14. Published as the single accompanying paper of the Bureau of Ethnology, *10th Annual Report, 1888–89.*

15. J. W. Powell, "Indian Linguistic Families of America North of Mexico," Bureau of Ethnology, *7th Annual Report, 1885–86.*

16. F. W. Hodge compiled a list of the bureau's publications and published it as a Bulletin in 1894–95. It contains all the major work of the bureau's first phase, including the distinguished series of *Annual Reports* with their accompanying papers, the *Bulletins,* and the added volumes of *Contributions to North American Ethnology,* begun under the Powell Survey.

17. There are 435 glass negatives of Hillers' Indian pictures preserved. See Steward, "Notes on Hillers' Photographs of Paiute and Ute Indians."

18. Matthew Stirling, the present head of the Bureau of American Ethnology, concurs in Holmes' eulogy of Powell's work in organizing ethnological research, but somewhat discounts his personal field work and his speculative contributions.

3

1. *The Education of Henry Adams,* p. 309.

2. Out of the report he prepared for the Bologna meeting, Wheeler published in 1885 his *Facts concerning the Origin, Organization, Administration, Functions, History, and Progress of the Principal Government Land and Marine Surveys of the World,* a useful volume, though marred in its American sections by self-glorification and by jealousy of rivals, especially Powell.

3. Later, WJ McGee read on the Major's behalf, before the Berlin meeting of the International Geological Congress, an amplification and justification of the Geological Survey's conventions. J. W. Powell, "Methods of Geological Cartography in Use by the United States Geological Survey," Congrés Géologique Internationale, C. R. 3rd Sess. (Berlin, 1888), pp. 221–40.

4. As we shall see, this trick later caused him to undergo some intensive questioning by a Congressional investigating committee. Senate Miscellaneous Document No. 82, 49th Cong., 1st Sess.

5. The history of the United States Geological Survey is told in Institute for Government Research, Service Monographs of the United States Government, *The Geological Survey* (New York, 1918). A fuller and more comprehensive history of the Survey is being prepared for the Geological Society of America by Professor Thomas Manning of Yale.

4

1. For this summary discussion of the colossal subject of the mapping of the continent I have drawn on Erwin Raisz, *General Cartography,* 2nd ed. (McGraw-Hill, 1948); Wheeler's *Facts concerning the Origin . . . of the Principal Government Land and Marine Surveys of the World;* Lieutenant Governeur Warren's able summary of American government explorations West of the Mississippi, in "Memoir to Accompany the Map of the Territory of the United States from the Mississippi to the Pacific Ocean," *Pacific Railroad Reports,* XI (1859); Herbert E. Bolton, *Pageant in the Wilderness;* Dale L. Morgan, *The Great Salt Lake* (New York, 1947); Bernard DeVoto's three-part history of the early West, *The Course of Empire, Across the Wide Missouri,* and *The Year of Decision;* J. O. Kilmartin, "Federal Surveys and Maps," in *The American Year*

Book, 1950; and a large body of the literature of western exploration from Lewis and Clark onward.

2. Miera's map was not published until 1950, in Herbert E. Bolton, *Pageant in the Wilderness,* though it was used by cartographers from Humboldt on, and was enormously influential in establishing some of the facts — and fantasies — of the interior West.

3. Published by White, Gallagher, and White in New York, 1828. A copy is in the Huntington Library. The Humboldt map may be found in Alexander von Humboldt, *A Political Essay on the Kingdom of New Spain,* translated from the original French by John Black (London, 1811).

4. United States Geological Survey, *4th Annual Report, 1882–83.* Since Powell made topography central in his bureau's activities, the report on mapping assumes great importance in the annual reports after 1882–83, though for the first two years of his administration the operations were largely clean-up of earlier work and preparation for the new comprehensive topographical survey.

5. Senate Miscellaneous Document No. 82, p. 689.

6. Letter, J. O. Kilmartin, Chief, United States Geological Survey Map Information Office, February 5, 1953. See also Department of the Interior, United States Geological Survey, "Status of Topographic Mapping," Map B, 2nd ed. (July, 1950).

7. Letter, J. O. Kilmartin, February 5, 1953.

8. The *Geologic Atlas of the United States* is of course in existence, but like the topographic maps, it is in a state of constant revision and perennially postponed completion.

5

1. *Paralysis agitans* first crippled and then killed Hayden. He was on crutches for several years before his death.

2. For Cope's career, appraised by a close friend, see Henry Fairfield Osborn, *Cope, Master Naturalist* (Princeton, 1931).

3. United States Geological Survey, Letters Sent, 1883, Nos. 84, 107, 124, 323, 455. Powell's letter to Cope dated May 31, 1883, is typical.

Dear Professor:

Your personal letter in relation to the progress of your work in the printer's hands, is just received.

I think from its tone that you are in error in some of your surmises. It is my belief that no one but the Public Printer, the Foreman of Printings, yourself and myself, has had anything to do with the arrangement or presentation of your work, and no outside influence has been exerted.

Again I can assure you that I only desire your work executed in the best manner, and in the shortest possible time.

Your book has been in the hands of the printer for several years, and his accounts have been running all that time. The new administration of the office is much more prompt and efficient than the old, and Congress has given the Bureau large appropriations to clear off all old work. Almost all such work is now off their hands; and they are exceedingly anxious to finish all. I think I fully understand and appreciate his wishes in the matter, and believe his reasoning to be good.

The Geological Survey is dependent upon the Public Printer for the prompt publication of its materials, and tries to co-operate with him in all his methods for speedy publication and for the rigid and economic expenditure of public funds.

The many delays in your work, exhibited in the failure to furnish MS to the printer, and the many changes you asked, has caused the officers of the Printing Bureau to feel that they could not depend upon you for any regular prosecution of the work of publication; and it was only by argument and earnest solicitation by myself that they were induced to take it up before the entire manuscript and drawings or illustrations were in their hands.

This they did, in violation of the general rule of the office, making your case an exception. If you fail to push the work from week to week until it is completed, it places me in an embarrassing position with them.

I beg you to consider this, and urge you to forward the copy in the shortest time possible. If you drop it now, it is impossible for me to say when it can be taken up again. In the meantime your unfinished work remains in their hands, a constant source of irritation.

In view of all this, I think it would be well if you would consider the volume at least as closed, and furnish a title and index, and let it go forth to the world.

I have just received a letter from Dr. Hayden suggesting this course (I enclose a copy for your information). His recommendations for the arrangement of your two volumes meet with my approval.

Very respectfully,

J. W. Powell.

4. Undated letter, Cope to W. H. Holmes, reproduced in New York *Herald,* January 12, 1890.

5. The purposes of the investigation and the testimony which it elicited are detailed in Senate Miscellaneous Document No. 82, cited previously. This is probably the best single source of information on the scope of the government's scientific bureaus in the eighteen-eighties, and the clearest reflection of the sharp disagreement between advocates of government science and those who would leave scientific investigation entirely to private enterprise.

6. J. W. Powell, testimony before the Joint Committee of Congress, *ibid.,* p. 179.

7. *Ibid.,* p. 180.

8. Reproduced in the New York *Herald,* January 12, 1890.

9. Senate Miscellaneous Document No. 82, p. 689. Because of the necessity of cleaning up the jobs left over from the King administration, it was not until the season of 1884–85 that Powell's mapping on the appropriate scales for topographical purposes began in earnest. See United States Geological Survey, *6th Annual Report, 1884–85.*

10. His letter was read into the record with other Herbert Agassiz correspondence by Representative Herbert, Senate Miscellaneous Document No. 82, pp. 1014–15.

11. After the partners in 1886 investigated King's conduct of the London office and found that he had neglected it shamefully, relied on a dishonest manager, failed to keep adequate records, mixed his personal and the corporate funds, and generally brought the company to the edge of ruin, there was a period when Agassiz apparently contemplated bringing King to law as a criminal. But that investigation of King's affairs would not occur for another

year, and there seem to have been no clear advance warnings to the partners of King's carelessness. Anger at King and all his works cannot therefore be adduced as a motive for Agassiz's letter. Presumably, without recognizing or admitting that the Coast and Geodetic Survey whose works he praised was also government science, and without admitting his own indebtedness to its organization and facilities, he felt a constitutional repugnance against the notion of science as a governmentally-sponsored matter. See Crosby, "So Deep a Trail."

12. Senate Miscellaneous Document No. 82, pp. 1070–84.

V. THE OPPORTUNITY

1

1. See Herbert O. Brayer, "The Influence of British Capital on the Western Range-Cattle Industry," *The Journal of Economic History,* Supplement IX (1949), 85–98.

2. Hamlin Garland, in *A Son of the Middle Border,* and O. E. Rölvaag, in *Giants of the Earth,* are as vivid reporters as any of the delights of a plains winter in a shack. Garland, of course, represented the "commuter," who homesteaded his land with the intention of selling it. Rölvaag's Per Hansa, and other immigrants like him, had no escape hatch; they had to stick it out or perish.

3. The effects of the drouth and of the collapse of the wild land-speculation boom in the eighteen-eighties are well summarized in Fred A. Shannon, *The Farmer's Last Frontier,* pp. 306–9. Shannon says, in part, "In the intermediate area [what Powell called the subhumid zone, approximately between the 96th and 101st meridians] when crop failure became evident in the early fall of 1887, the inhabitants became panicky and began dumping their speculative holdings on the market. There was a deluge of mortgage foreclosures, extending on down through the panic year of 1893. . . . Often, however, the farmer welcomed foreclosure, for the mortgage was worth more than the land. Half the population of western Kansas moved out between 1888 and 1892, and large portions of the plains from Kansas to North Dakota were virtually depopulated. As late as 1891, at least eighteen thousand prairie schooners entered Iowa from Nebraska. Many immigrants from Kansas braved it out with signs painted on their wagons such as: 'In God we trusted, in Kansas we busted.' Twenty towns in western Kansas were reported as totally depopulated."

4. In talking about homesteaders on the plains, I am drawing partly on the memories of a boyhood spent on just such a homestead from 1914 to 1919. Though it happened to be in Saskatchewan, it could as well have been in Dakota or Montana; though it happened to have been during the years of World War I, it could as easily have been in the eighteen-eighties. The conditions, the climate, the hopes, the people, the discomforts, the delusions — and the casualties — were identical. Saskatchewan in 1919 had learned practically nothing from the more than fifty years of attempts to break the plains in Kansas, Nebraska, and the Dakotas.

5. Garland, *A Son of the Middle Border,* p. 308.

6. For Powell's public opinions on the moral to be drawn from the Johnstown flood, and his attempt not only to allay popular fear of all dams, but to use the disaster as a moral imperative to over-all planning, see "The Lesson

of Conemaugh," *North American Review,* CXLIX (1889), 150–56.

7. Powell to the Secretary of the Interior, March 13, 1888, United States Geological Survey, Letters Sent, XLI, Nos. 362–88.

8. The needs, conditions, and policies outlined in Powell's letter of March 13 were essentially those on which he conducted his whole campaign for regional planning in the West during the next four years. They differ only in details, and in the greater amplification that years of experience had suggested, from those of the *Report on the Lands of the Arid Regions* ten years before.

9. The resolutions and acts bearing upon the initiation of the Irrigation Survey are listed in United States Geological Survey, *10th Annual Report, 1889,* pp. 1–80. The organic law, like much of that authorizing Geological Survey activity, was multiple and circuitous. The Joint Resolution of March 20, 1888, had the force of law, but the Irrigation Survey was not officially instituted until the Sundry Civil Expenses Bill, passed on October 2, 1888 (*24 Stat. L.,* 255) appropriated $100,000 for its operations. October 2, 1888, is therefore the true beginning date for the Irrigation Survey.

For the detailed activities of the Irrigation Survey, see United States Geological Survey, *10th, 11th, 12th,* and *13th Annual Reports,* the last three of which have Irrigation supplements; Everett W. Sterling, "The Powell Irrigation Survey, 1888–1893," *Mississippi Valley Historical Review,* XXVII, No. 3 (December, 1940), 421–34; Darrah, *Powell of the Colorado,* pp. 300–314; United States Geological Survey, Letters Sent and Letters Received, 1888–1892; and "Statement of Major J. W. Powell, Director of the Geological Survey," Senate Report No. 1466, 51st Cong., 1st Sess., July 2, 1890, pp. 46–109, 131–36. There is also useful material in Effie M. Mack, "William M. Stewart," unpublished University of California Ph.D. dissertation (Berkeley, 1930); G. R. Brown, ed., *The Reminiscences of Senator William M. Stewart of Nevada;* Harold H. Dunham, "Some Crucial Years of the General Land Office, 1875–90," *Agricultural History,* XI (1937), 129–30; R. P. Teele, *Economics of Land Reclamation,* 1927, pp. 202–54; and Benjamin Hibbard, *A History of the Public Land Policies* (New York, 1924), pp. 562–63. I have relied primarily on the letter books, the *Annual Reports,* Senate Report No. 1466, and Sterling.

10. "Statement of Major J. W. Powell," Senate Report No. 1466.

11. It is this Irrigation Survey, his second attempt to put into practice a sane reclamation policy for the West and to modify the land laws to preserve both natural and human resources, that makes Powell as important now as he ever was while alive. As we shall see, there is a clear line of development from his *Arid Regions* in 1878 to the multi-purpose river-control installations and the multi-bureaued federal administration of the Public Domain that we have known through much of the twentieth century and especially since the nineteen-thirties.

2

1. He paints his own portrait better than any one else could do it, in his *Reminiscences* and in his letters.

2. Powell to Secretary of the Interior John W. Noble, January 2, 1889. United States Geological Survey, Letters Sent, 173–13, p. 242.

3. Frederick Jackson Turner, *Frontier in American History* (New York, 1920).

4. The most thorough presentation of the aims and accomplishments of the last real flare-up of agrarian radicalism is John Hicks, *The Populist Revolt* (St. Paul, Minnesota, 1931).

5. United States Geological Survey, Letters Sent, 173–14, p. 27.
6. *Ibid.*, pp. 263–73.
7. *Ibid.*, 173–15, p. 3.
8. The inside account of the El Paso Dam and the machinations which prevented its being built is in Anson Mills, *My Story* (New York, 1918). See also George Wharton James, *Reclaiming the Arid West*, pp. 250–59; *Powell of the Colorado*, pp. 301–3; United States Geological Survey, Letters Sent, 173–16, p. 232; 173–14, pp. 316, 498.
9. The subject of water law in the West is so complex as to be utterly confusing to the layman. The best advice possible for anyone needing information in that direction is to see a lawyer, and not just any lawyer either, but one who has made a lifelong specialty of irrigation law. A general work intended for but not necessarily comprehensible to the layman is C. S. Kinney's *Law of Irrigation*, whose full title is a true indication of the entanglements to be found therein: *A Treatise on the law of irrigation and water rights and the arid region doctrine of appropriation of waters as the same is in force in the states of the arid and semi-arid regions of the United States; and also including an abstract of the statutes of the respective states, and the decisions of the courts relating to those subjects*, 2nd ed., revised and enlarged to October 1, 1912 (San Francisco, 1912).
10. United States Geological Survey, Letters Sent, 173–14, p. 464.
11. Stewart's speech repeats Powell's thesis of the history of irrigation agriculture, the effectiveness of irrigation as a civilizing agency, the notion that no settled agriculture historically appears except in lands which demand control of stream waters; and it borrows a host of Powell's illustrations from the history of Egypt, Mesopotamia, the Indus Valley, and the American Southwest. Compare J. W. Powell, "The Lesson of Conemaugh," and also "The History of Irrigation," *Independent*, XLV (May 4, 1893), 1–3.
12. This speech of Powell's has been several times reprinted. See *Reclamation Era*, XXVI, 201–2, or *Debates*, North Dakota Constitutional Convention, 1889 (Bismarck, N.D., 1889), pp. 410–12.
13. Powell, "The Lesson of Conemaugh."
14. Powell's biographers and writers on reclamation generally seem to have overlooked this speech, which is of first importance in any study of Powell's developing ideas for proper arid-land institutions. See *Proceedings and Debates, Montana Constitutional Convention, 1889*, pp. 803–23.

3

1. *Journals and Debates of the Constitutional Convention, Wyoming, September 2–30, 1889* (Cheyenne, Wyo., 1893), contains stiff and recurrent arguments on the proper basis of water rights. It was the constitution-framers' serious intention of setting a firm foundation of water law that led to their adoption of the Powell-Mead principle of water rights tied inseparably to land.
2. It is apparent from the transcript of the hearings before the Appropriations Committee, when the Irrigation Survey was not yet more than a vague idea, that Stewart and Powell had widely different views of what was necessary. One of the essential differences was the matter of preliminary topographical maps, the question of long-range *vs.* short-range planning. Senate Report No. 1814, 50th Cong., 1st Sess.
3. *Proceedings and Debates, Idaho Constitutional Convention, 1889* (Caldwell, Ida., 1912), pp. 1929–30.

4. For discussion of the meaning of the Acting Commissioner's action, and of the political whirlwind that followed, see Sterling, "The Powell Irrigation Survey, 1888–1893." A search of the letter books of the Survey and of the records of Congressional hearings and debates will document Sterling but not modify his conclusions. See also Darrah, *Powell of the Colorado,* pp. 299–314. Though few historians have made much of it, the closing of the entries was a most important event. No single action could have been a sharper blow at the typical Western expansiveness and wishfulness and optimism; hardly any act could have had such an immediate and explosive political reaction. Hardly any act could have posed the argument between fact and myth beyond the 100th meridian so dramatically. This was one of the major landmarks on the way to our contemporary land policies. The motive behind the closing of entries — the intention of partial predevelopment, of planned or steered settlement — is still heretical in some quarters in 1954 and was ten times as heretical in 1890.

5. United States Geological Survey, Letters Sent, 173–15, p. 388.

6. The resentment and uncertainty of local water companies was compounded by the widespread conviction that water was a States' rights matter. The El Paso–Elephant Butte dam dispute was one evidence of how utter was the chaos that Powell was trying to compel toward order. Other evidences may be extracted from the letter books, especially United States Geological Survey, Letters Sent, 173–12, p. 384 (the relation between irrigation works on the upper Missouri and navigation and flood control on the lower Mississippi); 173–13, p. 148 (in whose interest was the survey being made?); 173–15, p. 3 (the Clear Lake protests from Senator Hearst's constituents); 173–15, p. 13 (reasons for the segregation of the San Pitch reservoir site in Utah); 173–15, p. 388 (justification of request to segregate 8,000,000 acres of agricultural and forest and grazing land on the Snake River in Idaho and Wyoming); 173–16, p. 94 (answering questions of the Idaho Canal Company); 173–16, p. 155 (refusing an invitation to co-operate with George West of Greeley, Colorado, on a water deal); 173–16, p. 417 (private *vs.* government control of water); 173–16, p. 488 (a petition from the Florence Canal Company of Arizona to be confirmed in its title).

7. Much of this testimony is cited or summarized or repeated in Senate Report No. 1466, 51st Cong., 1st Sess., July 2, 1890; and in House Report No. 2407, 51st Cong., 1st Sess., June 4, 1890.

8. The most readily available expressions of these are in magazine articles. See "The Irrigable Lands of the Arid Region," "The Non-Irrigable Lands of the Arid Region," and "Institutions for the Arid Lands," in *Century,* XXXIX and XL (March, April, and May, 1890); "The History of Irrigation," *Independent,* XLV (May 4, 1893), 1–3; "The Lesson of Conemaugh," *North American Review,* CXLIX (August, 1889), 150–56; "Our Recent Floods," *North American Review,* CLV (August, 1892), 149–59; "The New Lake in the Desert," *Scribner's,* X (October, 1891), 463–68. The views expressed in these and others during the period are of course duplicated and elaborated in his testimony before Congressional committees and in the *10th, 11th, 12th,* and *13th Annual Reports* of the United States Geological Survey.

9. Powell's statement before the House Appropriations Committee, House Report No. 2407.

10. United States Geological Survey, Letters Sent, 173–16, p. 482.

11. House Report No. 2407.

12. Powell's first defense against this was a long letter to Secretary of the Interior Vilas on May 31, 1890 (United States Geological Survey, Letters Sent, 173–17, pp. 166 ff.). The letter includes quotations from the records of committee hearings during the formative weeks of the Irrigation Survey, and these indicate that Powell based the idea of the Survey solidly on topography from the beginning. Stewart and the others had simply not understood how thoroughly he meant it. See also House Report No. 2407 and Senate Report No. 1466.

4

1. The New York *Herald* on January 12 and again on January 19, when the dispute was continued and amplified, broke one of the most rancorous squabbles in the history of American science. The *Herald's* Hosea Ballou, who was actually Cope's ghost writer, rehearsed all the charges and defenses, cited all the documents, many of which turned out to have been distorted or used without their authors' permission, and lined up a formidable battery of scientists *pro* and *contra* Powell's organization of government science. See also Schuchert and LeVene, *O. C. Marsh, Pioneer in Paleontology,* and Henry Fairfield Osborn, *Cope: Master Naturalist* (Princeton, 1931), for somewhat partisan but also somewhat sheepish and embarrassed accounts of the row. Everybody connected with the dispute had reason to be sheepish, for the nature of the attack was such that no matter who won, everyone lost.

2. See Part IV, Chapter 5, *ante.*

3. New York *Herald,* January 19, 1890.

5

1. House Report No. 2407, containing as it does Major Powell's prepared answers to anticipated questions, constitutes a major document in the history of the Irrigation Survey. It gave Powell a chance not only to work on the opposition in Congress, but to broadcast his views to the public. This June 4 hearing and the July 2 one before the Senate Appropriations Committee represent the very peak and climax of his fight to institute planning in the West.

2. There had been no clear-cut definition of the arid lands throughout the entire controversy over the Irrigation Survey. Powell proceeded on a rational assumption and took in everything west of the 101st meridian, roughly. Finally, at the request of Commissioner L. A. Groff of the General Land Office, Powell on June 30, 1890, sent over a map indicating his understanding of what was meant by "irrigable lands" in the "arid regions." "As I understand it," he wrote, "the act of October 2, 1888, applies to these districts, the work of selecting reservoir sites, canal sites, and irrigable lands falls within these districts, and I am therefore of the opinion that the reservation of lands to be acquired from the General Government, only under the Homestead laws, after proclamation by the President, applies only to these districts." (United States Geological Survey, Letters Sent, 173–17, p. 289.) True to form, within two days Senator Stewart was using this explanatory map as the root of all the misunderstandings of the past two years, and basing on it a renewed attack on Powell.

3. Except in the general definition of policy, Dutton was the head of the Irrigation Survey. Even before November 21, 1888, when he was officially commissioned by Powell to direct the hydrographic work, all letters regarding

irrigation were referred to him without comment.

4. United States Geological Survey, Letters Sent, 173–17, p. 208.

5. Senate Report No. 1466.

6. See Part IV, Chapter 5, *ante*.

7. Elimination of the hydrographic work left Dutton out of a job. Though he might have been expected to continue his special arrangement with the Geological Survey which had absorbed his best energies since 1874, his testimony before the Irrigation Committee and his disagreement with Powell on the propriety of concentrating funds from both appropriations on topography led him to return to regular Army duty. He apparently believed, and apparently told Powell, that the topographical work being done with Irrigation Survey funds was illegal, though the record, read now, indicates that the irrigation clique approved topography until they found out what it entailed. See Letter from C. E. Dutton, Jr., appended to Stegner, "Clarence Edward Dutton," State University of Iowa unpublished Ph.D. dissertation, 1935.

8. The optimistic evolutionary aspect of Powell's thought is nowhere so compactly developed as in his essay, "Sociology," in *American Anthropologist*, n.s. I (July and October, 1899); but other essays in that series, which were to have been combined into the second volume of his *novum organum*, repeat the theme in manifold ways. See "Technology," *American Anthropologist*, n.s. I (April, 1899); "Esthetology," *American Anthropologist*, n.s. I (January, 1899); "Philology," *American Anthropologist*, n.s. II (October–December, 1900); and "Sophiology," *American Anthropologist*, n.s. III (January–March, 1901).

9. In a letter to a South Dakota correspondent on September 29, 1890, a month after the Senate had destroyed his Irrigation Survey and brought the General Plan to nothing, Powell wrote: ". . . I regret that a broader view of the subject could not have been taken and a sufficient appropriation made to carry on investigations in relation to all the waters of the arid and sub-humid regions which can be used in irrigation. Comparatively large appropriations should have been made and information given to the people at the earliest date and the largest extent. Such was my plan, and the House of Representatives deemed it wise, and the bill passed that body; but I was unable to represent the matter in such a convincing light as to carry the judgement of the Senate. . . .

"Were it in my power, such an investigation of this country would be made as to secure full information for the people, so that in settling in the sub-humid region they would be aware of the fact that it is absolutely necessary in that country to provide against years of drought by storing sufficient water for the agricultural lands and by building the necessary irrigation works, and the investigation would be carried on so thoroughly that the people would know just where the water would be found and how it could be used. . . ." United States Geological Survey, Letters Sent, 173–18, p. 151. His aim, that is, was always primarily an informational one; his difficulty was that information could not be made available without its clashing with fantasy and the practical politics and speculation that depended on it.

6

1. United States Geological Survey, *12th Annual Report, 1890–91.*

2. *Congressional Record*, Pt. 3, 45th Cong., 3rd Sess.

3. Shannon, *The Farmer's Last Frontier*, p. 309.

4. O. C. Marsh, *Odontornithes:* a monograph on the extinct toothed birds of

North America. United States Geological Exploration of the Fortieth Parallel Report, VII, Washington, 1880. What actually caused the trouble was not this publication by the King Survey, however, but Powell's reprinting of a forty-page abstract, in accordance with well-established practice, in the United States Geological Survey, *3rd Annual Report, 1881–82.*

5. Herbert's attacks on the Survey, on Marsh, and on Powell are distributed through several hundred pages of the *Congressional Record* (1892), XXIII, Part 2.

6. During February, April, and May, 1883 — significantly during the very time when Hayden and Powell were trying, with somewhat ill grace, to settle the details of completing the publications of the Hayden Survey — there was a series of ruffled letters from Smith to Powell's office. James Pilling eventually, on May 24, arranged for a personal meeting at the end of the month so that Smith could bring his objections of intrusions upon his state survey by the Geological Survey. On April 18 Powell himself had written to smooth Smith's feathers and promised the fullest co-operation and consideration of Smith's priorities and wishes. Apparently neither co-operation nor a personal interview cured Smith of his animus, and he remained one of the Cope crowd. United States Geological Survey, Letters Sent, 173–4, pp. 122, 236, 303.

7. Schuchert and LeVene, *O. C. Marsh, Pioneer in Paleontology,* pp. 319–20.

8. William E. Smythe, a writer for the Omaha *Bee* and a zealous worker for reclamation, organized the first national Irrigation Congress at Salt Lake City in 1891; he also founded and edited *Irrigation Age.* His persistent publicizing of irrigation problems, and his organization of arid-belt farmers into a politically coherent group, made him the single most influential figure, with the exception of Major Powell, in the early years of reclamation. His own account of his activities and the fight for adequate reclamation policies is in *The Conquest of Arid America* (New York, 1900).

9. In his "Institutions for the Arid Lands," Powell indicated what needed to be done in the West and remarked that of the three possible agencies of development — government, private corporations, and co-operative associations of citizens — he much favored the last. Federal and state governments, he believed, needed to do nothing but establish statutes on the rights of land and water, and provide adequate district and state courts. He thought that the federal government ought to survey the public domain, hold some of it in trust for the co-operative local districts, classify the public lands, and divide the waters by statute among the districts. Otherwise, control and administration of the timber, range, irrigable land, and water of the drainage-basin districts should be co-operative among the actual settlers. He hoped that such co-operative associations, once organized, might borrow corporation capital and thus bring together the small freeholders and the large corporations who were currently disputing control of the West, and tie them into some mutually profitable association.

10. International Irrigation Congress, *Proceedings* (1893), pp. 106–7.

7

1. Walcott was politically acceptable partly because he was a pure geologist, and had no interest in the Major's land-reform schemes.

2. United States Geological Survey, *15th Annual Report, 1893–94,* p. 7.

3. Speech by W J McGee before a meeting of the Smithsonian in the National Museum, September 26, 1902. In S. P. Langley *et al.*, "In Memory of John Wesley Powell," *Science,* n.s. XVI (1902), 782–90.

4. J. W. Powell, "The Larger Import of Scientific Education," *Popular Science Monthly,* XXVI (February, 1885), pp. 452–6.

5. J. W. Powell, *Truth and Error* (Chicago, 1898), p. 243.

6. Lester A. Ward, *Dynamic Sociology, or Applied Social Science* (New York, 1883). Ward's thoughts on every sort of scientific and philosophical topic are collected in the six volumes characteristically titled *Glimpses of the Cosmos* (New York, 1913–18). A considerably too enthusiastic estimate of Ward's thought and career as biologist, sociologist, and philosopher is Samuel Chugarman, *Lester Ward, the American Aristotle* (Durham, N.C., 1939).

7. Ward reviewed *Truth and Error,* not too favorably considering that the book was dedicated to him, in *Science,* n.s. IX (January 27, 1899), 126–37, and Powell replied — or retorted — in the same publication, IX (February 17, 1899), 259–63.

8. See especially "From Savagery to Barbarism," *Transactions of the Anthropological Society of Washington,* III (1885), 173–96; "From Barbarism to Civilization," *American Anthropologist,* I (1888), 97–123; and "Human Evolution," *Transactions of the Anthropological Society of Washington,* II (1883), 176–208.

9. The rather macabre settlement of the bet involved a study of Powell's brain, which was made with almost phrenological solemnity by Dr. D. S. Lamb after Powell's body had been embalmed in Haven, Maine, where he died, and brought to Washington. The solemn poking about in the "fissural complexities" of his brain was in keeping with Powell's own experimental habit, as well as with his positivist philosophy and his belief in *things,* concretions, as the sources of observation and hence of knowledge. The study was published by E. A. Spitzka as "A Study of the Brain of the late Major J. W. Powell," *American Anthropologist,* n.s. V (1903), 585–643.

VI. THE INHERITANCE

1

1. Garland tells of his acquaintance with Powell in *Roadside Meetings* (New York, 1930), pp. 361–63.

2. United States Department of the Interior, Bureau of Reclamation, "Present and Proposed Activities," January 1, 1951. A listing of Reclamation Bureau projects up to the year 1948 is in Department of the Interior, Bureau of Reclamation, *Reclamation Bureau Data* (Washington, 1948).

3. See Gifford Pinchot, *Breaking New Ground* (New York, 1947), for the story, somewhat marred by Pinchot's belligerent self-aggrandizement, of the Pinchot-Roosevelt promotion of conservation as a national program and a popular movement. Powell himself was looked upon by Pinchot with some suspicion: two such monumental bureaucrats, one fading as the other rose, would hardly have got along. Also, Powell had expressed himself as not favoring a federal forestry service, fearing that it might become corrupt. He constantly advocated conservation and reclamation, but just as constantly tried to develop cooperative local control. The verdict of history, at least as most

modern conservationists read it, has been that federal bureaus, though far from perfect, have been less susceptible to corruption than state governments exposed to almost irresistible local pressures, and that co-operative associations are likely to need the protection of federal power against private interests ambitious to dominate them.

4. United States Geological Survey, Letters Sent, 173–12, p. 162.

5. Louise Peffer points out in *The Closing of the Public Domain,* p. 170, that grazing was the last of the natural resources of the West to be dealt with, because of general suspicion of the "cattle interests." The terms of the Taylor Grazing Act, and its process of collaboration between local range users and government agencies, derive to some extent from the Mizpah-Pumpkin Creek grazing agreement authorized between the federal government and the state of Montana by an act of March 29, 1928. This was a hopeful experiment in joint leases, and it incorporated much of Powell's co-operative-user-control idea, but it had not time to work out fully before President Hoover's proposals to turn the public lands over to the states confused the situation and brought about a new cycle of policy conflicts that ended in the Taylor Grazing Act and some of the "rescue" legislation of the New Deal. Peffer, *The Closing of the*

6. Quoted in *ibid.,* p. 217.

7. *Ibid.,* p. 218.

8. In "The Non-Irrigable Lands of the Arid Region," for instance, he remarks that the pasturage must be carefully grazed, that ten, twenty, or even fifty acres are necessary to support one steer the year around, and that the land therefore should not be fenced except possibly by townships or tens of townships. This is to say, he approved of the handling of the range by the men actually running stock on it so long as they were restrained from monopolization of land and water to the exclusion of the small farmer.

9. The official closing of the old public domain should probably be set at July 16, 1946, when the General Land Office, after directing the disposal and reservation of the public lands continuously since 1812, formally closed and merged its functions in the newly-created Bureau of Land Management. The end of the one bureau and the creation of the new one highlighted the alteration of policy from disposal to something like Pinchot's "wise use." Peffer, *The Closing of the Public Domain,* p. 313.

10. Since large acreages were privately owned under practically all Bureau of Reclamation dams, the reclamation law could never be thought of as simply a means of reclaiming public lands, but must make allowances for the private holdings. It limited the amount of public land that could be acquired under any project to 160 acres, and to prevent profiteering by existing landholders, it limited the amount of water available to any owner to that which would irrigate 160 acres. That acreage-water limitation, which is completely in keeping with Powell's own small-farmer bias, has been one of the most bitterly fought clauses in any federal law. (See Paul S. Taylor, "The 160-Acre Water Limitation and the Water Resources Commission," *Western Political Quarterly,* III, No. 3 [September, 1950].) But the Newlands Act itself, despite local failures of administration or application, is perhaps the best and most responsible land-development law that the nation ever passed. It authorized the use of receipts from sale and disposal of public lands as a fund for the creation of irrigation works, and it withdrew all potential irrigable lands from entry except under the Homestead Act — thus returning the public domain to the condition it would have been in had Powell been allowed to complete his Irrigation Survey

in the eighteen-nineties. The early effects of the Newlands Act may be studied in James, *Reclaiming the Arid West,* and the later-developed policies of land management in Marion Clawson, *Uncle Sam's Acres.*

11. As this volume went to press in February, 1954, there were indications from several directions that the policies of federal ownership, federal management, extensive reservations, and "wise use" that developed between Powell's original *Arid Regions* proposals in 1878 and the inauguration of President Eisenhower in 1953 were to be systematically assaulted and if possible reversed. The turning over of the off-shore oil lands to the interested states was a symptom, although the off-shore oil was never part of the public domain as that concept historically developed. But in various public utterances both during the campaign and after his installation as Secretary of the Interior, Douglas McKay has indicated his intention of returning as far as possible on the road to the old policy of disposal which many had thought completely discredited and outgrown. By January, 1954, he had made ominous noises toward a revision and eventual breakup of the Indian reservations, had splintered a coherent reclamation project of the Bureau of Reclamation by awarding to private power companies two dam-sites on the Snake River, and was energetically going forward with a raid against the sanctity of the national parks (and perhaps angling for Reclamation Bureau support) by backing the proposed Reclamation dam in Echo Park, on the Green River, within the boundaries of Dinosaur National Monument. President Eisenhower, evidently concurring, has given his Secretary of the Interior a free hand; and in his State of the Union message he indicated his intention to push for a "revised public land policy" and "legislation to improve the conservation and management of publicly-owned grazing lands in national forests." Since the only alternatives at this time would be either to support the Forest Service in resisting pressure from stockmen for relaxation of rules in National Forest grazing lands, or to help the stockmen break the Forest Service down, there seems no doubt that his thinking and his intentions match those of Secretary McKay. There seems no doubt either that as the raids on federal reserves become more open, there will be a clear testing of the bi-partisan strength of the conservation movement and the principles that Powell's intense public career helped to create and promote. To a jaundiced historian, it appears that the "disposal" advocates make strong claims for state or local or private "development" when the pickings are good, and resources of real value are involved; but that they are very willing to have the federal government own, manage, and rescue lands which contain no valuable resources or which have been gutted by indiscriminate exploitation. Thus Texas, to take only one example, is hot for its share of off-shore oil and its right to the continental shelf. It never subscribed to the public domain notion and historically never surrendered its state-owned lands to the federal government upon annexation. But let a calamitous drouth hit Texas and listen to the cries for federal rescue. In the same way, stock interests have made tentative grabs at the range lands, many of them now restored to usefulness by the Soil Conservation Service and the controlled grazing under the Taylor Grazing Act; and lumber companies that have clear-cut their holdings without practicing forest management and replanting have put out their feelers toward government reserves, notably Olympic National Park and its virgin rain-forest. If that philosophy triumphs after so many years of gradual establishment of its opposite, Major Powell will undoubtedly rise from the dead in Arlington Cemetery and appear before a committee of Congress.

12. Paul S. Taylor, "The Central Valley Project: Water and Land," *Western Political Quarterly*, II, No. 2 (June, 1949); also "Extension of Remarks of Hon. Helen Gahagan Douglas of California in the House of Representatives," *Congressional Record* (June 20, 1947, June 1, 1948, and October 5, 1949). The most objective — and damaging — report on the competition between bureaus on the Kings and Kern, and the manipulation of bureaucratic rivalries for political advantage, is Arthur A. Maass, "The Kings River Project in the Basin of the Great Central Valley — A Case Study," Appendix 7 of *Task Force Report on Natural Resources* [Appendix L] prepared for the U.S. Commission on Organization of the Executive Branch of the Government (Washington, 1949).

13. Cited in Clawson, *Uncle Sam's Acres*, p. 259.

14. For a summary of this long and rather disgraceful squabble, see Peffer, *The Closing of the Public Domain*, pp. 194–95.

15. In this instance the forces of conservation were whipped into action by publicity, of which important early parts were Arthur Carhart, "Don't Fence Us In!", *Pacific Spectator* (Winter, 1947), and Bernard DeVoto's series of articles in the Easy Chair of *Harper's Magazine*.

16. Peffer, *The Closing of the Public Domain*, pp. 271–72.

17. The avowed tactics of the large landholders of the lower San Joaquin Valley, as reported in *Business Week*, May 13, 1944, are relevant here. They included attempts to repeal the 160-acre limitation directly, use of the Army Engineers to evade Reclamation Act restrictions, attempts to get the Central Valley Project back into the hands of the state of California, and use of deep-well pumps around the margins of irrigated areas to catch excess water for use on unauthorized lands.

18. Particularly with regard to the alleged tendency of the Bureau of Reclamation to ignore or slight the human consequences of its projects, and to consider feasibility the prime consideration in the building of a dam. The Sierra Club and other conservation groups have for years been pleading the recreational values of some of the sites that the Reclamation Bureau has marked for dams, and in particular have fought the proposed construction of dams within national parks and monuments. They have also supported the reservation of reservoir sites for the future, to be used only when the present reservoirs silt up. On both of these issues they have come into some conflict with Bureau of Reclamation policies.

19. Among his trainees and disciples were Elwood Mead, W J McGee, Arthur Powell Davis, and F. H. Newell, all later prominent in reclamation. It can almost be said that the Irrigation Survey trained the men who later made the Reclamation Service possible.

20. *The Education of Henry Adams*, p. 500.

21. *Ibid.*, p. 451.

22. Powell, *Truth and Error*, p. 419.

INDEX

Sentry Editions

1 A Week on the Concord and Merrimack Rivers *by Henry David Thoreau*

2 A Diary from Dixie *by Mary Boykin Chesnut, edited by Ben Ames Williams*

3 The Education of Henry Adams: An Autobiography

4 J.B. *by Archibald MacLeish*

5 John C. Calhoun *by Margaret L. Coit*

6 The Maritime History of Massachusetts: 1783–1860 *by Samuel Eliot Morison*

7 My Ántonia *by Willa Cather*

8 Patterns of Culture *by Ruth Benedict*

9 Sam Clemens of Hannibal *by Dixon Wecter*

10 The Great Crash, 1929 *by John Kenneth Galbraith*

11 The Year of Decision: 1846 *by Bernard DeVoto*

12 Young Man with a Horn *by Dorothy Baker*

13 Mein Kampf *by Adolf Hitler*

14 The Vital Center *by Arthur M. Schlesinger, Jr.*

15 The Course of Empire *by Bernard DeVoto*

16 O Pioneers! *by Willa Cather*

17 The Armada *by Garrett Mattingly*

18 American Capitalism *by John Kenneth Galbraith*

19 The Emancipation of Massachusetts *by Brooks Adams*

20 Beyond the Hundredth Meridian *by Wallace Stegner*

21 Paul Revere and the World He Lived In *by Esther Forbes*

22 Chosen Country *by John Dos Passos*

23 The Tragic Era *by Claude G. Bowers*

24 Parkinson's Law *by C. Northcote Parkinson*